CAMPUS SEXUAL ASSAULT RESPONSE TEAMS

Program Development and Operational Management

Donna M. Barry, APN, FN-CSA
Director, University Health Center
Montclair State University
Montclair, New Jersey
and
Paul M. Cell, Chief of Police
Montclair State University Police Department
Montclair, New Jersey

CRI
Civic Research Institute

4478 U.S. Route 27 • P.O. Box 585 • Kingston, NJ 08528

Printed in the United States of America

Library of Congress Cataloging in Publication Data
Campus Sexual Assault Response Teams: Program Development and Ongoing Operations/Donna M. Barry, APN, FN-CSA, and Paul M. Cell, Chief of Police

ISBN 1-887554-70-X

Library of Congress Control Number: 2009926654

Table of Contents

PART 1: CURRENT STATE OF COLLEGE CAMPUSES

Introduction: College Students—At Risk and Underserved P1-1
Donna M. Barry, APN, FN-CSA, and Paul M. Cell, Chief of Police

Chapter 1: Creating a Campus Culture That Supports Sexual Assault Response
Karen L. Pennington, Ph.D.

Chapter 2: Impact of Alcohol and Other Drugs on Campus Sexual Violence—Prevention and Response
William DeJong, Ph.D., and Linda Langford, Sc.D.

PART 2: CRITICAL COMPONENTS OF
A CAMPUS SEXUAL ASSAULT RESPONSE TEAM

Introduction: Doing the Groundwork—Research and Preparation P2-1
Donna M. Barry, APN, FN-CSA, and Paul M. Cell, Chief of Police

Chapter 3: Community Sexual Assault Response Teams—Structure, Function, and Efficacy
Donna A. Gaffney, APRN, BC, DNSc, FAAN

Chapter 4: How Federal Law Applies to Cases of Campus Sexual Assault
John Wesley Lowery, Ph.D.

Chapter 5: Navigating a Complaint of Sexual Assault Through a Campus Disciplinary Process
Liz Baldizan, Ed.D., Linda B. Falkson, J.D., and Mary Beth Grant, J.D.

Chapter 6: Role of Law Enforcement in Sexual Assault Response Teams
Paul M. Cell, Chief of Police

Chapter 7: Role of the Rape Care Advocate
Roberta Gibbons, M.A.

Chapter 8: Forensic Medical Examination of the Sexual Assault Victim
Donna M. Barry, APN, FN-CSA

PART 3: TRAINING AND IMPLEMENTATION

Chapter 10: Putting It All Together for a Best Practice Approach
Donna M. Barry, APN, FN-CSA, and Paul M. Cell, Chief of Police

Acknowledgments

The following individuals and organizations should be recognized, for without them this book and the Montclair State University Sexual Assault Response Team would not have been possible.

Assistant prosecutor Robert Laurino and SANE/SART Coordinator Alecia Seery, Essex County Prosecutor's Office (N.J.); Prosecutor James F. Avigliano, Passaic County Prosecutor's Office (N.J.); Felicia Infante, Union County SANE Coordinator (N.J.); Ursala Leibowitz, Essex County Rape Care Center (N.J.); Robert Ward, the American College Health Association; Jhon Velasco, The Center for Nonviolence and Prevention Programs (Montclair State University); the staff and the SANE nurses of the Montclair State University Health Center; the men and women of the Montclair State University Police Department; the Passaic County Police Chief's Association; and especially the contributing authors of this book.

A special word of thanks to Dr. Susan A. Cole and Dr. Karen L. Pennington for their visionary leadership and belief in a world without glass ceilings.

Most importantly, we would like to acknowledge and give thanks to our families for their patience, understanding, and sacrifices made during the creation of this book and to God for being with us throughout this journey.

Foreword

WHY ESTABLISH A CAMPUS SEXUAL ASSAULT RESPONSE TEAM?

Sexual assault is a critical issue for all college and university campuses. Even though many institutions officially report zero sexual assault crimes each year, sexual assault is known to be a historically underreported crime. As such, crime reports alone cannot provide the basis for determining the extent of the problem on any given campus. Community colleges, large residential campuses, and faith-based institutions are equally obligated to proactively and comprehensively address sexual assault within their communities. No campus is immune from this problem.

Studies have consistently shown that sexual assault primarily affects women and youths, and that most perpetrators are friends, acquaintances, or someone known to the victim.

- In 1994, Robin Warshaw demonstrated that one in four college women were victims of a completed or attempted rape and that in fully 84 percent of the attacks, the victim knew the perpetrator.
- The National Violence Against Women Survey of 1998 demonstrated that 83 percent of rape victims were under twenty-five years old when assaulted (Tjaden & Thoennes, 1998).
- In 2000, Bonnie Fisher, Francis Cullen, and Michael Turner's *The Sexual Victimization of College Women* survey estimated that colleges with 10,000 students might expect more than 350 rapes per year.

Addressing campus sexual assault is the right thing to do, and not only because it is a crime. Supporting a comprehensive institutional approach to address sexual assault ensures that all members of a campus community have access to the education and employment they seek. A single campus constituency cannot eradicate sexual assault on its own. Sexual violence on campus affects everyone. The entire campus community must work collectively to create a safer environment in which all members can live, work, and learn.

The impact of campus sexual assault can exact a tremendous toll on both the individuals involved and their institutions. For many victims of these violent crimes, immediate injuries endanger their physical health and well-being. Most victims also suffer emotional trauma and both short- and long-term psychological effects, including stress, feelings of isolation, low self-esteem, and self-blame. As a result of the incident, survivors may develop substance abuse problems, eating or sleep-related disorders, posttraumatic stress syndrome, or depression, which in some cases leads to suicide.

The academic consequences of sexual assault on campus are significant. Poor attendance and the inability to study can result in lower grades and, potentially, academic probation or dismissal. Some students may choose to suspend their studies or drop out entirely, thus losing their opportunity to obtain an education and compromising their ability to pursue professional and personal goals. Sexual assault on campus can also generate devastating, far-reaching consequences: "If college is a place for healthy risk-taking and for personal, social and vocational maturation, then rape and abuse represent blows to the search for self-identity and life roles" (Otten & Hotelling, 2001, p. 9).

Perpetrators of campus violence face potentially negative repercussions from identification, campus adjudication, and possible expulsion to prosecution and conviction with a prison sentence. However, if these individuals are not held accountable, their abusive behavior may escalate, further endangering students. Without appropriate intervention, perpetrators can continue to engage in violent behavior with future partners and perpetuate the cycle of violence.

By not effectively addressing sexual assault on campus, an institution sends a message that such violence will be tolerated and neglects both its moral obligations and academic purpose.

> By silencing inquiry, by discounting the seriousness of the problem, by responding inconsistently to sexual violence cases, and by failing to promulgate (or enforce) policies, the university fails in its most basic mission: to provide a nourishing learning environment free from intimidation and bias. (Otten & Hotelling, 2009, p. 9)

Thus, institutions of higher education can best serve members of their community by ensuring timely access to appropriate services and creating an environment intolerant of sexual assault. While the approach of each campus to addressing sexual assault will vary according to its needs and resources, this book provides suggestions and standards for every college and university campus.

Providing or ensuring access to specialized services for victims must be a priority of every campus plan to address sexual assault. Some colleges and universities may choose to support their own sexual assault victim services program on campus through college health centers, advocacy departments, and campus law enforcement. Others may establish referral relationships with external partners such as community Sexual Assault Response Team (SART) systems, established Sexual Assault Nurse Examiner (SANE) programs in local emergency rooms, local rape care centers, and municipal police departments. Whatever the methodology, every campus plan must include a range of services and be accessible to victims, including students, faculty, and staff, at all times.

Limited financial or personnel resources to support a campus-based sexual assault services program should not be seen as an insurmountable obstacle, especially when local qualified service providers are invited to participate in the campus victim services plan.

Many communities provide a full range of victim services. By developing a formal relationship with effective community service providers, campuses can help facilitate the quick mobilization of services for campus sexual assault victims.

When designing any type of victim services, campuses must take into consideration the particular needs of victims, with a special emphasis on the demographic make up of the campus community. This includes ensuring that services are accessible to, and appropriate for, all students, faculty, and staff—including both women and men, individuals with disabilities, cultural and religious minorities, lesbian/gay/transgendered individuals, commuting or parenting students, and older students.

When institutions of higher learning begin to address the issues associated with sexual assault by providing services for victims, holding perpetrators accountable, and promoting awareness through educational programs, administrators may see an increase in the number of violent incidents reported. This does not necessarily mean that there has been an increase in sexual assault. Instead, these numbers demonstrate that the campus system for responding to and dealing with violence is working and that victims feel confident enough to come forward and report. In the long run, the evidence of higher numbers signifies an important first step toward retaining students and eliminating the problem of violence against women on campus. This is why it is imperative to develop a campus SART *before* a campus implements training and prevention programs.

For victims of sexual assault to receive the care and services they are entitled to through federal and/or state regulations, campus response systems must be comprehensive and include all services—medical, forensic, advocacy, law enforcement, judicial affairs, housing and academic accommodations, and follow-up care. What is also crucial in this response is that these multidisciplinary teams provide a *coordinated* response with objective administrative oversight and evaluation to ensure an effective response.

TRAINING AND PREVENTION PROGRAMS

College and university campuses are microcosms of the larger communities in which they reside. As such, campuses experience the same social problems faced by all communities including sexual assault. Students, staff, and faculty alike are at risk for sexual victimization. Moreover, all three groups can also be potential perpetrators of sexual assault. However, prevention education and training on sexual assault and institutional policies can prepare campus community members for these realities and improve response services. In addition, training on campus sexual assault policies clearly conveys the institution's expectations of acceptable behavior for all members of the campus community.

An appropriate place to begin is with training for faculty and staff, including campus security and law enforcement. These individuals have relationships with students who may view them as trusted resources within the campus community. In turn, professors, teaching assistants, janitors, administrative support staff, and student leadership must be prepared to appropriately respond to disclosures of sexual victimization. When employees are thus empowered, necessary resources and services can be mobilized without delay. Unfortunately, a recent study found that "few campuses provide sexual assault response and/or sensitivity training to those most likely to first hear of sexual assaults on their campus: friends and fellow students, campus law enforcement/security officers, and faculty members" (Karjane, Fisher, & Cullen, 2002, p. ix).

Faculty and staff not only provide resources for victims, but they are also vulnerable to assaults themselves. A national victimization study sponsored by the U.S. Department of Justice reported that approximately 51,000 employees are raped or sexually assaulted each year (Warchol, 1998). Informing staff members about available resources is a proactive way of ensuring their prompt access to treatment and services.

There are a number of reasons why colleges and universities must provide sexual assault prevention education to members of their campus communities. As educational institutions, they assume a role in the development of individuals—fostering character and helping people understand their roles and responsibilities in society. In addition, sexual assault is a crime primarily committed against youths, the population traditionally served by many colleges and universities. Institutions of higher education also sponsor and support a number of social organizations frequently associated with high-profile sexual assault crimes, including fraternities, sororities, and athletic teams, which garner significant media attention when incidents occur.

Campuses also have the unique opportunity to educate and eradicate sexual assault through primary prevention programs. This strategy ranges from engaging men in dialogs that can create cultural change to bystander intervention programs. It can also be used within the campus health care system by integration of questions in patient assessments that measure vulnerability and risk taking behaviors.

Campus sexual assault prevention education activities take many forms, including public media campaigns aimed at raising awareness about the prevalence and dynamics of acquaintance rape, consciousness-raising groups for men to explore their role in supporting sexually exploitative behavior, and peer educator presented role plays and workshops in residential buildings. Including training and prevention as part of campuses overall response to sexual assault is imperative and is clearly a proactive and preventative response to sexual violence issues.

Training and education also needs to be done extensively with members of SARTs to understand the dynamics of victim response, victim rights, and perpetrator behaviors in order to provide the highest quality response system. This includes campus responders as well as community team members. Many municipal agencies do not understand the dynamics of a campus environment and can respond ineffectually to college victims. Community responders also need specific training in the additional rights and options of campus victims in order to provide a fully comprehensive response.

This foreword stresses the importance of comprehensive services for victims of sexual assault in the form of coordinated and comprehensive SARTs and the provision of training and prevention programs for team members and campus communities at large.

This book will provide the foundation to assist campuses in the development of a comprehensive plan to address sexual assault. The chapters are written to inform, educate, and empower people to action. Go forth and take action!!!

The California Coalition Against Sexual Assault

Authors' Note

Portions of the foreword have been excerpted with permission from the California Campus Blueprint to Address Sexual Assault and the Campus Violence Prevention Resource Guides, resources of the California Coalition Against Sexual Assault. All Rights Reserved.

References

Fisher, B. S., Cullen, F. T. &Turner, M. G. (2000, December). *The sexual victimization of college women.* Washington, DC: National Institute of Justice.

Karjane, H., Fisher, B. S., & Cullen, F. T., (2002). *Campus sexual assault: How America's institutions of higher education respond.* Final report. Newton, MA: Education Development Center.

Otten, A. J., & Hotelling, K. (Eds.). (2001). *Sexual violence on campus: Policies, programs and perspectives.* New York: Springer Publishing Company, Inc.

Tjaden, P., & Thoennes, N. (1998, November). *Prevalence, incident and consequences of violence against women: Findings from the National Violence Against Women Survey.* Washington DC: National Institute of Justice and the Centers for Disease Control and Prevention.

Warchol, G. (1998). *Workplace violence, 1992-1996: National crime victimization survey special report,* Washington, DC: U.S. Department of Justice, Bureau of Justice Statistics.

Warshaw, R. (1994). *I never called it rape: The Ms. report on recognizing, fghting and surviving date and acquaintance rape.* New York: Harper Perennial.

Preface

I was raped last night at a party and I need someone to help me.

These were the words Susan used when she appeared at the front desk of our campus health center. Frantic, tearful, and feeling alone, Susan shared the story of her experience. She was angry that this had happened to her and needed someone to assure her she was safe. The only help that we knew to offer was to send her to a local hospital, but she declined. Susan feared going to a strange environment and was embarrassed to tell anyone else of her victimization despite our encouragement. In the end, Susan never went to the hospital for care, never reported the crime to police, and, ultimately, never returned to school.

This incident occurred more than seven years ago and was the sole motivation to improve services at our university in New Jersey, and resulted in the creation of our campus Sexual Assault Response Team (SART). From the very beginning, we made a personal and professional commitment to do whatever was necessary to assure that Susan's experience would never occur again amongst our students.

Working together, the external resources available to our University Police Department and the University Health Center were evaluated in order to identify ways to improve services to our campus victims. Through this process, the concept of the SART was discovered—a multidisciplinary response system composed of rape care advocates, law enforcement, and forensic/medical professionals. This traditional SART format existed primarily in municipal and county agencies but seldom in a university environment. Although many campuses throughout the country have used the acronym SART, our research demonstrated these were not fully comprehensive services under the traditional definition. Although many counties in the state of New Jersey were creating SART services, further investigation made it evident that a community SART system did not exist within our local area. There were also no external quality services for partnership except the local Rape Care Center. Thus, our campus SART system needed to be created from the ground up.

We followed the state standards created for the care of sexual assault victims within our state and replicated these services on campus. A year later, after intensive work and some occasional obstacles, the Montclair State University (MSU) SART was launched as a fully comprehensive, on-campus service available 24/7, 365 days a year. Seven years later, the MSU SART has been sustained effectively and serves our students well.

Despite its success, we have continued to look for ways to improve and expand the service. As of 2007, all counties in New Jersey have established SART systems. We have now partnered with one of our local counties to educate community SART responders regarding campus victims—a high-risk population with unique needs, rights, and options. If our students choose not to use the MSU SART and seek services within the community, these needs will hopefully be recognized and their rights upheld. In doing so, our students will be empowered to move forward and make informed decisions about their options.

The decision was also made to bring our SART model to other campuses through workshop presentations at national conferences with the objective of encouraging other institutions to develop comprehensive services. The response has been overwhelmingly positive and enlightening as well. The majority of schools we encountered had similar resources to what we had offered before the MSU SART was formed. Advocacy was reported as being the primary focus and mainstay of response. Campus and municipal law enforcement frequently lacked specialized training in responding to the needs of sexual assault victims. Forensic/medical examinations were often the "weak link" in existing services, and, many times, the examinations were done by providers without appropriate training. Our anecdotal experiences were confirmed by a recent survey done by the American College Health Association. Results of this survey can be found in Appendix G. This and other research makes it evident that a significant need still exists for the development of comprehensive services on campuses to address the high risk population of college students. The SART model has been highly successful throughout the country and is a benchmark program for campus response.

Our audiences also expressed a strong sense of determination and commitment to improve existing services. Many schools have contacted us to consult regarding issues specific to their own campus SART development. The most frequent inquiry we have received has been "Is there a manual available we can follow as a guide?" This question and the recognition by other campuses of the need to improve services made it evident that a text was the next logical step to assist our fellow institutions with SART development.

This book is based on several fundamental principles:

1. A solid understanding of the nuances of college students is of critical importance in all aspects of campus sexual violence prevention, response, investigation, and prosecution. This includes factors such as individual campus cultures, dynamics, and administrative governance—and recognition of their impact on student vulnerability to sexual assault, victim response, and perpetrator behaviors. Without this understanding, success in dealing with all issues of campus sexual violence will be difficult if not impossible.

2. Most institutions of higher education must abide by federal statutory regulations that mandate specific actions regarding sexual assault. In fact, colleges and universities are actually held to a higher standard than our communities. It is imperative that campus professionals possess a working knowledge of these regulations in order to integrate these mandates into SART development. In addition, institutions also maintain an internal code of conduct and disciplinary process that can be most foreign to community responders. In order for community partners to effectively work with campus victims, an understanding of this process and victim options must occur.

3. Familiarity with the traditional community SART system is crucial in order to understand each member's role and purpose and to create an effective team approach. Coordination and oversight is also a vital aspect of a successful SART. However, SART development cannot occur through a cookie-cutter approach. The only template that exists is one of primary team membership—advocacy, law enforcement, and the forensic/medical provider. A successful SART needs to be individualized to each campus environment and dependent on multiple variables. Each institution must discern what will work best on its own campus in order to provide effective, comprehensive, and compassionate services.

Part 1 offers research and concepts to provide the reader with a deeper understanding of the college environment. The chapters address the recognition of an at-risk population; the impact of campus culture and dynamics on sexual assault; and a discussion of alcohol/drugs and their relationship to sexual violence.

Part 2 is designed to assist multidisciplinary professionals in getting started with comprehensive descriptions of the critical components of campus SART development. The chapters are planned in a stand-alone format and written in a user-friendly manner. Thus, any discipline can turn directly to a chapter for rapid location of information. This part, in effect, serves as a manual that has been requested by many of our constituents. It will assist the reader to pose difficult questions that are necessary in order to complete an accurate needs assessment of services.

Part 3 discusses the internal aspects of protocol development and critical training needs, and it also demonstrates integration of all services into a successful campus SART system. The appendices offer extensive resources that are highly recommended as tools for the creation of an effective campus SART.

We would be remiss if we did not clarify certain writing techniques at this point:

- Throughout the book, the term *victim* is used instead of *survivor.* The choice was intentional, because our students have truly been victimized when a sexual assault occurs. It is through effective response that those victims become survivors and is a primary goal of SARTs.

- The pronoun *she* has been used throughout the text in reference to victims since most victims are female. It was used for continuity purposes only and does not exclude sexual assault against males or same-sex assaults. We know that these types of assaults do occur and are most definitely underreported to a far greater extent. MSU's SART is designed to be gender neutral, and we encourage readers to develop responses that will provide comprehensive services to male victims as well as being inclusive of same sex assaults.

- Campus victims are part of a population with special needs and are the focus of this book. The text does not address other populations with special needs but assumes that campuses will integrate the needs of these populations into their response system. A list of resources is included in Appendix F to assist the reader.

- All SART members need to develop cultural competency in order to understand the specific dynamics and mores of their campus and provide an effective response. However, many colleges and universities are also highly diverse with respect to race, ethnicity, and sexual orientation. It is important to address the needs of these groups as well and recognize the impact of these factors on victim behavior and response.

Our hope is that this book will serve our colleagues not only as an effective training tool and comprehensive foundation for campus SART development, but as a manuscript for discussion, program planning, and professional development. In the end, we will have provided a roadmap of our experience including the speed bumps that we needed to navigate in achieving our final goal. It has been an enlightening and rewarding journey. We invite you to share the experience and the rewards, and we wish you the best in your endeavors. It is a journey worth taking!

Donna M. Barry and Paul M. Cell
2009

About the Editors and Contributors

Donna M. Barry, RN, APN, MSN, FN-CSA, has been in the health care field for over twenty-five years as a registered nurse, professor of nursing, and nurse practitioner. In 1997, Ms. Barry completed her post-master's certificate as a family nurse practitioner and began specializing in college health at Montclair State University (MSU) as a clinical care provider. She holds licensure as a nurse practitioner and certification as a forensic examiner. Ms. Barry earned a master's degree in nursing from Seton Hall University and a post-master's certificate from Rutgers University. She has also received advanced training through the International Association of Chiefs of Police as a law enforcement trainer in sexual assault, domestic violence, and stalking.

Ms. Barry's areas of expertise have focused on campus sexual assault response, disaster and public health medical response, and college heath. In 1999, she was appointed director of the Montclair State University Health Center and continues to serve in that capacity today as well as provide direct care to the student population. In this role, she serves as the chief administrator of student health services and the Montclair State University Sexual Assault Response Team (MSU SART); medical advisor to the university's Emergency and Pandemic Response Teams; response coordinator for public health incidents; and a member of the Students of Concern Team.

After certification as a sexual assault forensic examiner in 2001, Ms. Barry developed and implemented the MSU SART that is now recognized as a model practice for other colleges and universities across the country. MSU SART was recognized in 2008 for its excellence in victim services by the International Association of Chiefs of Police. She currently serves as coadministrator for MSU SART with the Chief of University Police and responds as a forensic examiner for sexual assault victims at the university and her home county in New Jersey. In 2002 and again in 2005, Ms. Barry wrote and served as project director for two $200,000 grants from the Violence Against Women Office of the Department of Justice to Reduce Violence Against Women on Campus.

Considered an expert in the field of campus sexual assault response, she currently serves on the National SART Toolkit Advisory Board representing institutions of higher education, as a consultant to the American College Health Association for a Centers for Disease Control sexual violence grant, chair of the American College Health Association Campus Violence Coalition, American College Health Association representative for the 2008 U.S. Department of Justice Community Oriented Policing Services Campus Safety Summit, and as a past member of the 2007 National SART Training Conference Planning Committee. She is a frequently requested speaker for national conferences on the topic of sexual assault response.

Ms. Barry has received awards for these initiatives including a vice presidential award from Montclair State University in 2004, the New Jersey College and University Public Safety Association 2004 Distinguished Assistance Civilian Award and was recognized as a "Vagina Warrior" by MSU and Eve Ensler in 2004.

Ms. Barry is also a member of the NJ-1 Disaster Medical Assistance Team under the auspices of the U.S. Department of Health and Human Services' National Disaster Medical System and was deployed as a medical responder post-Hurricane Rita in 2005. She also participates regularly in federal, state, and county emergency preparedness and disaster response exercises. Ms. Barry is certified through the American College of Forensic Examiners' Medical Publication and Safety, First Responder Division, in preparation and response, level III.

Chief Paul M. Cell has twenty-eight years of law enforcement experience and has been Chief of the Montclair State University Police Department since 2001. He is a graduate of the 217th class of the prestigious FBI National Academy and of the FBI Mid-Atlantic Law Enforcement Executive Development Seminar. In 2003, Chief Cell was part of a law enforcement delegation that traveled to South Africa to work with the national South African Police Services to discuss policing policies and strategies. During that time, he had the opportunity to work on a tactical police squad in the highly volatile Soweto area of Johannesburg.

Throughout his career, Chief Cell has received advanced training in two distinctive fields of law enforcement study: sexual assault investigations and domestic preparedness. His scope of expertise concentrated on sexual assault investigations during his tenure assigned to the Detective Bureau.

One of the founders and coadministrator of the Montclair State University Sexual Assault Response Team, he is an integral force in providing sexual assault training for law enforcement. In 2004, Chief Cell was recognized for his work to reduce violence against women through the Eve Ensler initiative. In 2007, he was selected to attend the International Association of Chiefs of Police National Law Enforcement Leadership Institute on Violence Against Women. In 2008, MSU SART was recognized by the International Association of Chiefs of Police for its excellence in victim services.

In addition to his background in criminal investigations, he has also received trainer certifications in domestic preparedness initiatives including terrorism training for law enforcement, law enforcement response to weapons of mass destruction incidents, incident response to terrorist bombing, community emergency response team development, and he received advanced training in weapons of mass destruction enhanced threat and risk assessment. He is also certified through the American College of Forensic Examiners' Law Enforcement and Military Division in homeland security preparation and response teams, level III. In 2006, he authored and presented the *Magna* national audio conference on campus preparedness entitled "Are You Ready?"

Considered a police expert in the field of campus safety, Chief Cell is an invited speaker and frequent presenter at national conferences on various topics involving campus safety initiatives. His specialty is in the field of campus Sexual Assault Response Team development. In addition, he serves as a consultant for a variety of media and print sources seeking expert advice when campus emergency situations arise throughout the nation. Chief Cell has appeared on television and radio talk shows and in a *Newsweek* article entitled "Is Your Campus Safe?" (August 2007). This article has been reprinted in the 2008 fall and winter editions of the Kaplan Newsweek *How to Get Into College 2008* magazine. Most recently his department was featured on the cover of the March 2008 issue of *Police Chief Magazine,* which included his article on "New Developments in University Safety."

As an active member in local, state, national, and international professional law enforcement associations he has held several board positions within these organizations. Chief Cell is the 2009 president of the NJ Passaic County Police Chiefs Association and past president in 2004 and 2005. He currently serves as vice president of the Passaic County Law Enforcement Foundation and sergeant at arms for the New Jersey State Association of Chiefs of Police both since 2007. In addition, he is an active member of the New Jersey President's Council of Colleges and Universities Homeland Security Committee.

Police Lieutenant Kieran Barrett has been working at the Montclair State University (MSU) Police Department for eleven years, has a B.S. in criminal justice, and will complete his master's studies in history in 2009. Lt. Barrett led the MSU Police Department's Investigations Unit for five years and currently is administrative commander in charge of such things as budget, professional standards, internal training, as well as community programming. Lt. Barrett is a certified police instructor in the State of New Jersey and in 2006 received advanced training through the International Association of Chiefs of Police National Violence Against Women Trainer Development Program. In his spare time, Lt. Barrett enjoys his continued study of generational history, hiking, and any time spent outdoors. A lifelong resident of northern New Jersey, Lt. Barrett married an MSU alumni and had his first child, Andrew, in July 2006.

Elizabeth Mary Baldizan, Ed.D., is the assistant dean for the Academic Success Center and Director of the Jean Nidetch Women's Center at the University of Nevada Las Vegas (UNLV). Dr. Baldizan is an adjunct professor in the Department of Educational Leadership at UNLV and was also adjunct faculty and graduate intern coordinator at Seattle University.

Her professional involvement includes serving as president of the Association for Student Judicial Affairs, board of director member for the National Association of Student Personnel Administrators (NAPSPA), editorial board for the Council on Law in Higher Education, and is a current member of the *NASPA Journal* editorial board. She is a graduate of the University of Northern Colorado, magna cum laude, where she earned her bachelor's degree in communications and environmental studies and received her master of arts in education from the University of New Mexico. Her doctorate was earned in educational administration from UNLV.

The California Coalition Against Sexual Assault, founded in 1980, is the only statewide organization whose sole purpose is to promote public policy, advocacy, training, and technical assistance on the issue of sexual assault. The primary members are California's rape crisis centers and rape prevention programs and affiliate members that include organizations, businesses, and individuals committed to their mission and vision of the elimination of sexual violence. The California Coalition Against Sexual Assault provides leadership, vision, and resources to rape crisis centers, individuals, and advocates for the needs of sexual assault survivors and its membership through public policy initiatives, technical assistance, listservs, a Rape Prevention Resource Library, research reports, and special initiatives such as the Campus Program, My Strength Campaign, and the Prevention Connection.

William DeJong, Ph.D., is a professor of social and behavioral sciences at the Boston University School of Public Health. Dr. DeJong is director of research and development for Outside the Classroom, Inc., in Needham, MA, which provides online alcohol education programs to U.S. college and university students. He is also the principal investigator for the Social Norms Marketing Research Project, a large-scale evaluation of social norms marketing campaigns focused on reducing student alcohol use, which was funded by the National Institute on Alcohol Abuse and Alcoholism and the U.S. Department of Education. Between 1995 and 2004, Dr. DeJong served as director of the U.S. Department of Education's Higher Education Center for Alcohol and Other Drug Abuse and Violence Prevention, for which he still serves as a senior advisor. He is a graduate of Dartmouth College and received his doctorate in social psychology from Stanford University.

Linda B. Falkson, J.D., became the Cornell University assistant ombudsman in April 2008. Prior to receiving this appointment, she served as Cornell's associate judicial administrator and then as deputy judicial administrator for ten years enforcing Cornell's Code of Conduct. As a conduct officer, she was active with the professional organization, Association of Student Judicial Affairs (ASJA). She served as Ithaca City Prosecutor from 1994 to 1998. Prior to serving as a prosecutor, she engaged in general legal practice, including criminal defense. She is a 1989 graduate of State University of New York at Buffalo Law School and a 1986 graduate of Cornell University.

Donna Gaffney, APRN, BC, DNSc, FAAN, is on the faculty of the International Trauma Studies Program in New York City. She has long addressed the issues of trauma in women and children's lives. In 1994, she collaborated with and was funded by the New York State Department of Health and the Division of Criminal Justice Services to design and implement the first forensic curriculum for evaluating and treating sexual assault survivors in New York State. In 2004, she developed an online sexual assault examiner course for Seton Hall University and The New York City Alliance Against Sexual Assault. She also consulted with the New York State Department of Health on the design and implementation of the New York sexual assault forensic examiner (SAFE) certification guidelines and process. Dr. Gaffney was a consultant and contributor for UNICEF's pilot training program for the Democratic Republic of the Congo Sexual Assault Care Guide.

Dr. Gaffney consulted with the Air Force JAG School in Alabama and since that time has trained Air Force Special Investigators at the USAF Academy as well as investigators at regional workshops held at bases across the United States. In these workshops Dr. Gaffney addresses the dynamics of sexual assault and the psychological impact of sexual violence, drug facilitated sexual assault, and the nature of the forensic examination.

Following the arrest of former nurse and serial killer, Charles Cullen, in 2003, Dr. Gaffney raised public awareness regarding the role of forensic nursing in the reporting of criminal acts. In addition to numerous academic publications, Dr. Gaffney is the author of *The Seasons of Grief, Helping Children Grow Through Loss and Adolescent Sexuality: A Guide for Clinicians.* She has been a contributor to *Sexual Assault Report* and the *International Journal of Forensic Nursing.* Dr. Gaffney is a member of the American Academy of Nursing, the American Nurses Association, the American Psychological Association, and the International Association of Forensic Nurses. She is also a forensic nurse consultant and has a private practice focusing on women and children.

Roberta Gibbons, M.A., is the associate director of the Aurora Center for Advocacy and Education, the on-campus violence intervention and prevention center at the University of Minnesota-Twin Cities. For the past eight years she also has served as the principal investigator for the U.S. Department of Justice's *Grants to Reduce Violent Crimes Against Women on Campus.* As adjunct faculty at both the University of Minnesota and Metropolitan State University, Ms. Gibbons has taught courses through the departments of public policy, women's studies, family education, and human services. Ms.Gibbons earned her master's degree in political science in 1991, holds a certificate in program evaluation, and is currently a Ph.D. candidate in educational policy and administration. She worked in nonprofit management and for the legislatures of both Minnesota and Wisconsin before joining the University of Minnesota in 1999.

Mary E. ("Mary Beth") Grant, J.D., has served as Cornell University's judicial administrator since 1999. Prior to joining Cornell, Ms. Grant worked as a civil rights attorney and a community educator with the Legal Aid Society of Minneapolis, served as a judicial clerk, and completed a stint in a law firm. Ms. Grant earned her B.A. *with high distinction* from the University of Iowa and her J.D. from Cornell Law School. Ms. Grant makes her home in Ithaca, NY, with her husband and two daughters, where she enjoys attending live music events, volunteering in the community, poking around in her garden, and relaxing with a good book.

Linda Langford, Sc.D., is an associate director at the Center for College Health and Safety at Education Development Center in Newton, MA. She has worked at the U.S. Department of Education's Higher Education Center for Alcohol and Other Drug Abuse and Violence Prevention since 1998, serving as evaluation director for four years and since 2002 directing the center's violence prevention initiatives, including developing a comprehensive framework for campus violence prevention. Previous projects include working with statewide campus coalitions to promote coordination between sexual violence and alcohol prevention efforts and directing a pilot study of a high school social norms marketing alcohol prevention campaign. Her work focuses on strategic planning, evaluation, and health communications with special interests in environmental prevention approaches, practitioner-researcher collaborations, and translating research to practice. She holds a doctorate in behavioral sciences from the Harvard School of Public Health and taught in Tufts University School of Medicine's health communications program from 1998-2007.

John Wesley Lowery, Ph.D., is associate professor in the Department of Student Affairs in Higher Education at Indiana University of Pennsylvania. He previously served on the faculty at Oklahoma State University and the University of South Carolina. He also held administrative positions at Adrian College and Washington University. He earned his doctorate at Bowling Green State University in higher education administration. Dr. Lowery is actively involved in numerous professional associations including ACPA, ASJA, and NASPA. He has a master's degree in student personnel services from the University of South Carolina and an undergraduate degree from the University of Virginia in religious studies. He is a frequent speaker and author on topics related to student affairs and higher education, particularly legislative issues and judicial affairs on which he is widely regarded as a leading expert. Over his career, Dr. Lowery has been honored by several professional organizations. At the 2007 Association for Student Judicial Affairs Conference, he received the D. Parker Young Award for "outstanding ongoing scholarly research contributions to the fields of higher education and student judicial affairs."

Karen L. Pennington, Ph.D., is a native of Pennsylvania and has spent the last twenty-six years working in the higher education arena. She has served in a variety of student affairs administrative positions including director of student activities, director of residence life, dean of students, and vice president at six colleges and universities in Pennsylvania, New York, and Ohio. Dr. Pennington received a B.A. and M.A. in history at the University of Scranton (PA), an M.Ed. in secondary education counseling at Gannon University (PA), and a Ph.D. in higher education administration from the State University of New York at Albany. She is past president of the National Association of Student Personnel Administrators (NASPA), an international association serving over 9,000 members. She is a member of the board of advisors for Archbishop Prendergast High School in Drexel Hill, PA, and a member of the board of trustees of the University of Scranton. A resident of New Jersey since January 1998, Dr. Pennington resides in Upper Montclair.

Part 1

Current State of College Campuses

Introduction: College Students—At Risk and Underserved

by Donna M. Barry, APN, FN-CSA, and Paul M. Cell, Chief of Police

I was just hanging out in my room with a guy I knew from class. We were wasting time talking and stuff before dinner. He started hitting on me pretty hard and I kept putting him off, but he wouldn't stop. He raped me and then left, like it was no big deal. I didn't know what to do and none of my friends were around, so I went to the emergency room. I told them I had been raped, but I didn't want to tell the police. I just wanted to make sure he hadn't hurt me and get medication in case he had something.

The nurse put me in a room by myself. I could hear lots of people outside of my room, and once in a while someone would yell or cry. It was a Friday night, and they were really busy. Two hours went by before someone came in to see me. She stuck her head in the door and said "Oh—you're the one who was raped. Someone will be in soon." But no one came in; I finally left after another two hours went by. The next morning I tried a local doctor's office near campus. When I told them what had happened to me, they charged me $75.00 and brought me to an exam room to get undressed. Then the doctor came in and said he couldn't help me, and I would have to go to the clinic down the street. So I got dressed and went looking for the clinic. I never got my $75.00 back. The clinic said they couldn't help me either. So here I am. All I want is for someone to listen to me, and tell me I'm going to be ok. It's taken almost 24 hours and four places for that to happen. Doesn't it matter to anyone that I was raped?

Individuals who have worked in the field of sexual violence, regardless of the discipline, have heard the horror stories of someone who has been victimized, was unaware of how to get help, and then subjected to cold, inadequate services. Those who work within the college environment hear it far too often. The questions that arise are several: Are college students really more vulnerable to sexual assault? What types of services do colleges and universities currently provide to assist victims? What can be done to reduce sexual violence, improve services, and ease access to care?

In 2005, approximately 17.5 million students were enrolled in colleges and universities throughout the United States. Sixty percent of enrolled students were between eighteen and twenty-four years of age, and females made up 57 percent of the coeducational enrollment population (United States Department of Education, National Center for Education Statistics, 2008, chap. 3). In a 2000 study for the National Institute of Justice (NIJ), Fisher, Cullen, and Turner (2000) revealed that all women in the United States between the ages of seventeen and twenty-four are at the greatest risk for sexual assault. The National Violence Against Women Survey in 2006 showed that 29.4 percent of female victims were eighteen to twenty-four years old when they were raped (NIJ, 2006).

Studies that focused exclusively on college students resulted in similar outcomes. The NIJ study in 2000 found that 35 out of every 1,000 (2.8 percent) female college students had experienced rape or attempted rape within the same time frame (Fisher et al., 2000). Four years later, the National College Health Assessment survey found that 5.8 percent of female college students reported incidents of rape and attempted rape within a nine-month period (American College Health Association [ACHA, 2004).

Yet, crime reporting statistics demonstrate a vastly different picture. Less than 5 percent of completed or attempted rapes committed against students were reported to campus or community law enforcement in the Fisher et al. (2000) survey. Victims were more likely to turn to a peer or mentor for support as opposed to administrators or officials on or off campus. The same survey showed that 90 percent of the women knew their assailant, and many had difficulty defining their experience as rape. This was most evident in those assaults in which the offender was known, no weapon was used, no sign of physical injury was evident, and alcohol was involved (Bondurant, 2001).

The results of the aforementioned surveys over the past seven years have not changed significantly. They reveal an obvious vulnerability and high incidence of sexual assault for college students, in particular female students, yet significantly low reporting rates influenced by college victims' failure to recognize their experience as assault. Multiple factors increase vulnerability such as individual campus cultures and the prevalence of alcohol and drug use. These variables are discussed at length in Chapters 1 and 2.

Despite the obvious risk, campus and community providers have been slow to provide comprehensive services and actions that encourage risk reduction. Awareness programming has been the primary focus historically. For more than thirty years, campuses across the country have attempted to educate students on the risks of sexual assault. Women's centers and advocacy groups have been formed at most institutions with an emphasis on awareness, prevention, and advocacy support for victims. In 1998, the Violence Against Women Office of the United States Department of Justice began to provide grant funding to further expand these efforts and involve community partnerships with the goal of reducing the occurrence of sexual assault, improving services, increasing reporting, and moving institutions forward in providing comprehensive services.

A 2005 NIJ study of how schools were responding to sexual assault on campus examined a sample of almost 2,500 schools participating in federal financial aid programs. It found only 37 percent of the respondents reported crime statistics in the required manner; fewer than two in five schools offered sexual assault training for campus security; only 46 percent offered anonymous reporting; less than half provided services after business hours; and only one third to one half offered educational programs that included nonstranger assault prevention. The same study found only 25 percent of the respondent schools provided coordinated, comprehensive victim services and identified this as a promising practice for the future (NIJ, 2005). Yet, results of a 2008 Sexual Assault Response Team survey by the ACHA identified less than twenty schools with coordinated, comprehensive services for victims out of 154 respondents (ACHA, 2008; see Appendix G).

College students continue to be identified as at risk for sexual assault year after year. The incidence of assault has fluctuated very little, and reporting rates remain low. Yet, institutions have been slow to address risk reduction, improve access to care, coordinate comprehensive services, and comply fully with federal regulations.

References

American College Health Association. (2006). *National college health assessment.* Retrieved December 15, 2007, from http://www.acha.org

American College Health Association. (2008). *Survey on campus sexual assault services.* Retrieved April 1, 2008, from http://www.acha.org

Bondurant, B. (2001). University women's acknowledgment of rape: Individual, situational and social factors. *Violence Against Women, 7*(3), 294-314.

Fisher, B. S., Cullen, F. T., & Turner, M. G. (2000, December). *The sexual victimization of college women.* Washington, DC: National Institute of Justice.

National Institute of Justice. (2005). *Research for practice: Sexual assault on campus: What colleges and universities are doing about it.* Washington, DC: U.S. Department of Justice Office of Justice Programs.

National Institute of Justice. (2006). *Extent, nature and consequences of rape victimization: Findings from the national violence against women survey.* Washington, DC: U.S. Department of Justice Office of Justice Programs.

United States Department of Education, National Center for Education Statistics (2008). *Digest of educational statistics, 2007* (NCES 2008-22). Retrieved November 20, 2008, from http://nces.ed.gov.

Chapter 1

Creating a Campus Culture That Supports Sexual Assault Response

by Karen L. Pennington, Ph.D.

ACT I, Scene I

Location: Almost Perfect University

                    Parents Campus Safety Presentation at Freshman Orientation

Time: The present

Parent: I am concerned about my daughter's safety if she comes here in the fall. I was looking at your recent Clery[1] report and saw that the number of reported rapes for last year was fourteen. That is very high to me. But even worse, that is a 500 percent increase over the previous year. You have a real problem here!

Administrator: Thank you so much for noticing! We are very proud of that increase! That means we are well on the way to correcting our problem of sexual assault.

                   (Parent faints)

Can such an exchange occur at an orientation program? It can if there is a campus culture that encourages members of the community to come forward and report sexual assault. But, too often, the thought of coming forward is frightening, not only because of the way the individual feels she will be perceived, but because she dreads the expected response. There are countless stories of campus victims who report that they were ignored, chastised, accused of lying, encouraged to forget it, or in other ways made to feel violated by those they expected to help them.

---

[1]For the requirements of the Jeanne Clery Disclosure of Campus Security Policy and Campus Crime Statistics Act of 1998 (Clery Act; 20 U.S.C. § 1092(f)), see Chapter 4 and Appendix D.

If anyone wants to find an easy answer to why reports of sexual assault on a campus are low, it is not because they do not happen, but rather because there is a culture—either formal or informal—that discourages sexual assault reporting. While this is certainly not the case on all campuses, there are still some where reporting is not encouraged and may in fact be discouraged. For those working on a campus in the latter group, this chapter will explore ideas that will help professionals create a new culture by changing the way campus officials view sexual assault reports and encourage the creation of campus services for both victims and perpetrators.

ROOTED IN THE PAST

For many individuals, the mystique and allure of college remains rooted in a simpler time. Beginning with the founding of Harvard College in 1636, institutions of higher education were founded to give the elite men of the colonies training in the classics, theology, and other subjects that would permit them to take their rightful place as leaders. Drawings of the time emphasize the gentility of the campus, with ivy covered walls and students seated at the foot of the master. There was no discord, no disruption, and certainly nothing that indicated violence occurred on campus. The reality, of course, was quite different; from the beginning, students rebelled, fought, and rioted. In fact, one of the earliest recorded instances of student unrest occurred at the University of Paris in 1229, where riots caused the death of several students and closed the university for two days.

But the more common view of college, which is held by many trustees, parents, community members, and even some students of today, is the happy-go-lucky college days in films such as *Knute Rockne: All American* (1940) or *Love Story* (1970). The vision in these films is of a traditional college student, and the college experience is created by visualizing Sandra Dee, Annette Funicello, and Bobby Darren. Even if the trustees, parents, and community members have never seen a movie with these stars from the 1950s or have never even heard their names, the image of a pristine campus with clean-cut men and women earnestly seeking higher education and only engaging in innocent fun before turning in at 10:00 p.m. is what many individuals want to believe is the life of a typical college student in 2009.

The world has obviously changed from those days of perceived innocence, and the reality of college life is often represented by movies such as this top- ten list from Kate Tobin (2008) of New York University:

1. *Old School* (2003): This film provides "all the fun of college. None of the education" (Tobin, 2008).

2. *Animal House* (1978): "Set in 1962, this screwball comedy is raunchy [and] highly inappropriate" (Tobin, 2008).

3. *Good Will Hunting* (1997): In this film a janitor turns into a student.

4. *Scent of a Woman* (1992): This is another coming of age story.

5. *The Rules of Attraction* (2002): "The film features sex, drugs, and . . . [reminds] us, 'There Are No Rules'" (Tobin, 2008).

6. *PCU* (1994): This film is an anti–political-correctness comedy.

7. *Higher Learning* (1995): The film deals with "normal adolescent problems, as well as serious prejudice, intolerance, racism and sexism among the student body" (Tobin 2008).

8. *Revenge of the Nerds* (1984): This story appeals to the dork in all of us.

9. *With Honors* (1994): This film "makes the point that book-smarts aren't much without a real world application, explaining the difference between a degree and an education" (Tobin 2008).

10. *Back to School* (1986): "Wild parties, extreme pool diving sequences and general insanity ensue" (Tobin 2008) as a result of a fun-loving millionaire enrolling in college to convince his disillusioned son not to drop out.

Yet, despite the more contemporary reality of the films enumerated above, there remains a nostalgic belief and feeling toward the college experience that is rooted in a pre-1960s sense of the societal norms.

PLANTED IN THE PRESENT

The acknowledgment of sexual assault in society only came late in the twentieth century. Ironically, it was the issue of spousal or marital rape that brought the issue into public awareness.

> Until the late 1970s, most states did not consider spousal rape a crime. Typically, spouses were exempted from sexual assault laws. For example, until 1993 North Carolina law stated that "a person may not be prosecuted under this article if the victim is the person's legal spouse at the time of the commission of the alleged rape or sexual offense unless the parties are living separate and apart." [North Caroline Gen. Stat. § 14-27 (1979)] These laws are traceable to a pronouncement by Michael Hale, who was Chief Justice in England in the seventeenth century, that a husband cannot be guilty of rape of his wife "for by their mutual matrimonial consent and contract the wife hath given up herself in this kind unto the husband which she cannot retract" [Russell (1990)]. In the late 1970s, advocates began efforts to change these laws. Currently, rape of a spouse is a crime in all fifty states and the District of Columbia. (VAWnet.org, 2000)

Until the late 1970s, it was difficult to find any recognition of this or any other kind of nonstranger rape. Sexual assault on college campuses was unheard of. It was not acknowledged or spoken of; educating about or responding to it was inconceivable. Why should there be a response to something that doesn't happen?

A 1991 *Time* magazine article changed the focus on the issue forever. In a June 3 article, the magazine related "the story of Katie Koestner, a woman who dared to speak out against a silent epidemic. A graduate of the College of William and Mary, Katie was sexually assaulted by a fellow student, someone she met during her first week of school" (Trellisinteractive, 1991).

Despite the awakening that occurred on campuses across the nation, there remains, for many, a sense of denial. There is denial that sexual violence occurs, but even more insidious is the tendency of some to try to hide it and keep it from being reported. For as many task forces, committees, hotlines, and educational posters that have been created, there are as many individuals who encourage students to change their story, forget it happened, and, above all, to not report. It is this act of choosing to ignore the cries of those who have been sexually assaulted that creates a culture where addressing sexual violence is unacceptable.

CHANGING THE CULTURE

So how do campus service providers encourage leaders to change their thinking and foster an atmosphere where reporting and action are considered positive campus activities? It is necessary first to look at the barriers to doing so.

Aside from the tendency to want to see only the positive "ivy covered wall" side of college life, it is important to consider the factors that capture the thoughts of boards of trustees, presidents, parents, and community members. Although they genuinely care about students, these groups, as well as others, have to be additionally concerned about public perception and image. The future of the institution depends on the external assessments of others.

Some of these external constituents include:

- *Legislatures and politicians:* Regardless of whether an institution is public or private, urban or rural, large or small, how an institution is viewed by local and state legislatures has an impact on the incitation. Direct and indirect funding, grants, and aid can easily be influenced by the positive intervention of those elected to represent the people served by the institution. Too much press that may be considered negative can have an impact on their willingness to fight for dollars on behalf of the college or university.

- *Alumni:* The respect that alumni feel for their alma mater weighs heavily on the mind of campus leaders. Not only do they play a significant role in the annual donation and endowment strategy of an institution, they also play an important role in furthering enrollment. Dissatisfied alumni will not "talk up" the college to young people they know, and they can have a profoundly negative impact on those thinking about attending the institution if they so choose.

- *Media:* Giving the local media an impression that there is "a problem" at the institution may also affect enrollment. This could be true not only for new, but for current students as well. Reports of sexual assault, even scrutiny of the annual Clery (see Chapter 4 and Appendix D) statistics could raise awareness of the issue that is unwelcome.

- *Community members:* Most people do not want to live in a community that has a crime problem. If a college or university begins to report large numbers of sexual assaults, it could appear that the surrounding communities are unsafe, thus inhibiting growth of the area and the financial well-being that accompanies it.

- *Parents:* No parents look to send their child off to a place that may be unsafe. Reports of any crime may make the parents uneasy, but violations of a sexual nature naturally cause great concern. Unless an institution is prepared with an active strategy that encourages education, reporting, and response, such information only will serve to frighten caring parents away for fear their child will be in danger on the campus.

- *University counsel:* The liability that may be incurred by admitting that a violation of a sexual nature happened on campus may cause legal representatives of the college or university to shy aware from admitting that there is a problem for fear of being sued and having to pay damages because the school is perceived as having "deep pockets."

- *Law enforcement:* Campus and local law enforcement may be enmeshed in traditional and outmoded beliefs that "she asked for it," "boys will be boys," or "no doesn't mean no." It may also be that the local ethos of the community has not evolved beyond these same sentiments, and to take reports and try and prosecute offenders is a waste of their time and efforts.

There are also internal constituents that may thwart an atmosphere of openness:

- *Faculty and staff:* For many of the same reasons listed above, faculty and staff may be reluctant to support a culture that actively encourages reporting sexual assaults. They may feel that to work in an institution where such things occur is beneath them or will impact the way they are perceived by colleagues at other colleges or universities. They may unintentionally project attitudes and beliefs that dissuade students from feeling safe in this environment.

- *Students:* It can be difficult for adolescents (i.e., traditionally aged students) to admit that they cannot handle all matters that come their way. They may be reluctant to admit, even to their peers, that they found themselves in a situation that went awry. Thus, peer pressure may create an informal culture that actively discourages students from coming forward and reporting sexual assault. Since most assaults against students are committed by someone known, and often trusted, by the victim, students struggle to recognize the incident as a sexual assault because it would mean applying the label "rapist" to a peer. If the offender is well known and popular on campus, victims may also incur pressure from friends to discourage reporting. The involvement of alcohol and/or drug use by the victim exacerbates these issues. Victims may blame the incident on their own behaviors, fear punishment from administrators, and fear not being believed by administrators due to poor recollection of the incident.

Therefore, whether overt or covert, external or internal, the messages that reinforce denial and silence may be very strong on the campus. Breaking these barriers and eliminating the fears that accompany them are essential to creating a culture of openness.

BLOSSOMS FOR THE FUTURE: FUNDAMENTAL PRINCIPLES OF VICTIM SUPPORT

The change in culture required to create an effective campus sexual assault response must first come from "the top." The highest level administrators must, whether through explicit or implicit action, give permission for the campus responders and care givers to act. They must understand that encouraging students to report will cause an increase in national Clery (see Chapter 4 and Appendix D) statistics and other publicity. However, if necessary they must be persuaded that a perceived negative can actually be a positive. The most important factor in this change is to turn a culture of silence into one that embraces variance and does not shy away from conflict. This is not at all easy, but the fundamental principles of victim support must be maintained and promulgated. These include:

- Don't criticize;

- Do understand;

- Do listen to their reasons;

- Do help distinguish between "if only's" and "guilt";

- Don't oversimplify;

- Do reassure them that you are there;

- Don't take control;

- Do help them to feel safe;

- Don't frighten them;

- Don't direct anger at them;

- Don't blame yourself;

- Don't speak for them;

- Do encourage a medical checkup; and

- Don't expect too much of yourself (Healthyplace.com, 2008).

It is unrealistic to expect that all members of the community will be able to remember all of these points or be able to effectively manage them if they do. The responsibility of senior management is to provide an environment where the appropriate constituents can serve as both educators and advocates. Making this an active and expected first step for community response will encourage the campus to support students in their efforts to report.

While it is difficult, insensitive, and even crass to discuss, the public reaction to sexual assault on campus is a critical component of the campus culture. Liability and public image are probably the greatest inhibitors to a climate of openness, and they are also the most important to change. In fact, gaining control of these factors will be 95 percent of all that is necessary to change a campus culture.

Institutional liability is a grave concern of presidents and senior management. Colleges and universities that hid what happened on campus and pretended that the ivy tower facade was impenetrable were places that faced greater criticism and more damage when a sexual assault occurred.

In today's society, where the media and the Internet often report and control a story before the university's public relations staff has a chance to decide how to release that story and manage the details, it is naive to believe that no one will care about such a story or that the press will not try to get every juicy detail. The transparency that an institution displays and the readiness to share information is clearly the best way to survive such a public relations attack.

Making this kind of incident an unfortunate but not sensational event can mitigate the public relations damage as well as the institutional liability. Publicly acknowledging that sexual assault can and does happen on campus can help the institution come out on the plus side of a news story or a lawsuit. Despite their care for students, senior management is also responsible to the institution, alumni, and boards. Unfortunately, some members of those groups may be more interested in how the institution is perceived in these situations than in the best interests of a victim. Providing a proactive defense by actively addressing sexual assault through education, prevention, and response will not only serve students well, but all other constituents as well. This is a win-win-win proposition and one that, if embraced by management, can make a positive change in the campus culture.

The remaining 5 percent required to change the culture is the confidence senior management has in the services that sexual assault response care givers provide to victims. Also related to the liability concern, is that, if there is a belief that students will be taken care of quickly and appropriately, the problems associated with lawsuits and poor publicity will be minimized. That makes the role of the Sexual Assault Response Team (SART) extremely important to the institution, senior management, and students. This is another win-win-win proposition.

CONCLUSION

A successful institutional commitment to providing an appropriate and supportive response to sexual assault is dependent upon a campus culture that has a high tolerance for risk. The key to developing such a culture is having open-minded senior administrators at the top. If they do not already fit that description, it is necessary to try to change them and the culture that they create and maintain.

The three most important factors that will affect the ability to make that change are:

- The senior officers have a belief in the need to support and care for campus victims of sexual assault.

- The senior officers have confidence in the abilities of the SART.

- The senior officers understand that contrary to conventional wisdom, truth and openness about the fact that such heinous acts occur on campus, and that they have a coordinated response plan, can actually put the institution in a positive and constructive light.

While the methods to secure change on the second two points will vary from campus to campus, without the fundamental belief in victim support and advocacy expressed in the first bulleted item, there is no chance of making a change in the campus culture. However, this level of callousness is extremely rare in higher education and is often mistaken for what is actually the fear of bad publicity. This can be corrected by sharing with the senior officers the positive and negative press that institutions have received for being open or hiding the facts, respectively.

The desire to help and assist victims will make these efforts meaningful and less onerous. While it may take a while to convince those in a position to approve the creation of a SART, the endeavor will obviously be a significant step toward building a supportive campus environment. Changing campus cultures may not be easy or insignificant but are certainly worth the effort. Building a peaceful and nonviolent campus atmosphere is a major component of the foundation that supports positive student development. Serving as a catalyst for this type of change is a considerable achievement for any professional.

Finally, or more aptly, the beginning of creating a new campus culture will be a result of these efforts, and the community, with all of its many constituent groups, will be a better place to live, work, and learn.

References

Armstrong, S., Gordon, J., Weinstein, B., Weinstein H. (Executive Producers), & Van Sant, G. (Director). (1997). *Good Will Hunting* [Motion picture]. United States: Be Gentlemen Limited Partnership.

Avary, R., Butan, M., Deutch, J., Hadida, S., Oglesby, M., Ortenbergy, T., et al. (Executive Producers), & Avary, R. (Director). (2002). *The rules of attraction* [Motion picture]. Netherlands: Kingsgate Films.

Endler, E., Endler, M., Ramis, H. (Executive Producers), & Metter, A. (Director). (1984). *Back to school* [Motion picture]. United States: Paper Clip.

Field, T., Samuelson, P. (Producers), & Kanew, J. (Director). (1984). *Revenge of the nerds* [Motion picture]. United States: Interscope Communications.

Golden, D. (Executive Producer), & Hiller, A. (Director). (1970). *Love story* [Motion picture]. United States: Love Story Company.

Guber, P., Peters, J. (Executive Producers), & Keshishian, A. (Director). (1994). *With honors* [Motion picture]. United States: Spring Creek Productions.

Hall, P., Singleton, J. (Producers), & Singleton, J. (Director). (1995). *Higher learning* [Motion picture]. United States: Columbia Pictures.

Healthyplace.com. *Supporting someone who has been raped or sexually assaulted.* Retrieved May 19, 2008, from http://www.healthyplace.com/Communities/Abuse/lisk/family_friends.html

Pollock T., Reitman, I. (Executive Producers), & Phillips, T. (Director). (2003). *Old school* [Motion picture]. United States: Dreamworks Pictures.

Reitman, I., Simmons, M. (Producers), & Landis, J. (Director). (1978). *Animal house* [Motion picture]. United States: Universal Pictures.

Russell, D. E. H. (1990). *Rape in marriage* (Rev. ed.). Bloomington: University of Indiana Press.

Schiff, P. (Producer), & Bochner, H. (Director). (1994). *PCU* [Motion picture]. Canada: Twentieth Century Fox.

Schwary, R. L.(Executive Producer), & Brest, M. (Director). (1992). *Scent of a woman* [Motion picture]. United States: City Light Films.

Tobin, K. (2008). Top 10 college movies of all time. *Young Money.* Retrieved July 11, 2008, from http://www.youngmoney.com/entertainment/movies/040305_01

Trellisinteractive.com. (1991). "Date Rape" College of William and Mary. Retrieved May 18, 2008, from http://www.trellisinteractive.com/nfa/colchronology.html

VAWnet.org. (2000). Spousal rape laws. Retrieved May 20, 2008, from http://new.vawnet.org/Assoc_Files_VAWnet/SpousalRape.pdf

Wallis, H. B. (Executive Producer), & Bacon, L. (Director). (1940). *Knute Rockne: All American* [Motion picture]. United States: First National Pictures.

Chapter 2

Impact of Alcohol and Other Drugs on Campus Sexual Violence— Prevention and Response

by William DeJong, Ph.D., and Linda Langford, Sc.D.

ALCOHOL AND OTHER DRUG USE ON COLLEGE CAMPUSES

The problem of sexual assault on American college campuses cannot be addressed without understanding common patterns of student alcohol and other drug (AOD) use. This section, examines the scope of AOD-related problems at U.S. institutions of higher education (IHEs), the factors that cause students to drink or use other drugs, and whether there is a campus culture of alcohol use.

Extent of Alcohol Use

National surveys typically find that about 40 percent of undergraduates engage in heavy episodic drinking, which is often defined as having five or more drinks in a row at least once in a two-week period (O'Malley & Johnston, 2002). Half of these students, or about 20 percent overall, report drinking at this level three or more times in the previous two weeks (Wechsler et al., 2002a). One study estimated the rate of alcohol dependence among college students at 6 percent, based on self-reported drinking behaviors (Knight et al., 2002).

Each year, approximately 1,700 students (eighteen to twenty-four years old) enrolled in two- and four-year institutions die from alcohol-related causes, mostly due to motor vehicle crashes. More than 600,000 students in this age range are hit or assaulted by another drinking student, while an estimated 97,000 are victims of alcohol-related sexual assault or date rape (Hingson, Heeren, Winter, & Wechsler, 2005).

The National Institute on Alcohol Abuse and Alcoholism (NIAAA) summarized this data by characterizing heavy drinking by college students as widespread, dangerous, and disruptive (NIAAA Task Force on College Drinking, 2002).

Predictors of Campus Alcohol Use

Several factors predict which students are most likely to drink heavily: (1) male gender (O'Malley & Johnston, 2002), (2) white race/ethnicity (O'Malley & Johnston, 2002), (3) fraternity or sorority membership (Baer, 2002), and (4) participation in competitive athletics (Baer, 2002). Students younger than twenty-one years tend to drink on fewer occasions than their older peers, but they drink more per occasion and have more alcohol-related problems than students of legal drinking age (Wechsler, Lee, Nelson, & Kuo, 2002b).

What motivates students to use alcohol? Researchers have identified three psychological functions or needs that alcohol use fulfills: (1) to facilitate affiliation with other people, (2) to induce positive emotions, and (3) to mitigate or avoid negative emotional states (Cooper, Russell, Skinner, & Windle, 1992; Cronin, 1997; Stewart, Zeitlin, & Samoluk, 1996). Some researchers have proposed a fourth motivate for college students: to conform to perceived social norms (Cooper, 1994; Perkins, 2002). Borjesson and Dunn (2001) found that, for both males and females, drinking correlated most strongly with expectancies of social facilitation.

Other researchers have studied how people's beliefs about the behavioral, emotional, and cognitive effects of alcohol affect alcohol consumption (Baer, 2002). Generally, heavy alcohol use and problem drinking are more common among people who have positive expectancies about what alcohol can do (Carey, 1995; Werner, Walker, & Greene, 1995). Interestingly, positive alcohol expectancies are associated with increased negative consequences, even when controlling statistically for the level of alcohol use (Park & Grant, 2005).

Positive alcohol expectancies can be divided into three primary domains: activity and performance enhancement, tension reduction, and social lubrication (Sher, Wood, Wood, & Raskin, 1996). Believing that alcohol use can disinhibit sexual behavior or enhance the sexual experience is associated with both increased drinking (Carey, 1995; O'Hare, 2005) and sexual risk-taking (Fromme, D'Amico, & Katz, 1999; Leigh, 1990; O'Hare, 2005).

Is There a Campus Drinking "Culture?"

The landmark report on college drinking by the NIAAA (2002) concluded that drinking in higher education settings can be characterized as a "culture," meaning that there are alcohol-related traditions, beliefs, and expectations that permeate campus life and are handed down through generations of college students. Indeed, alcohol is easy to spot in campus communities. It is served at tailgating parties before sporting events, promoted through drink specials at neighborhood bars, glamorized in images of intoxicated students on television shows depicting spring break, and normalized in conversations among students and in tales told by their parents. There is no question that these images actively promote collegiate drinking and reinforce its status as a cultural rite of passage.

It is important to realize, however, that these visible reminders actually misrepresent the true extent of campus drinking. While a substantial minority of college students drink in high-risk ways and cause significant consequences, data show that drinking levels among college students are overestimated, both by students themselves and the public at large (Perkins, 2002, 2003). About one in five college students abstains from alcohol entirely, which equals the proportion of students who drink most heavily, and the remaining 60 percent of students drink more moderately (Wechsler et al., 2002a). Thus, while there are many drinking rituals embedded in college culture, it is important to note that heavy drinking is *not* the general norm among college students.

Other Drug Use

Among U.S. college students, marijuana is the most commonly used illicit drug. In 2006, the Monitoring the Future study reported that 30.2 percent of the full-time students surveyed used marijuana in the past year, while 18.1 percent had used illicit drugs other than marijuana. Among the other street drugs, hallucinogens (at 5.6 percent) were the most commonly used. Additional illicit drug use levels were as follows: cocaine—5.1 percent; inhalants—1.5 percent; and methamphetamine—1.2 percent (Johnston, O'Malley, Bachman, & Schulenberg, 2007).

College students also abuse several prescription medications. In 2006, annual rates of prescription opioid misuse stood as follows: Vicodin, 7.6 percent and OxyContin, 3.0 percent. Fully 3.9 percent reported misuse of the stimulant Ritalin in the past year, while tranquilizer misuse stood at 5.8 percent and sedative (barbiturate) misuse at 3.4 percent. Steroid use was uncommon, at 0.8 percent (Johnston et al., 2007).

Ecstasy (or MDMA) was the most frequently used "club drug," with 2.6 percent of students reporting use in 2006. Usage peaked in the early 2000s, when nearly 10 percent of college students reported using the drug in the past year. Other club drugs are used far less often: gamma hydroxybutyrate (GHB), less than 0.05 percent; ketamine, 0.9 percent; and Rohypnol, 0.2 percent (Johnston et al., 2007). These three drugs are frequently cited in press accounts as "date rape drugs," but the drug most commonly used in predatory sexual assaults is alcohol (ElSohly & Salamone, 1999).

A survey conducted by the National Center on Addiction and Substance Abuse at Columbia University (2007) found that students with diagnosed depression, compared to other students, are more likely to have used marijuana, used other illicit drugs, and abused prescription drugs. Other factors predicting other drug use include male gender (Johnston et al., 2007), white race/ethnicity (Johnston et al., 2007), and membership in a fraternity or sorority (National Center on Addiction and Substance Abuse at Columbia University, 2007).

Students name a variety of reasons for using other drugs. Generally, students say they use drugs out of curiosity, to fit in socially, to relieve boredom, or simply to feel "high" (National Center on Addiction and Substance Abuse at Columbia University, 2007). Other cited reasons vary by drug. According to the National Institute on Drug Abuse (NIDA), people use marijuana to enhance sensation, relieve stress, or feel "high." Cocaine use can create a powerful euphoria and a rush of energy (National Institute on Drug Abuse [NIDA], 2007). College students report using Ecstasy and other club drugs to improve mood, boost energy, increase sociability, release inhibitions, increase mental clarity, and enhance sensory perception and sexual experience (Wish, Fitzelle, O'Grady, Hsu, & Arria, 2006). Students often use stimulants to fuel concentration and longer study sessions (NIDA, 2007; Teter, McCabe, LaGrange, Cranford, & Boyd, 2006) but also to intensify the experience of "partying"

(White, Becker-Blease, & Grace-Bishop, 2006) or to lose weight (National Center on Addiction and Substance Abuse at Columbia University, 2007).

It should be noted that there is a clear relationship between drinking and other substance use. A 1993 national survey of college students showed that alcohol abstainers were the least likely to have used other drugs during the past year, while heavy drinkers were the most likely (Wechsler, Moeykens, Davenport, Castillo, & Hansen, 1995). Despite the dangers of other drug use, illicit drugs create far fewer health and safety problems on campus than alcohol.

SCIENCE-BASED APPROACHES TO AOD PREVENTION

There are several science-based approaches to AOD prevention. This work is of direct relevance to the subject of sexual violence, not only because this problem is impacted by the fact that large numbers of students drink and use drugs, but also because the philosophical approach that guides AOD prevention work can be adapted to address campus sexual assault.

For many years, campus officials limited their AOD prevention efforts to changing people's knowledge, attitudes, and behavioral intentions (e.g., awareness programs, peer education); protecting students from short-term consequences (e.g., safe ride or designated driver programs); and intervening with and treating students with substance use problems (DeJong & Langford, 2002). One of the chief lessons taught by nearly two decades of prevention research is the need for a more comprehensive approach, one that not only addresses the educational and treatment needs of individuals but also seeks to bring about basic change at the institutional, community, and societal level, often through changes in public policy (DeJong & Langenbahn, 1996).[1]

Environmental Prevention Strategies

Guided by the research of DeJong and Langenbahn (1996), campus administrators have begun to embrace *environmental management*, a broader approach to AOD prevention that focuses on environmental change to reduce both the appeal and availability of AODs (DeJong et al., 1998). Research evidence supports this approach (Bonnie & O'Connell, 2004; NIAAA Task Force on College Drinking, 2002). A recent evaluation of ten campus and community coalitions found small but significant decreases in student alcohol use and related problems at the five campuses that implemented the greatest number of environmental change strategies, compared with control group campuses (Weitzman, Nelson, Lee, & Wechsler, 2004).

Environmental management has five constituent strategies, each of which focuses on a specific problem in typical college environments. Each strategy involves multiple program and policy options for administrators to consider (Zimmerman & DeJong, 2003).

---

[1]This approach to prevention is intellectually grounded in the field of public health, which emphasizes the broader physical, social, cultural, and institutional forces that contribute to problems of human health and safety (Wallack, Dorfman, Jernigan, & Themba, 1993). Prevention work in the public health arena has been guided by a social ecological framework, which recognizes that any health-related behavior, including college student drinking, is affected through multiple levels of influence: intrapersonal (individual) factors, interpersonal (group) processes, institutional factors, community factors, and public policies (Stokols, 1996).

Strategy #1: Offer and Promote Events and Activities That Do Not Include AOD.
Many campus administrators are investing additional resources to create and promote
substance-free events and activities; provide greater financial support to substance-
free student clubs and organizations; open or expand a student center, gym, or other
substance-free settings; and develop student service learning or volunteer activities.

Strategy #2: Create an Environment That Supports Health-Promoting Norms.
Available options include modifying the academic schedule to increase the number of
early morning and Friday classes, increasing academic standards so that students will
need to spend additional time studying out of class, increasing faculty-student contact,
and improving faculty-student mentoring (DeJong & Langenbahn, 1996).

Social norms marketing campaigns are designed to convey accurate information
about student alcohol use in order to counter widespread misperceptions of campus
drinking norms and thereby drive down consumption. Several colleges and universities have reported success using campus-wide media campaigns, with student surveys
revealing both more accurate perceptions of actual drinking behavior on campus and
decreases in reported heavy episodic drinking (Perkins, 2003).

Strategy #3: Limit Availability of AODs On and Off Campus. Campus officials can
enforce policies that limit the times and places that alcohol is available to students on
campus. Key strategies include prohibiting delivery or use of kegs or other common
containers, controlling or eliminating alcohol sales at sporting events, and disseminating
and enforcing guidelines for registered parties (Toomey, Lenk, & Wagenaar, 2007).

Community-based strategies include limiting both the number of alcohol outlets
near campus and the days or hours of alcohol sales, eliminating low-cost promotions, requiring keg registration, and prohibiting home delivery of alcohol purchases
(Toomey et al., 2007). Another key strategy is to implement responsible beverage
service (RBS) training programs (Saltz & Stanghetta, 1997).

Vigorous federal, state, and local enforcement efforts are already in place to
reduce the supply of illicit drugs. Campus officials can work with law enforcement
agencies to identify where students are getting illicit drugs and then take action by
arresting and prosecuting dealers (DeJong, 2006).

Strategy #4: Restrict Marketing and Promotion of AODs. Campus officials have
wide latitude to ban or restrict alcohol advertising on campus and to limit the content of party or event announcements (DeJong, in press). Likewise, they can prohibit
on-campus advertising of rave clubs and related events where club drug use may be
encouraged or tolerated. Student party announcements that allude to illicit drug use
can similarly be forbidden (DeJong, 2006). Off-campus, campus, and community
officials can work together to eliminate alcohol promotions that offer low-priced drink
specials or otherwise promote high-risk drinking (DeJong & Langenbahn, 1996).

Strategy #5: Develop and Enforce Campus Policies and Government Laws.
Campus administrators should authorize and encourage campus police to work in
partnership with local law enforcement agencies to uphold campus policies and local,
state, and federal laws. Statutes of particular concern include laws that prohibit the
distribution or possession of illegal drugs, alcohol possession by minors, providing
alcohol to minors, alcohol-impaired driving, and neighborhood disturbances (DeJong,
in press). After reviewing the scientific literature, the NIAA Task Force on College

Drinking (2002) also recommended that campus and other local officials focus on restricting the density of alcohol retail outlets and increasing prices and excise taxes on alcoholic beverages.

While strongly reinforcing the environmental management approach, the NIAAA Task Force also noted the importance of targeting individual students who are identi-fied as problem, at-risk, or alcohol-dependent drinkers (NIAAA Task Force on College Drinking, 2002). Required here are strategies to engage these students in appropriate screening and intervention services (Larimer & Cronce, 2007).

A program called BASICS (Brief Alcohol Screening and Intervention for College Students), for example, uses two brief motivational interview sessions to give students feedback about their drinking and provide them with an opportunity to craft a plan for reducing their alcohol consumption (Baer, Kivlahan, Blume, McKnight, & Marlatt, 2001). Researchers are investigating Web-site–based tools with computerized feedback as a means of implementing this type of brief intervention program on a larger scale (Lewis, Neighbors, Oster-Aaland, Kirkeby, & Larimer, 2007; Neighbors, Larimer, & Lewis, 2004).

Build Campus and Community Infrastructure

Moving forward with a comprehensive prevention agenda requires a layered infrastructure (DeJong et al., 2007). On campus, there needs to be a *permanent task force* that represents several important constituencies, including key administrative staff, faculty, and students, and reports directly to the president. To facilitate prevention work in the surrounding community, campus officials need to participate in a *campus and community coalition*. The coalition's membership must be broad and include such groups as neighborhood residents, the business community, public health agencies, health care providers, faith-based institutions, law enforcement, and substance abuse treatment. Action at the state level, including the development and operation of multiple campus and community coalitions and the development of state-level policy, can be fostered through campus membership in a *statewide association of academic prevention leaders*.

Engage in a Strategic Planning Process

Because the extent and nature of AOD problems vary across IHEs, and because each campus community is unique, there is no simple or "one-size-fits-all" solution to student AOD problems. The key to implementing successful programs and policies is a *strategic planning process* that enables campuses to tailor promising approaches to their local problems, structures, and culture (Langford & DeJong, 2008). Effective strategic planning involves the steps listed below. While this process is presented as a linear progression, in practice a planning group will often rework earlier steps as more information is gathered and assessed.

1. *Conduct a problem analysis.* This step involves gathering evidence on the nature and scope of the problem, examining available resources and assets in the campus community, and analyzing and summarizing this information to clarify needs and opportunities.

2. *Establish long-term goals and objectives.* Each item should focus on the *changes* in people or the environment that are needed to reduce the magnitude of the problem.

3. *Consult research, program experience, and behavior change theory to identify potential strategies.* This step should be done only after the institution's long-term goals and objectives are specified.

4. *Create a strategic plan.* This step involves assessing the intervention options and deciding on a set of strategies; translating the selected strategies into specific activities, such as new policies, media campaigns, and student services programs; creating a "logic model" that describes the intervention components and explains how they are expected to achieve the desired goals and objectives; and creating a work plan.

5. *Execute an iterative evaluation plan.* Work is required to monitor implementation of the work plan, evaluate the programs and policies, and using the findings to guide improvements, and then continuing to evaluate.

A good planning process will result in a well-designed statement of problems, assets, and needs, which also provides baseline data for the evaluation; the selection of policies and programs that have demonstrated effectiveness or a solid foundation in behavior change theory; precisely stated goals and objectives, which allow measurable outcomes to be specified; a summary of the prevention initiative that links each program and policy to specific objectives; and the marshalling of adequate resources to ensure full implementation of the program plan.

Conclusion

While its scope is frequently overestimated, substance abuse is an ongoing problem on college campuses with significant negative effects on campus health and safety. In the last decade, the higher education field has made great strides in determining the best approaches to campus AOD prevention, which entails engaging in a strategic planning process to assess local campus problems and adopting locally tailored, multifaceted, and sustained approaches, all informed by an environmental management framework. Understanding the complex causes of substance abuse and the best approaches to prevention are critical in addressing alcohol-related sexual violence.

SUBSTANCE ABUSE AND SEXUAL VIOLENCE ON COLLEGE CAMPUSES

Like substance abuse, sexual violence[2] among college students is a serious and multifaceted problem, which is made even more complex by the frequent AOD involvement of both perpetrators and victims. This section describes how the public health-based approaches described above apply to sexual violence on college campuses; reviews the research on the extent and nature of AOD involvement in sexual violence; and describes how AOD involvement affects institutional, social, and victim responses to sexual violence. The chapter concludes with recommendations for addressing AOD-related sexual assault as part of a comprehensive program.

---

[2]The term *sexual violence* is used as general term in this chapter to describe a continuum of behaviors, including rape, attempted rape, unwanted touching, sexual harassment, and non-contact sexual abuse (e.g., voyeurism, online harassment; Basile & Saltzman, 2002).

Applying a Public Health Approach to Sexual Violence

Building Comprehensive Efforts. While application of the public health model to substance abuse is not new, use of this framework to address violence, injury, and suicide is relatively recent (American College Health Association [ACHA], 2004; Centers for Disease Control and Prevention, 2004; Commission for the Prevention of Youth Violence, 2000; Davis, Parks, & Cohen, 2006; Mercy, Rosenberg, Powell, Broome, & Roper, 1993; National Center for Injury Prevention and Control, 1993; U.S. Public Health Service, 1999). Traditionally, campus responses to crime and violence have focused on only one aspect of this model: reacting to specific incidents with a mix of criminal justice, disciplinary, mental health, and victim advocacy interventions. Such efforts are essential to maintaining a safe environment, and strong enforcement and victim advocacy efforts send a clear message about an institution's intolerance for violent behavior. Importantly, the public health model emphasizes the importance of expanding these traditional efforts to include both prevention and early intervention.

Thus, public health initiatives to address sexual violence fall into three categories based on when those interventions occur (Centers for Disease Control and Prevention, 2004):

- *Primary prevention* takes place before sexual violence occurs. These approaches aim to prevent violence altogether by targeting underlying causes and creating safe and health-promoting environments.[3]

- *Secondary prevention* approaches address early signs of violence to prevent further escalation.

- *Tertiary prevention* includes steps taken after an act of sexual violence to minimize long-term consequences and recurrence.

The terms *prevention, early intervention,* and *response and treatment* are more commonly used to describe this continuum of interventions (see Table 2.1). Collectively, these efforts constitute a comprehensive approach to campus violence and safety.

Also important is *where* problems occur. While colleges and universities generally have less control over off-campus settings, it is important to remember that many assaults occur off campus. This underscores the importance of collaborating with community-based organizations when striving to create a comprehensive effort.

Addressing Underlying Causes. A public health approach to sexual violence suggests that, like infectious diseases, violent behavior has multiple determinants that can be identified and addressed, thereby preventing the targeted problems. The strategic planning process described above (see "Engage in a Strategic Planning Process") can also guide this work. The early stages of this process are particularly critical for creating

---

[3]An important distinction has emerged in the literature between *prevention* and *outreach/ awareness* activities. Outreach/awareness efforts focus on conveying basic information such as definitions of sexual assault and rape, prevalence data, the problem's underlying dynamics, laws and statutes, and guidelines for helping a survivor. By themselves, these efforts establish an important foundation for prevention but are not sufficient to change behavior and prevent sexual violence from occurring. True prevention efforts require an intensive set of programs that focus on addressing the underlying factors—at all levels of the social ecological model— that promote sexual violence (Campus Response Committee of the Oregon Attorney General's Sexual Assault Task Force, 2006).

Table 2.1
Continuum of Prevention and Response to Sexual Violence

	Prevention	Early Intervention	Response and Treatment
Goals	Prevent problems by reducing risk factors, promoting protective factors, and creating health-promoting environments	Intervene early to address problem behaviors, situations, and environments	Assist victims, sanction and treat offenders, respond to crisis, and assist the community in dealing with the aftermath of violence

successful primary prevention efforts: conducting a thorough analysis of the problems, identifying the risk and protective factors that contribute to those problems, and setting clear goals and objectives for change based on this analysis.

As the social ecological model suggests, prevention efforts will need to address a broad spectrum of factors that contribute to sexual violence as identified through a local assessment of campus conditions. A comprehensive program will seek to make changes in multiple domains, including factors such as individual attitudes, beliefs, perceptions, and skills; normative factors; policies and enforcement; student support services for students, and disciplinary measures. While the concept of *environmental management* originally focused on AOD prevention (DeJong et al., 1998), the importance of supplementing individual change efforts with initiatives designed to shape the social, cultural, and legal environment is equally important for sexual violence prevention (Langford, 2004).

Sexual violence efforts should draw from existing research and theory to inform programs and policies. The literature in this field continues to grow, and recent major reviews of sexual assault prevention interventions offer useful guidance, especially about what *does not* work. Despite these advances, however, there is no simple answer to the question of "what works" to prevent sexual violence. Many campus-based sexual violence programs and policies have not been evaluated, and the existing studies often lack rigor, making definitive conclusions impossible (Bachar & Koss, 2000). In addition, every campus community is unique, and therefore even the best studies will not yield a simple or "one-size-fits-all" solution to sexual violence.

As with AOD programs, campus officials will need to tailor sexual violence efforts to their local problems, structures, and culture (Langford, 2004). To do this, it is critical to develop a thorough understanding of the research literature that describes the extent of AOD involvement in sexual violence, the nature of these links, and the effect of AOD involvement on institutional, social, and victim responses to sexual violence. This literature, reviewed below, can be used as part of the strategic planning process to guide a local problem analysis and inform the process of developing or revising programs and policies.

AOD Involvement in Campus Sexual Violence

This section reviews the research on the co-occurrence of AOD and campus sexual violence. While both alcohol and drugs are implicated in campus sexual violence, the focus is more on alcohol because it is by far the most commonly used substance on college campuses, and there is more research on this topic. It is important to state at the outset that, while AOD use appears to be one contributor to sexual violence, substance use does not justify sexually aggressive behavior by perpetrators, nor does it make victims culpable for their victimization.

Co-Occurrence of Alcohol Use and Sexual Violence. Research finds a consistent positive association between alcohol use and sexual violence (Abbey, 2002; Abbey, Zawacki, & McAuslan, 2000; Bachar & Koss, 2000; Wood & Sher, 2002). In a review of the literature, Abbey (2002) concluded that at least half of all sexual assaults involving college students are associated with alcohol consumption by the victim, the offender, or both. While the literature reports a confusing array of statistics regarding alcohol involvement in sexual assault,[4] this estimate is based on a review of many studies and therefore can be considered reliable. Importantly, this estimate was also confirmed by a recent longitudinal study (Banyard et al., 2005a).

When alcohol is involved in a sexual assault, the majority of the time both the victim and the perpetrator have been drinking (Abbey, Clinton-Sherrod, McAuslan, Zawacki, & Buck, 2003; Abbey, McAuslan, & Ross, 1998; Zawacki, Abbey, Buck, McAuslan, & Clinton-Sherrod, 2003). Notably, alcohol is present in many social interactions where no assault occurs, indicating that alcohol consumption *alone* does not cause sexual violence. As described earlier, studies show that a substantial minority of college students drink in high-risk ways (Wechsler et al., 2002a), but most of these students are not involved in sexual violence. Likewise, many men assault women without being intoxicated. Thus, substance use is neither necessary nor sufficient for sexual aggression (Abbey, 2002; Marchell & Cummings, 2001; Testa, 2004; Wood & Sher, 2002).

Co-Occurrence of Other Drugs and Sexual Violence. While alcohol is by far the most frequent substance involved in sexual violence, other drugs may be involved as well. Studies find that when these drugs are used by victims or perpetrators, they are often used in conjunction with alcohol (Testa & Livingston, 1999; Ullman, Karabatsos, & Koss, 1999b; Wood & Sher, 2002). Research finds frequent use of "drug tactics" by college students, which is defined as the deliberate use of drugs or alcohol to coerce victims into unwanted intercourse and to decrease their likelihood of reporting (Warkentin & Gidycz, 2007). Perpetrators may also take advantage of a victim's voluntary use of substances to obtain sex. Both overt and covert use of drugs and alcohol often serve to decrease the perpetrator's sense of responsibility for the assault and can heighten a victim's self-blame (Warkentin & Gidycz, 2007). In most state statutes, however, the legal definition of rape includes penetration while the victim is incapacitated or otherwise incapable of giving consent due to self-induced or forced intoxication, among other reasons (National Institute of Justice, n.d.).

Drug-facilitated sexual assault (DFSA) occurs when the voluntary or involuntary ingestion of a drug by a victim results in an act of sexual activity without consent (Papadodima, Athanaselis, & Spiliopoulou, 2007). Drugs used to facilitate rape can

---

[4]Differences among individual study findings are attributable to methodological differences such as the source of the data, the definitions and measures of substance use and sexual violence, the population studied, the characteristics of respondents, the perceived confidentiality of responses, and the study context (e.g., a "health survey" may elicit different responses than a "crime survey"; Bachar & Koss, 2000; Wood & Sher, 2002). When examining statistics, it is advisable to examine each study's definitions and data collection methods and consider the implications of these choices for the reported data (Langford, Isaac, and Finn, under review).

include marijuana, cocaine, benzodiazepines (including Rohypnol), GHB, barbiturates, morphine, lysergic acid diethylamide (LSD), and others (Fitzgerald & Riley, 2000). Sometimes referred to as "date rape drugs," these substances may be taken knowingly or may be slipped surreptitiously into the drink of an unsuspecting person who is then assaulted (Langford, Isaac, & Finn, under review). As noted earlier, a very small percentage of students—less than 0.05 to 0.9 percent—report using GHB, ketamine, or Rohypnol recreationally.

Some of these drugs result in sedation, total or intermittent unconsciousness, and amnesia, making it difficult for victims to recount what occurred, which can delay or inhibit reporting (Fitzgerald & Riley, 2000; Pope & Shouldice, 2001). Even when suspected assaults are reported as soon as the victim recovers consciousness, standard toxicological screens often fail to test for common drugs and, if testing occurs, it may be too late to detect their presence or effects (Pope & Shouldice, 2001).

While concern about DFSA has centered around a few drugs, in particular GHB and Rohypnol, one community-based study tested urine samples from victims of sexual assaults in which drug use was suspected, finding that alcohol was by far the most frequently detected substance (ElSohly & Salamone, 1999). The tests also detected nearly twenty different other drugs besides GHB and Rohypnol, indicating that focusing on any one or two drugs is insufficient. While this study was not exclusive to college students, there is no reason to believe that the diversity of drugs would be any less in a campus setting. It is likely that use of rape-facilitating drugs varies from campus to campus based on factors such as drug availability and peer behavior, and therefore measures should be in place to monitor and address local use and trafficking of these drugs. Again, it is important to remember that alcohol is the most commonly used rape-facilitating drug.

Characteristics of AOD-Related Sexual Violence. In general, sexual assaults involving AOD largely resemble those not involving AOD (Abbey, Zawacki, Buck, Clinton, & McAuslan, 2001). Research shows that the most common campus sexual violence scenario involves a male offender and a female victim who are at least casually acquainted and who interact socially prior to the assault (Abbey, 2002; Abbey et al., 2001). The majority of victims employ some form of resistance or protective action but are not physically injured in the assault (Fisher, Cullen, & Turner, 2000). Despite their overall similarly to other sexual assaults, there are a few differences in AOD-involved assaults that should be noted.

Assault Severity and Outcomes. Research finds that alcohol involvement in AOD is associated with more severe forms of victimization and that the amount of alcohol consumed plays a role in assault outcomes (Abbey et al., 2003; Testa & Livingston, 1999; Ullman, Karabatsos, & Koss, 1999a; Ullman et al., 1999b). Studies find that intoxicated victims are more likely to experience completed (rather than attempted) rapes, most likely due to a decreased ability to resist an attacker (Abbey et al., 2001). Perpetrator use of alcohol appears to have a curvilinear relationship with severity. Consistent with other research, a study by Abbey et al. (2003) found that perpetrators who consumed more alcohol during sexual assaults used more aggression to obtain sex, and greater alcohol use by victims was associated with more severe forms of assault. For perpetrators, however, severity of assault initially increased with greater alcohol consumption but then declined at the highest levels of alcohol use, most likely because highly intoxicated perpetrators may be less able to complete a rape (Abbey et al., 2003).

Some research has begun to look beyond the question of whether any AOD use was involved to explore the effects of different levels and patterns of AOD use on sexual violence (Wood & Sher, 2002). One study, for example, queried respondents about both their most recent date and a date involving sexual aggression. Light AOD use was not related to sexual violence, but sexually aggressive dates were more likely to involve heavy AOD by both partners (Muehlenhard & Linton, 1987). In general, alcohol use just prior to the assault is thought to be a stronger predictor than measures of typical alcohol use (Zawacki et al., 2003). In contrast, the study by Abbey et al. (2003) found that the perpetrators' self-reported usual frequency of drinking independently predicted the severity of sexual assault, over and above their drinking level at the time of the assault. This finding underscores the importance of examining both preassault and typical AOD use as risk factors for sexual violence.

Situational and Relationship Characteristics. Alcohol-related sexual violence is more likely than other assaults to be preceded by time spent together at a party or bar (Zawacki et al., 2003). Alcohol-involved sexual assaults are more likely to occur when the victim and offender are casually acquainted, as compared to couples in more intimate relationships or strangers (Abbey et al., 2001; Koss, Dinero, Seibel, & Cox, 1988). One explanation for the latter finding is that a man may feel more entitled to sex in an intimate relationship and therefore have less need to employ AOD use to justify or excuse forceful sexual behavior.

Perpetrator Characteristics. Research suggests that the typical campus sexual assault involves a male assailant and female victim. Recent studies have begun to examine the extent to which men report unwanted sexual contact. In one study, a similar proportion of men and women (21 and 28 percent, respectively) reported being recipients of at least one of five types of unwanted contact. There were, however, some differences in the assaults. Women were more likely to report having physical force used against them and being given alcohol or drugs by a partner to promote intercourse (although intercourse did not occur; Larimer, Lydum, Anderson, & Turner, 1999). Only men reported giving alcohol or drugs to a partner in an attempt to promote intercourse. Despite these differences, men who reported unwanted sexual contact experienced more depressive symptoms than other men, suggesting the need to provide services for men as well as women who go through this type of experience.

Another recent study examined the characteristics of perpetrators of alcohol-involved sexual assaults compared to other sexual assault perpetrators and nonperpetrators. Consistent with other research, results showed that both groups of sexual assault perpetrators (AOD-involved and not) were similar on most characteristics compared to nonperpetrators, including history of delinquency, aggressive and dominant personality traits, more engagement in and endorsement of casual sexual behavior, greater sexual dominance, stronger attitudes supporting violence against women, and more frequent misperception of women's friendliness as sexual interest (Zawacki et al., 2003). Alcohol-involved perpetrators did differ in some alcohol-related behaviors and beliefs. Specifically, alcohol-involved perpetrators reported stronger beliefs that alcohol enhances sex drive and that women's drinking signifies sexual interest, greater alcohol consumption during sexual interactions, and greater consumption while misperceiving sexual intent. This group of perpetrators also reported greater impulsivity, which may further enhance the likelihood that they will act on their misperceptions of women's sexual motives or interest (Zawacki et al., 2003).

Despite the fact that many campus sexual assaults share similar characteristics, not all offenders are the same. Among college men who are sexually aggressive, there is a substantial subset of repeat offenders who have been described as having a "predatory" approach to sexual assault (Lisak & Miller, 2002). Also noteworthy is the fact that two thirds of college men who report any acts meeting the definition of sexual assault have committed multiple offenses (Abbey et al., 1998; Lisak & Miller, 2002). In one study, 76 repeat rapists were responsible for a total of 439 completed or attempted rapes, or an average of 6 each (Lisak & Miller, 2002). A 2005 prospective study of undergraduate men found that those with a history of severe sexual aggression over a three-month period, compared to those who had not been aggressive, were fifteen times more likely to commit an act of sexual aggression over the next four months (Loh, Gidycz, Lobo, & Luthra, 2005). Research on serial rapists shows that they extensively plan and premeditate their crimes, use sophisticated strategies to select and groom their victims, and often use AOD deliberately as a means of gaining control over their victims (Lisak & Miller, 2002). Many of these offenders also commit other types of crimes, such as battering and assault (Lisak & Miller, 2002).

While these data are extremely alarming, it is important to remember that most college men are not coercive, do not want to victimize others, and are willing to help address the sexual assault problem. In one study, the overwhelming majority of men responding to a survey administered across multiple campuses agreed with various statements about gaining consent for sex, such as "I respect my partner's wishes about sexual activity." Similarly, most men surveyed indicated their willingness to intervene to prevent a sexual assault (Rape, Abuse and Incest National Network [RAINN], 2005). Other surveys have yielded similar findings (Berkowitz, 2006).

How Do AODs Contribute to Sexual Violence?

Nature of Relationship Between AOD Use and Sexual Violence. Although the associations between AOD and sexual violence are well documented, this does not mean that AOD causes violence (Abbey, 2002; Wood & Sher, 2002). Many people drink or use drugs without assaulting, and many sexual assaults occur without AOD use. For example, while alcohol may precede and contribute to sexual violence, the direction of causation also may be the opposite; for example, a person who intends to be sexually aggressive may drink to bolster his confidence or justify his behavior (Abbey, 2002; Abbey et al., 2001; Ullman, 2003; Wood & Sher, 2002).

Substance abuse may also be a consequence of sexual violence. A number of studies have found that sexual violence survivors consume more alcohol than nonvictimized women (Kaysen, Neighbors, Martell, Fossos, & Larimer, 2006; Parks & Fals-Stewart, 2004; Testa, Livingston, & Collins, 2000). Kaysen et al. (2006) followed female students at three campuses prospectively over a three-year period and found that alcohol-related sexual assault was associated with higher rates of alcohol use and related negative consequences in the year prior to the assault, during the year the rape took place, and in subsequent years. Other studies have shown increased alcohol use after sexual violence only among certain subgroups of survivors (Gidycz, Coble, Latham, & Layman, 1993). These findings highlight that the interrelationships among AOD and sexual violence are complex, dynamic, and reciprocal (Flack et al., 2007). Given that alcohol consumption is one factor that appears to increase victims' vulnerability to revictimization, the potential for increased postassault alcohol consumption is a cause for concern (Marx, Heidt, & Gold, 2005).

Risk, Protective, and Vulnerability Factors. Primary prevention efforts seek to identify and change the factors that lead to sexual violence. Like AOD, sexual violence has multiple determinants that can be organized according to a social ecological framework (Centers for Disease Control and Prevention, 2004; Chalk & King, 1998; Reiss & Roth, 1993). Recent conceptual models of the alcohol-violence relationship underscore the need to consider alcohol as one contributor in a complex interplay of factors, including individual characteristics, group-level factors, and attributes of campus and community environments (Abbey, 2002; Burkhart, Bourg, & Berkowitz, 1994; Marchell & Cummings, 2001; Reiss & Roth, 1993; Wood & Sher, 2002). No one factor causes sexual violence, and therefore prevention efforts need to address multiple contributing factors through a set of complementary and synergistic effects (Langford et al., under review).

Causative factors may operate by increasing the risk of perpetration or the likelihood of victimization. Bachar and Koss (2001) make this distinction by defining *risk* as a combination of societal, institutional, dyadic, and individual-level influences that *increase the likelihood of perpetration* (i.e., causing harm), while defining *vulnerability* as a combination of societal, institutional, dyadic, and individual-level influences that *heighten the likelihood of victimization* (i.e., suffering harm; Centers for Disease Control and Prevention, 2007). Recent work also has highlighted the role of bystanders and the need to identify the multiple factors that affect whether a person observing violence will intervene (Banyard, Plante, & Moynihan, 2003; Berkowitz, 2002; Center for the Study of Sport in Society, 2007).

A comprehensive review of the many factors that contribute to sexual violence is beyond the scope of this chapter. The next section offers a conceptual model that describes how alcohol can contribute to sexual violence, which can guide efforts to analyze other contributing factors to sexual violence and inform the design of comprehensive prevention efforts.

Conceptual Model of Alcohol-Related Sexual Assault. Abbey (2002) proposed an explanatory model for acquaintance sexual assaults perpetrated by men against women. The model underscores the proposition that alcohol often exacerbates the dynamics that exist in the absence of alcohol, including those related to preexisting beliefs and other situational factors. More research is needed to determine the extent to which the model would apply to other types of assaults, such as those involving other drugs, strangers, male victims, or GLBT (gay, lesbian, bisexual, transgender) victims, but it still provides a useful rubric for examining AOD-related sexual violence.

Abbey (2002) outlines three pathways through which alcohol might contribute to sexual violence, emphasizing that these alcohol effects may be independent and synergistic:

1. *Preexisting beliefs about alcohol's effects on sexual behavior and aggression.* Studies show that men who perpetrate AOD-related sexual assault are more likely to hold particular beliefs (e.g., that alcohol enhances sexual experiences, that women who drink are signaling their sexual interest, and that some types of sexual pressure are acceptable). In addition, when men believe intoxication excuses aggressive behavior, they may be more likely to exhibit coercive behavior after drinking or may drink if they intend to be aggressive.

2. *Effects of alcohol during heterosexual interactions.* Alcohol can affect appraisal of sexual motives and intent, interpersonal communication, and compliance

with perceived peer group attitudes and behaviors. For example, the narrowing of attention caused by alcohol may cause a man to overestimate his partner's interest in intimacy, to misread her nonverbal cues, and to misinterpret what she says. In addition, alcohol may increase aggressiveness during the encounter and reduce the ability to consider long-term negative consequences of behavior. All of these effects may be exacerbated in peer contexts where peer norms are perceived to support heavy drinking, uninhibited behavior, casual sex, and sexual coercion.

3. *Effects of alcohol just prior to forced sex.* At this juncture, alcohol can contribute to sexual violence by impairing the ability to rectify mistaken assumptions about sexual intent, diminishing the victim's ability to resist, and serving as a means for perpetrators to justify their aggressive behavior. For example, an intoxicated man may focus narrowly on his own sexual arousal and think that his aggressiveness is justified if he perceives that he was "led on" and therefore is entitled to sex. Men may use alcohol as a tool to render a victim unable to resist sexual advances and then justify their behavior based on preexisting beliefs about women and alcohol and a distorted interpretation of situational cues.

While not addressed directly by the model, it is likely that these three factors assume different weight depending on the type of sexual assault. Berkowitz (2007) distinguishes among unintentional, opportunistic, and predatory perpetration. Misinterpretation of cues about the victim's desire for sexual contact would more often be a factor in unintentional assault, while predatory acts involving deliberate alcohol incapacitation would most likely be associated with attributions of promiscuity for women who drink and a pattern of using alcohol to justify aggression.[5]

In addition to the factors described above, an individual's past experiences (e.g., childhood sexual abuse) and personality traits (e.g., impulsivity) can also interact with alcohol in the context of sexual assault. However, these risk factors are not as amenable to change by campus sexual violence prevention programs (Abbey, 2002).

Environmental Contributors to Sexual Violence. The conceptual model described in the previous section focuses primarily on individual and peer contributors to sexual violence, as well as situational factors. Also important are factors at the institutional, community, and societal levels of the social ecological model, which collectively have been referred to in the prevention literature as environmental factors. Because students act within a particular context, it is important to analyze the extent to which this physical, social, economic, cultural, and legal environment may be contributing to sexual violence problems (DeJong et al., 1998).

Institutional factors generally include campus-level traits such as sexual assault policies and their level of enforcement. Physical characteristics of the campus setting such as campus lighting and access to buildings are also considered to be institutional-level factors. While changes to the physical environment may be part of an overall campus safety effort, they are unlikely to have a strong effect on alcohol-related sexual

---

[5]This heterogeneity of sexual violence is reflected in recent research on rape resistance training, which has focused on identifying and analyzing the range of dynamics and contexts in which assault occurs in order to better prepare women to recognize and resist different types of sexual aggression (Macy, Nurius, & Norris, 2006, 2007; Nurius, Norris, Macy, & Huang, 2004).

violence. Recent work in bystander intervention has sought to alter the campus environment by creating a "community of responsibility" in which students are trained to recognize and intervene in incidents of violence (Banyard et al., 2003; Banyard, Plante, & Moynihan, 2005b).

Community factors are defined as the characteristics of the community surrounding the campus that may influence sexual assault, such as easy availability of alcohol due to lax enforcement of underage drinking laws or the willingness and ability of the local criminal justice system to investigate and prosecute campus sexual assaults.

Societal influences operate at a broader level, outside the immediate campus community. These include state and federal laws and broad social and cultural norms toward gender roles, sexuality, violence, and their intersection (DeJong & Langford, 2002; Langford, 2004). A thorough analysis of sexual violence should seek to identify environmental factors that may be amenable to intervention (Langford et al., under review).

Understanding Context and Meaning of Alcohol-Involved Sexual Violence. In order to intervene effectively, it is important to understand both the context of these incidents and how students view them. Recent qualitative studies have begun to examine these issues. Peralta and Cruz (2006) conducted in-depth interviews with a convenience sample of seventy-eight college students at a Midwestern campus to explore their perceptions of drinking behaviors and violence (including but not limited to sexual violence). The majority of both male and female respondents believed that alcohol causes violence, and they viewed aggression as a normal and expected expression of power and masculinity by young men. In addition, several male respondents who admitted being sexually aggressive attributed this behavior to their alcohol use.

In another study, researchers at a large Midwestern university conducted an ethnographic investigation of a women's floor in a residence hall that had a reputation for high-frequency alcohol use (Armstrong, Hamilton, & Sweeney, 2006). They concluded that "party rape" (i.e., the assault of an intoxicated woman at an on- or off-campus party) was a frequent and predictable outcome of a combination of *individual characteristics* (e.g., use of partying as a way to fit into college life and perception of men's sexual interest as an indicator of attractiveness and social status); *organizational practices* (e.g., lax enforcement of alcohol policies in fraternity houses and male control of fraternity parties, including gendered themes, easy alcohol access, and transportation); and *interactional factors* (e.g., expectations of men to pursue sex and use of alcohol to inhibit resistance to sexual advances). Because the women viewed fraternity parties as an important means of meeting men, fitting into a social scene, and feeling sexually attractive, they resisted criticizing the party scene or the men's behavior despite the fact that many of them knew women who had been sexually assaulted. Instead, they tended to blame victims for being assaulted.

These studies illustrate the challenge that students face in making sense of campus sexual assault since it occurs in the context of settings and behaviors generally perceived to be part of the "normal" college experience (Adams-Curtis & Forbes, 2004). College students commonly overestimate the extent of both drinking and sexual activity among their peers (Berkowitz, 2006; Perkins, 2002, 2003) and therefore see frequent participation in these activities as normative behavior. And the majority of campus sexual assaults are perpetrated by someone known to the victim and are proceeded by social or romantic interaction at a party or on a date. In at least half of assaults, the victim, the offender, or both have been drinking (Abbey, 2002). Thus, college students are forced to try to strike a balance between exploring personal relationships and managing risk in the context of apparently ordinary circumstances (Macy et al., 2007).

The embeddedness of sexual violence risk factors in the fabric of campus life can make it difficult to craft simple prevention messages. While the underlying message is correct, slogans like "No Means No" are unlikely to convey accurately to students what they need to know about campus sexual violence. The best prevention programs "start where people are," (i.e., they reflect a deep understanding of their audience's existing beliefs, values, and priorities; Backer, Rogers, & Sopory, 1992). The research described above underscores the importance of examining sexual violence within the context of students' meaning systems and then applying those insights when designing prevention efforts.

Effect of AOD on Responses to Sexual Violence

To this point, how AOD contributes to sexual violence and the implications this linkage has for creating prevention and early intervention efforts have been described. What happens after a sexual assault? Again, AOD involvement is a complicating factor, with a strong influence on how the survivor experiences the assault, how others view it, and how institutions respond.

Consequences of AOD-Involved Sexual Assault. Victims of sexual violence commonly experience an array of serious consequences, including depression, social isolation, and posttraumatic stress disorder, which may result in social and academic difficulties and reduced quality of life (Campbell, 2002; Menard, 2002; Tjaden & Thoennes, 1998; Zweig, Crockett, Sayer, & Vicary, 1999). Some research has examined whether the effects of AOD-involved sexual violence are similar to those resulting from other types of assaults.

Schwartz and Leggett (1999) compared postassault consequences among thirty college women raped by physical force to those experienced by thirty-five victims raped while incapacitated by alcohol or drugs. The vast majority of women in both categories reported some level of distress. Importantly, women raped while incapacitated were just as likely as those raped by force to report negative psychological and emotional consequences (Schwartz & Leggett, 1999). Another study found, however, that women who were using alcohol at the time of a sexual assault rated the attack itself as less severe, possibly due to blunted physical reactions due to intoxication (Clum, Nishith, & Calhoun, 2002). Both of these studies were small and localized, so their generalizability is limited. A third study of noncollege women ages eighteen to forty-nine compared victims raped by physical force, verbal coercion, and intoxication, finding that, while survivors in the physical force group experienced the most extreme negative consequences, intoxicated victims also scored fairly high on measures of assault seriousness and life disruption (Abbey, BeShears, Clinton-Sherrod, & McAuslan, 2004). More research is needed to clarify the most common reactions to alcohol-related sexual assault and the factors that mediate those consequences, but it is apparent that many survivors of AOD-related assault, whatever the circumstances, do experience significant distress.

Failure to Define AOD-Related Assaults as Rape. While the law in most jurisdictions is clear that rape has occurred if the woman is incapable of giving consent as a result of intoxication, questions frequently arise about whether a victim under the influence of alcohol or drugs has truly been raped or instead is a victim of consensual but "regretted" sex (Schwartz & Leggett, 1999). This skepticism may be enhanced if the victim experiences memory impairment due to voluntary or involuntary AOD use (Hensley, 2002).

Studies show that the public at large, including law enforcement officers and victims themselves, holds stereotypes about what they consider a "real" rape. According to this stereotypic (and inaccurate) view, rape is an act of penetration perpetrated by a stranger using violence or a weapon that results in physical injury incurred during vigorous resistance by a moral and sober victim. Those who hold these stereotyped beliefs often will discount or excuse acts that fall outside these parameters, even when they meet the legal definition of rape or attempted rape. The extent to which an assault matches these stereotypes is associated both with victims' willingness to report rape and the likelihood that police and prosecutors will investigate and prosecute these offenses. In fact, data from the National College Women Sexual Victimization (NCWSV) study shows that most campus sexual assaults do not conform to the stereotypical definition: most victims are assaulted by someone they know and are not physically injured (Fisher et al., 2000).

Survivors themselves may share the public's confusion about the definition of rape. In the NCWSV study, nearly half (48.8 percent) of the women who had experienced an assault meeting the legal definition of completed or attempted rape did not consider the incident to be rape, and another 5 percent were uncertain (Fisher et al., 2000). AOD involvement in an assault may reduce further the likelihood that a victim will consider it to be rape even when it meets the legal definition (Harned, 2005). One small study found, for example, that only one of thirty-five (3.3 percent) victims who were raped while intoxicated thought they had been raped compared to five of thirty victims (23.8 percent) who were raped by physical force (Schwartz & Leggett, 1999). These findings were supported in a qualitative study that explored women's labeling of unwanted sexual experiences. In this study, many participants did not label their assault as rape due to the presence of AOD use, either because they thought they may have consented or because they blamed themselves for becoming intoxicated. Interestingly, several respondents who did label their experience as rape cited incapacitation by alcohol or drugs as the very reason they considered the assault to be rape (Harned, 2005). Thus, it appears that understanding the concept of AOD-related incapacitation was important in determining whether women would label sexually aggressive acts as rape.

Blaming the Victim. Even if an incident is acknowledged as rape, AOD involvement increases the likelihood of the victim being viewed as partially or fully responsible for the incident. Rape victims blame themselves more than other victims of crime, particularly when they were under the influence of alcohol or drugs when the sexual assault occurred (Abbey, 2002; Fisher, Daigle, Cullen, & Turner, 2003; Ullman & Filipas, 2001). Other people also assign more blame to victims of AOD-involved assault. Studies using written scenarios show that females who are drinking are judged to be more responsible for a sexual assault compared to those not drinking (Sims, Noel, & Maisto, 2007). While few studies examine victim-blaming and other drug use, one recent study examined the role of Ecstasy use in perceptions and attributions of responsibility in acquaintance rape, finding that respondents considered women who were raped while intoxicated with Ecstasy to be more responsible for being victimized than while sober (Castello, Coomer, Stillwell, & Cate, 2006). In contrast, the presence of AOD in a sexual assault may serve to mitigate the perpetrator's perceived responsibility for the assault (Abbey, 2002).

AOD and Reporting of Sexual Violence. Sexual violence is one of the most under-reported crimes, particularly on college campuses, and AOD involvement appears to exacerbate reporting issues. The NCWSV study found that about two thirds of the college women who had survived an attempted or completed rate said that they told someone about it, usually a friend, yet fewer than 5 percent of these incidents, without regard to AOD involvement, were reported to law enforcement officials (Fisher et al., 2000). Consistent with other studies, these assaults were most likely to be reported when they were more "believable" (i.e., more serious, perpetrated by a stranger), when they occurred on campus property, and when the victims defined the incident as rape (Fisher et al., 2003). AOD use by the victim, offender, or both made victims even less likely to disclose their assault to campus authorities, yet more likely to tell a friend (Fisher et al., 2003).

Common reasons cited by victims for not reporting sexual violence include the following: not sure that the incident was serious enough; not sure if a crime or harm was intended; did not want other people or family to know; lack of proof the incident happened; fear of reprisal; police would not think it was serious enough; feelings of shame, guilt, or embarrassment; concerns about confidentiality; and fear of not being believed or that the incident would be viewed as their fault (Fisher et al., 2003; Sable, Danis, Mauzy, & Gallagher, 2006; Thompson, Sitterle, Clay, & Kingree, 2007).

Victims of drug-facilitated sexual assault may not report due to uncertainty about what occurred. While most studies do not ask respondents directly whether AOD use was a barrier to reporting, it is likely that AOD involvement plays a role in victims' assessments of known reporting-related factors such as the seriousness and believability of an attack and whether the police should be involved. In fact, research supports the notion that there is less support for reporting certain types of crimes to authorities. For example, a set of experimental studies found that college students were less likely to advise students who were drinking to report sexual assault and other crimes to the police, particularly when the victim was under age (Ruback, Menard, Outlaw, & Shaffer, 1999). In part, these findings may reflect the general tendencies to minimize the occurrence and effects of AOD-related sexual assaults and to hold victims responsible. Another contributing factor is that under-age students and survivors who used illicit drugs may fear prosecution or sanctioning for their substance use (Negrusz, Juhascik, & Gaensslen, 2005).

Thus, while overall reporting of campus rapes is low, AOD-involved assaults appear to be reported to authorities even less frequently than other assaults. Low reporting is problematic: offenders are less likely to be sanctioned, and victims may not be informed of available services, decreasing the likelihood of their successful recovery (Thompson et al., 2007). Failure to report sexual violence also may contribute to the perception that it is a rare problem on college campuses, thereby decreasing the perceived need for prevention and intervention. Clearly, a priority for comprehensive sexual violence programs should be to address AOD-specific barriers to reporting.

Help-Seeking and Recovery. Other research has identified key factors that negatively influence the recovery process and postassault symptoms of sexual violence survivors generally, including disbelieving and blaming reactions from others (often termed secondary victimization; Ullman, 1996) and inadequate community services (Campbell et al., 1999). In general, studies do not find a direct effect of AOD involvement on recovery and later symptoms. Research is needed to explore the possibility of an indirect influence on longer-term outcomes due to AOD involvement resulting in greater skepticism, increased victim blame, and decreased reporting.

Some survivors may cope with postassault distress by increasing their AOD use (Kaysen et al., 2006; Parks & Fals-Stewart, 2004; Testa et al., 2000), placing them at heightened risk for revictimization. Substance use subsequent to an attack may also be an important barrier to recovery from sexual assault. One study found, for example, that alcohol abuse predicted posttraumatic stress disorder one year after a rape (Darves-Bornoz et al., 1998).

Little research has examined the effect of AOD on service utilization by survivors. One study examined alcohol involvement as one of several factors affecting both the postrape use and responsiveness of the legal, medical, and mental health systems. Consistent with the research on stereotypic beliefs about rape, these systems responded best to assaults that involved weapons and injuries, which did not tend to involve alcohol (Campbell, 1998). Most of the alcohol-related incidents involved a perpetrator known to the victim, no weapon, and alcohol use by the victim. Survivors of these assaults experienced particularly poor responsiveness from the legal system, which tended to drop the cases early on even though many of the victims wanted to pursue prosecution. The response of the mental health system was mixed. In particular, the victims' family and friends often did not receive information about rape and its effects, which was inconsistent with the victims' wishes. These survivors found the medical system most responsive to their needs (Campbell, 1998).

IMPLICATIONS FOR SEXUAL ASSAULT RESPONSE TEAM GROUPS

AOD and sexual violence are both complex problems that require multifaceted prevention and response approaches that can be sustained over time. While AOD appears to contribute to sexual violence through multiple pathways, AOD involvement is not a necessary or sufficient factor in sexual violence, and eliminating alcohol problems on campus, even if it were possible, would not eliminate sexual violence (Abbey et al., 2001; Banyard et al., 2005a). It is important, therefore, to address both AOD and sexual violence as both individual and overlapping problems. To be most effective, prevention and response programs must reflect the complex associations between AOD and sexual violence and work in collaborative and mutually supportive ways. The following are recommendations for addressing AOD-involved sexual violence.

Coordinate Sexual Violence Prevention and Response Efforts

A strong response to sexual violence incidents is essential to assist survivors and send a clear message about an institution's intolerance for violent behavior. Recent work has challenged practitioners to expand their efforts to feature both *primary prevention* and *early intervention* (Centers for Disease Control and Prevention, 2004). As the social ecological model suggests, when developing this work, campuses will want to address a broad spectrum of contributors to sexual violence as identified through a local assessment of campus and community conditions.

While the emphasis of most Sexual Assault Response Team (SART) programs is victim response, many member agencies also conduct community outreach and prevention efforts. Even when a SART program does not have direct responsibility for prevention work, efforts to implement a comprehensive approach will be strengthened when SARTs work collaboratively with campus and community prevention partners, striving to help ensure that every agency's programs and policies are coordinated and work in sync.

Build Collaborative Efforts to Address AOD and Sexual Violence Jointly

AOD use and sexual violence are both serious problems in campus communities. At many colleges and universities, these two issues are addressed by diverse departments with separate initiatives. Best practices in prevention science suggest that one-time or fragmented programs are ineffective in effecting sustained change (Anderson & Whiston, 2005). Campus officials working on AOD and sexual violence issues can bridge their efforts so that programs in each area reinforce and support each other's messages resulting in a stronger overall effort (Bachar & Koss, 2001).

In addition, research demonstrates that alcohol and drugs are important environmental as well as individual contributors to sexual violence. Communities with higher levels of alcohol abuse experience more crime and violence, including sexual violence (Grossman & Markowitz, 1999; Wechsler et al., 2002a). To the extent that factors like alcohol availability and lax enforcement of policies are contributing to the overall sexual assault rate in campus communities, it is in the interest of sexual assault prevention advocates to support comprehensive environmental approaches to alcohol prevention. While decreasing substance use clearly is not sufficient to reduce sexual assault, strong AOD prevention efforts are an important component of an overall plan. Likewise, AOD prevention specialists will benefit from helping to create sexual violence programs and policies that will support and reinforce their efforts. Given the associations between alcohol and sexual assault, effective prevention planning will require connecting these efforts to develop coordinated, synergistic programs (Bachar & Koss, 2001).

Collaboration between sexual violence and AOD professionals may require grappling with differences in terminology, philosophy, and approach. SART groups can set the tone for this work by involving campus and community AOD prevention professionals in their efforts, initiating respectful discussions of professional differences, and helping to identify shared priorities for sexual violence and AOD work. Specifically, SART programs can provide an opportunity for diverse stakeholders to develop a common approach and language for discussing AOD and sexual violence that reflects the complexity of this relationship and yet is understandable and acceptable to all campus constituents. SART groups also can collaborate on all of the steps of the strategic planning process, including examining local data; identifying and prioritizing local problems; targeting those problems with an appropriate mix of strategies; constructing a program logic model, work plan, and evaluation plan; creating infrastructure to support implementation; and evaluating the effectiveness of these efforts (Langford et al., under review).

Likely benefits of strong sexual violence and AOD collaboration include: (1) increased coordination and synergy of prevention programs, (2) less duplication of efforts, (3) more information and data sharing, (4) stronger institutional power to advocate for comprehensive prevention efforts on campus, and (5) advancement of both fields through the sharing of concepts and approaches from each other's work (Langford et al., under review).

Use Research on AOD and Sexual Violence in Designing Prevention Programs

The public health approach emphasizes the importance of matching solutions to the scope and nature of the problem. To the extent that SART members are involved in designing and delivering prevention initiatives, they can improve these efforts by taking into account the research literature about the complex intersections between AOD and sexual violence.

Recent research findings about predatory rapists are particularly important in light of typical campus sexual violence educational programs. These programs commonly focus on defining sexual violence, teaching sexual negotiation, and understanding consent (Anderson & Whiston, 2005; Sochting, Fairbrother, & Koch, 2004), thereby implying that perpetrators generally are well intentioned and that most sexual violence results from mistakes stemming from ignorance or miscommunication. Studies of predatory rapists reveal that a different dynamic is involved, which requires targeted approaches such as educating bystanders to intervene (Banyard et al., 2003; Banyard et al., 2005b) and developing campus systems that can identify repeat offenders. It should be noted that SART programs may be especially well positioned to work with law enforcement agencies to identify and prosecute serial offenders.

The research also highlights important information for education and outreach efforts. For example, students hold common misperceptions that can be challenged in prevention programs, such as the belief that violence is a "normal" response to alcohol consumption, especially for men, and that alcohol use mitigates responsibility for sexual assault. Campus disciplinary systems should include procedures that hold intoxicated offenders accountable, and these measures should be explained to students as part of campus prevention programs.

Because the research literature continues to grow, the most effective planning efforts will include regular reviews of new research findings to ensure that decisions are based on the best available information.

Ensure That Responses to Sexual Violence Address the Dynamics of AOD-Involved Assaults

Protocols for responding to reports of sexual violence should take into account the possibility of AOD involvement. Each SART program will want to review its policies and procedures to ensure that they address situations in which survivors, offenders, or both are impaired by AOD, either voluntarily or involuntarily. All team members should be trained in the complex dynamics of AOD-related sexual violence and the rationale for the action steps specified in the protocols.

The following are examples of additional actions that campuses may wish to take to strengthen their responses to AOD-related sexual violence:

- Victims are less likely to report rapes that do not meet the stereotypical definition. Policies and protocols should define clearly the acts that constitute sexual violence, consistent with state laws regarding AOD-incapacitated assault. Victims should be encouraged to report AOD-involved assaults.

- Officials across multiple campus and community systems (e.g., medical, legal, counseling, women's center, rape crisis center) should be educated about common biases against victims of AOD-involved acquaintance rape and then be trained in specific guidelines for responding sensitively and professionally to a victim reporting an AOD-involved assault. All reports of sexual violence should be treated with equal credibility by authorities. A victim's lack of recall about an incident should not be interpreted to mean that the story is suspect or that the assault is less serious.

- Given that relatively few sexual assaults are reported to campus authorities, all students should all be given simple information about how to respond nonjudgmentally and helpfully to a friend who discloses sexual violence.

- Both on- and off-campus medical protocols should specify what steps are to be taken in cases of AOD-involved sexual assault, taking into account a victim's ability to be interviewed productively and to consent to examination. If drug-facilitated rape is suspected, prompt and appropriate testing should be performed for a full array of possible substances. SART programs should consider whether to advocate for systematic AOD testing for all victims and, if so, whether to recommend the circumstances under which victims can opt in or out of testing (Konradi, 2003).

- SART advocates may want reported sexual assault offenses to be investigated vigorously, like any crime, including gathering evidence and interviewing others who may have information about the assault. SART programs may be able to work with campus and community officials to review their law enforcement and disciplinary procedures to assess the likelihood that they can detect and respond to repeat predatory offenders.

- Campus policies and protocols should make clear how AOD involvement is to be considered in the disciplinary process. Student conduct staff can work closely with rape care advocates to balance the rights of the accused and the accuser. Sanctions for perpetrators of AOD-related sexual assault should be commensurate with the seriousness of the act (Berkowitz, 2007). Campuses may wish to consider offering alternative and potentially more victim-friendly approaches such as restorative justice models (Koss, Bachar, Hopkins, & Carlson, 2004).

- Follow-up services for victims should take into account the possibility of AOD-related consequences and postassault sequelae. Advocates, counselors, and medical clinicians can screen for increased postassault AOD consumption and offer appropriate services. Some literature suggests that victims who cannot recall their assault due to AOD may require different therapeutic approaches than other victims—for example, they may not be able to retell their story as a way of dealing with trauma (Hensley, 2002).

Strive for Coordination and Synergy Across Sexual Violence and AOD Prevention and Intervention Efforts

Sexual violence results from the complex interplay of numerous factors, and changing any one risk factor while neglecting others will be of limited effectiveness in reducing the overall problem. Successful prevention initiatives target multiple contributing factors that operate at various levels of the social ecological model, using a rich combination of programs, policies, and services. It is not sufficient, however, simply to keep adding individual program components. Prevention research shows that coordinated and sustained activities rather than one-time or fragmented programs are needed to make sustained change (Anderson & Whiston, 2005). Thus, ensuring that diverse campus efforts work synergistically is one of the most important steps practitioners can take to improve their initiatives to combat sexual violence. For example, programs such as staff training on policies and procedures, student education and outreach programs, and disciplinary procedures for policy violations should all be examined and revised to ensure that their messages and implementation are consistent and clear.

Planners also can seek opportunities to create synergy among other prevention and student development efforts to maximize their collective effect. Since health and safety programs often address shared underlying risk factors, planners are likely to find several opportunities to reinforce common themes. Another possibility is to connect disparate efforts by choosing a theme that transcends specific problem behaviors—for example, increasing civility, fostering healthy norms, or promoting core values. By building upon positive values and behaviors, campuses may enhance all of their prevention efforts.

CONCLUSION

AOD involvement in campus sexual violence exacerbates an already complex problem. Alcohol and drug use interacts with other factors to increase the likelihood of sexual assault, while also affecting how survivors are treated after an assault. While reducing AOD use is not sufficient for eliminating sexual violence, supporting comprehensive AOD prevention efforts is an important component of an overall sexual violence prevention strategy.

SART programs can play an important role in highlighting the extent and nature of the links between AOD and sexual violence and then working to ensure that campus and community programs, policies, and services address these complex dynamics. A critical role for SART groups is to work collaboratively with campus and community partners to engage in a strategic planning process that aims to identify and address the specific ways in which AOD is contributing to sexual violence, shape more humane and effective responses to sexual violence survivors, and coordinate sexual violence response efforts with ongoing prevention initiatives. Stated simply, effective collaboration among AOD and sexual violence partners has enormous potential to improve the safety of campus communities, and SART programs can lead the way to realize that potential.

References

Abbey, A. (2002). Alcohol-related sexual assault: A common problem among college students. *Journal of Studies on Alcohol, Supplement No. 14*, 118–128.

Abbey, A., BeShears, R., Clinton-Sherrod, A. M., & McAuslan, P. (2004). Similarities and differences in women's sexual assault experiences based on tactics used by the perpetrator. *Psychology of Women Quarterly, 28*(4), 323-332.

Abbey, A., Clinton-Sherrod, A. M., McAuslan, P., Zawacki, T., & Buck, P. O. (2003). The relationship between the quantity of alcohol consumed and the severity of sexual assaults committed by college men. *Journal of Interpersonal Violence, 18*(7), 813-833.

Abbey, A., McAuslan, P., & Ross, L. T. (1998). Sexual assault perpetration by college men: The role of alcohol, misperception of sexual intent, and sexual beliefs and experiences. *Journal of Social and Clinical Psychology, 17*(2), 167–195.

Abbey, A., Zawacki, T., Buck, P. O., Clinton, A. M., & McAuslan, P. (2001). Alcohol and sexual assault. *Alcohol Research & Health, 25*(1), 43-51.

Abbey, A., Zawacki, T., & McAuslan, P. (2000). Alcohol's effects on sexual perception. *Journal of Studies on Alcohol, 61*(5), 688-697.

Adams-Curtis, L. E., & Forbes, G. B. (2004). College women's experiences of sexual coercion: A review of cultural, perpetrator, victim, and situational variables. *Trauma, Violence, & Abuse, 5*(2), 91-122.

American College Health Association. (2004). *Standards of practice for heath promotion in higher education.* Retrieved November 12, 2007, from http://www.edc.org/hec/thisweek/acha-standards.doc

Anderson, L. A., & Whiston, S. C. (2005). Sexual assault education programs: Meta-analytic examination of their effectiveness. *Psychology of Women Quarterly, 29*(4), 374-388.

Armstrong, E. A., Hamilton, L., & Sweeney, B. (2006). Sexual assault on campus: A multi-level, integrative approach to party rape. *Social Problems, 53*(4), 483-499.

Bachar, K., & Koss, M. (2001). From prevalence to prevention: Closing the gap between what we know about rape and what we do. In C. Renzetti, J. Edleson & R. Bergen (Eds.), *Sourcebook on violence against women* (pp. 117-142). Thousand Oaks, CA: Sage.

Bachar, K. J., & Koss, M. P. (2000, May). *Rape prevention education: Towards closing the gap between theory and practice.* Dallas, TX: National Sexual Violence Prevention Conference.

Backer, T. E., Rogers, E. M., & Sopory, P. (1992). *Designing health communication campaigns: What works?* Thousand Oaks, CA: Sage.

Baer, J. S. (2002). Student factors: Understanding individual variation in college drinking. *Journal of Studies on Alcohol, Supplement No. 14*, 40-53.

Baer, J. S., Kivlahan, D. R., Blume, A. W., McKnight, P., & Marlatt, G. A. (2001). Brief intervention for heavy-drinking college students: 4-year follow-up and natural history. *American Journal of Public Health, 91*(8), 1310-1315.

Banyard, V. L., Plante, E. G., Cohn, E. S., Moorhead, C., Ward, S., & Walsh, W. (2005a). Revisiting unwanted sexual experiences on campus: A 12-year follow-up. *Violence Against Women, 11*(4), 426-446.

Banyard, V. L., Plante, E. G., & Moynihan, M. M. (2003). Bystander education: Bringing a broader community perspective to sexual violence prevention. *Journal of Community Psychology, 32*(1), 61–79.

Banyard, V. L., Plante, E. G., & Moynihan, M. M. (2005b). *Rape prevention through bystander education: Bringing a broader community perspective to sexual violence prevention* (NCJ 208701). Washington, DC: U.S. Deptartment of Justice, National Institute of Justice.

Basile, K., & Saltzman, L. (2002). *Sexual violence surveillance: Uniform definitions and recommended data elements Version 1.0.* Atlanta, GA: Centers for Disease Control and Prevention, National Center for Injury Prevention and Control.

Berkowitz, A. D. (2002). Fostering men's responsibility for preventing sexual assault. In P. A. Schewe (Ed.), *Preventing violence in relationships* (pp. 163–196). Washington, DC: American Psychological Association.

Berkowitz, A. D. (2006). *Fostering healthy norms to prevent violence and abuse: The social norms approach.* Retrieved September 9, 2008, from http://alanberkowitz.com/Preventing%20Sexual%20Violence%20Chapter.pdf

Berkowitz, A. D. (2007). *Guidelines for sanctioning perpetrators of sexual assault.* Unpublished Manuscript.

Bonnie, R. J., & O'Connell, M. E. (2004). *Reducing underage drinking: A collective responsibility.* Washington, DC: National Academy of Sciences, Institutes of Medicine, National Research Council.

Borjesson, W. I., & Dunn, M. E. (2001). Alcohol expectancies of women and men in relation to alcohol use and perceptions of the effects of alcohol on the opposite sex. *Addictive Behaviors, 26*(5), 707-720.

Burkhart, B., Bourg, S., & Berkowitz, A. (1994). Research on men and rape: Methodological problems and future directions. In A. Berkowitz (Ed.), *Men and rape: Theory, research, and prevention programs in higher education, new directions for student services* (pp. 67-71). San Francisco: Jossey-Bass.

Campbell, J. C. (2002). Health consequences of intimate partner violence (review). *Lancet, 359*(9314), 1331–1336.

Campbell, R. (1998). The community response to rape: Victims' experiences with the legal, medical, and mental health systems. *American Journal of Community Psychology, 26*(3), 355-379.

Campbell, R., Sefl, T., Barnes, H. E., Ahrens, C. E., Wasco, S. M., & Zaragoza-Diesfeld, Y. (1999). Community services for rape survivors: Enhancing psychological well-being or increasing trauma? *Journal of Consulting and Clinical Psychology, 67*(6), 847-858.

Campus Response Committee of the Oregon Attorney General's Sexual Assault Task Force. (2006). *Recommended guidelines for comprehensive sexual assault response and prevention on campus*. Retrieved December 1, 2007, from http://www.oregonsatf.org/documents/Campus_SA_Guidelines_Final.pdf

Carey, K. B. (1995). Alcohol-related expectancies predict quantity and frequency of heavy drinking among collage students. *Psychology of Addictive Behaviors, 9*(4), 236-241.

Castello, J., Coomer, C., Stillwell, J., & Cate, K. L. (2006). The attribution of responsibility in acquaintance rape involving ecstasy. *North American Journal of Psychology, 8*(3), 411-419.

Center for the Study of Sport in Society. (2007). *Mentors in Violence Prevention (MVP)*. Retrieved February 28, 2007, from http://www.sportinsociety.org/vpd/mvp.php

Centers for Disease Control and Prevention. (2004). *Sexual violence prevention: Beginning the dialogue*. Atlanta, GA: Centers for Disease Control and Prevention, National Center for Injury Prevention and Control.

Centers for Disease Control and Prevention. (2007). *Sexual violence: Fact sheet*. Retrieved April 30, 2007, from http://www.cdc.gov/ncipc/factsheets/svfacts.htm

Chalk, R., & King, P. A. (Eds.). (1998). *Violence in families: Assessing prevention and treatment programs*. Washington DC: National Academy Press.

Clum, G. A., Nishith, P., & Calhoun, K. S. (2002). A preliminary investigation of alcohol use during trauma and peritraumatic reactions in female sexual assault victims. *Journal of Traumatic Stress, 15*(4), 321.

Commission for the Prevention of Youth Violence. (2000). *Youth and violence*. Retrieved July 1, 2007, from http://www.ama-assn.org/ama/upload/mm/386/fullreport.pdf

Cooper, M. L. (1994). Motivations for alcohol use among adolescents: Development and validation of a four-factor model. *Psychological Assessment, 6*, 117-128.

Cooper, M. L., Russell, M., Skinner, J. B., & Windle, M. (1992). Development and validation of a three-dimensional measure of drinking motives. *Psychological Assessment, 4*, 123-132.

Cronin, C. (1997). Reasons for drinking versus outcome expectancies in the prediction of college student drinking. *Substance Use & Misuse, 32*, 1287-1311.

Darves-Bornoz, J. M., Lepine, J. P., Choquet, M., Berger, C., Degiovanni, A., & Gaillard, P. (1998). Predictive factors of chronic post-traumatic stress disorder in rape victims. *European Psychiatry, 13*(6), 281-287.

Davis, R., Parks, L. F., & Cohen, L. (2006). *Sexual biolence and the dpectrum of prevention: Towards a community solution*. Enola, PA: National Sexual Violence Resource Center.

DeJong, W. (2006). Environmental management and the prevention of other drug abuse. *Catalyst, 4*(2), 2-3.

DeJong, W. (in press). *Alcohol and other drug policies for colleges and universities: A guide for university and college administrators*. Washington, DC: U.S. Department of Education, Higher Education Center for Alcohol and Other Drug Abuse and Violence Prevention.

DeJong, W., Anderson, J., Colthurst, T., Davidson, L., Langford, L., Mackay-Smith, V., et al. (2007). *Models of effective prevention: The U.S. Department of Education's alcohol and other drug prevention models on college campuses grants*. Washington, DC: U.S. Department of Education, Higher Education Center for Alcohol and Other Drug Abuse and Violence Prevention.

DeJong, W., & Langenbahn, S. (1996). *Setting and improving policies for reducing alcohol and other drug problems on campus: A guide for administrators*. Washington, DC: U.S. Department of Education, Higher Education Center for Alcohol and Other Drug Prevention.

DeJong, W., & Langford, L. (2002). A typology for campus-based alcohol prevention: Moving toward environmental management strategies. *Journal of Studies on Alcohol, Supplement No. 14*, 140–147.

DeJong, W., Vince-Whitman, C., Colthurst, T., Cretella, M., Gilbreath, M., Rosati, M., et al. (1998). *Environmental management: A comprehensive strategy for rducing alcohol and other drug use on college campuses*. Washington, DC: U.S. Department of Education, Higher Education Center for Alcohol and Other Drug Prevention.

ElSohly, M., & Salamone, S. (1999). Prevalence of drugs used in cases of alleged sexual assault. *Journal of Analytical Toxicology, 23*, 141-146.

Fisher, B. S., Cullen, F. T., & Turner, M. G. (2000, December). *The sexual victimization of college women*. Washington, DC: National Institute of Justice.

Fisher, B. S., Daigle, L. E., Cullen, F. T., & Turner, M. G. (2003). Reporting sexual victimization to the police and others: Results from a national-level study of college women. *Criminal Justice and Behavior, 30*, 6-38.

Fitzgerald, N., & Riley, K. J. (2000). Drug-facilitated rape: Looking for the missing pieces. *National Institute of Justice Journal, April*, 8-15.

Flack, W. F., Jr., Daubman, K. A., Caron, M. L., Asadorian, J. A., D'Aureli, N. R., Gigliotti, S. N., et al. (2007). Risk factors and consequences of unwanted sex among university students: Hooking up, alcohol, and stress response. *Journal of Interpersonal Violence, 22*(2), 139-157.

Fromme, K., D'Amico, E., & Katz, E. (1999). Intoxicated sexual risk taking: An expectancy or cognitive impairment explanation? *Journal of Studies on Alcohol, 60*(1), 54-63.

Gidycz, C. A., Coble, C. N., Latham, L., & Layman, M. J. (1993). Sexual assault experience in adulthood and prior victimization experiences: A prospective analysis. *Psychology of Women Quarterly, 17*, 151-168.

Grossman, M., & Markowitz, S. (1999). *Alcohol regulation and violence on college campuses, NBER Working Paper No. 7129*. Cambridge, MA: National Bureau of Economic Research.

Harned, M. S. (2005). Understanding women's labeling of unwanted sexual experiences with dating partners: A qualitative analysis. *Violence Against Women, 11*(3), 374-413.

Hensley, L. G. (2002). Drug-facilitated sexual assault on campus: Challenges and interventions. *Journal of College Counseling, 5*(2), 175.

Hingson, R. W., Heeren, T., Winter, M., & Wechsler, H. (2005). Magnitude of alcohol-related mortality and morbidity among U.S. college students ages 18-24: Changes from 1998-2001. *Annual Review of Public Health, 26*, 259-279.

Johnston, L. D., O'Malley, P. M., Bachman, J. G., & Schulenberg, J. E. (2007). *Monitoring the future national survey results on drug use, 1975-2006. Volume II: College students and adults ages 19-45* (NIH Publication No. 07-6206). Bethesda, MD: National Institute on Drug Abuse.

Kaysen, D., Neighbors, C., Martell, J., Fossos, N., & Larimer, M. E. (2006). Incapacitated rape and alcohol use: A prospective analysis. *Addictive Behaviors, 31*(10), 1820–1832.

Knight, J. R., Wechsler, H., Kou, M., Seibering, M., Weitzman, E. R., & Shuckit, M. A. (2002). Alcohol abuse and dependence among U.S. college students. *Journal of Studies on Alcohol, 63*(3), 263-270.

Konradi, A. (2003). A strategy for increasing postrape medical care and forensic examination: Marketing sexual assault nurse examiners to the college population. *Violence Against Women, 9*(8), 955-988.

Koss, M. P., Bachar, K. J., Hopkins, C. Q., & Carlson, C. (2004). Expanding a community's justice response to sex crimes through advocacy, prosecutorial, and public health collaboration: Introducing the RESTORE Program. *Journal of Interpersonal Violence, 19*(12), 1435–1463.

Koss, M. P., Dinero, T. E., Seibel, C. A., & Cox, S. L. (1988). Stranger and acquaintance rape: Are there differences in the victim's experience? *Psychology of Women Quarterly, 12*(1), 1-24.

Langford, L. (2004). *Preventing violence and promoting safety in highereducation settings: Overview of a comprehensive approach.* Washington, DC: U.S. Department of Education, Higher Education Center for Alcohol and Other Drug Abuse and Violence Prevention.

Langford, L., Isaac, N. E., & Finn, P. (under review). *Preventing sexual violence in college and university settings: Planning for a comprehensive approach.* Washington, DC: U.S. Department of Education, Higher Education Center for Alcohol and Other Drug Abuse and Violence Prevention.

Langford, L. M., & DeJong, W. (2008). *Strategic planning for prevention professionals on campus.* Washington, DC: U.S. Department of Education, Higher Education Center for Alcohol and Other Drug Abuse and Violence Prevention.

Larimer, M., & Cronce, J. (2007). Identification, prevention, and treatment revisited: Individual-focused college drinking prevention strategies, 1999-2006. *Addictive Behaviors, 32*, 2439-2468.

Larimer, M. R., Lydum, A. R., Anderson, B. K., & Turner, A. P. (1999). Male and female recipients of unwanted sexual contact in a college student sample: Prevalence rates, alcohol use, and depression symptoms. *Sex Roles, 40*(3/4), 295-308.

Leigh, B. C. (1990). The relationship of sex-related alcohol expectancies to alcohol consumption and sexual behavior. *British Journal of Addiction, 85*(7), 919-928.

Lewis, M. A., Neighbors, C., Oster-Aaland, L., Kirkeby, B. S., & Larimer, M. E. (2007). Indicated prevention for incoming freshmen: Personalized normative feedback and high-risk drinking. *Addictive Behaviors, 32*, 2495-2508.

Lisak, D., & Miller, P. M. (2002). Repeat rape and multiple offending among undetected rapists. *Violence and Victims, 17*(1), 73-84.

Loh, C., Gidycz, C. A., Lobo, T. R., & Luthra, R. (2005). A prospective analysis of sexual assault perpetration: Risk factors related to perpetrator characteristics. *Journal of Interpersonal Violence, 20*(10), 1325–1348.

Macy, R. J., Nurius, P. S., & Norris, J. (2006). Responding in their best interests: Contextualizing women's coping with acquaintance sexual aggression. *Violence Against Women, 12*(5), 478-500.

Macy, R. J., Nurius, P. S., & Norris, J. (2007). Latent profiles among sexual assault survivors: Implications for defensive coping and resistance. *Journal of Interpersonal Violence, 22*(5), 543-565.

Marchell, T., & Cummings, N. (2001). Alcohol and sexual violence among college students. In A. Ottens & K. Hotelling (Eds.), *Sexual violence on campus: policies, programs, and perspectives* (pp. 30-52). New York: Springer.

Marx, B. P., Heidt, J. M., & Gold, S. D. (2005). Perceived uncontrollability and unpredictability, self-regulation, and sexual revictimization. *Review of General Psychology, 9*(1), 67-90.

Menard, S. (2002). *Short- and long-term consequences of adolescent victimization.* Washington, DC: U.S. Department of Justice, Office of Juvenile Justice and Delinquency Prevention.

Mercy, J. A., Rosenberg, M. L., Powell, K. E., Broome, C. V., & Roper, W. L. (1993). Public health policy for preventing violence. *Health Affairs, 12*(4), 7-29.

Muehlenhard, C. L., & Linton, M. A. (1987). Date rape and sexual aggression in dating situations: Incidence and risk factors. *Journal of Counseling Psychology, 34*(2), 186-196.

National Center for Injury Prevention and Control. (1993). *The prevention of youth violence: A framework for community action.* Atlanta, GA: Centers for Disease Control and Prevention.

National Center on Addiction and Substance Abuse at Columbia University. (2007). *Wasting the best and the brightest: Substance abuse at American colleges and universities.* New York: Author.

National Institute of Justice. (n.d.). *Rape and sexual violence*. Retrieved November 12, 2007, from http://www.ojp.usdoj.gov/nij/topics/crime/rape-sexual-violence/welcome.htm

National Institute on Drug Abuse. (2007). *Drug abuse and addiction*. Retrieved July 27, 2007, from http://www.drugabuse.gov/scienceofaddiction/addiction.html

Negrusz, A., Juhascik, M., & Gaensslen, R. E. (2005). *Estimate of the incidence of drug-facilitated sexual assault in the U.S.* (NCJ 212000). Rockville, MD: National Criminal Justice Reference Service.

Neighbors, C., Larimer, M. E., & Lewis, M. A. (2004). Targeting misperceptions of descriptive drinking norms: Efficacy of a computer-delivered personalized normative feedback intervention. *Journal of Consulting & Clinical Psychology, 72*(3), 434-447.

NIAAA Task Force on College Drinking. (2002). *A call to action: Changing the culture of drinking at U.S. colleges*. Bethesda, MD: National Institute on Alcohol Abuse and Alcoholism.

Nurius, P. S., Norris, J., Macy, R. J., & Huang, B. (2004). Women's situational coping with acquaintance sexual assault: Applying an appraisal-based model. *Violence Against Women, 10*(5), 450-478.

O'Hare, T. (2005). Risky sex and drinking contexts in freshman first offenders. *Addictive Behaviors, 30*(3), 585.

O'Malley, P. M., & Johnston, L. D. (2002). Epidemiology of alcohol and other drug use among American college students. *Journal of Studies on Alcohol, Supplement No. 14*, 23-39.

Papadodima, S. A., Athanaselis, S. A., & Spiliopoulou, C. (2007). Toxicological investigation of drug-facilitated sexual assaults. *International Journal of Clinical Practice, 61*(2), 259-264.

Park, C. L., & Grant, C. (2005). Determinants of positive and negative consequences of alcohol consumption in college students: Alcohol use, gender, and psychological characteristics. *Addictive Behaviors, 30*(4), 755.

Parks, K. A., & Fals-Stewart, W. (2004). The temporal relationship between college women's alcohol consumption and victimization experiences. *Alcoholism: Clinical and Experimental Research, 28*(4), 625-629.

Peralta, R. L., & Cruz, J. M. (2006). Conferring meaning onto alcohol-related violence: An analysis of alcohol use and masculinity in a sample of college students. *Journal of Men's Studies, 14*(1), 109-125.

Perkins, H. W. (2002). Social norms and the prevention of alcohol misuse in collegiate contexts. *Journal of Studies on Alcohol, Supplement No. 14*, 164-172.

Perkins, H. W. (Ed.). (2003). *The social norms approach to preventing school and college age substance abuse: A handbook for educators, counselors, and clinicians*. San Francisco: Jossey-Bass.

Pope, E., & Shouldice, M. (2001). Drugs and sexual assault: A review. *Trauma, Violence, & Abuse, 2*(1), 51-55.

Rape, Abuse and Incest National Network. (2005). *Social norms campaign: Engaging men in the prevention of sexual assault*. Retrieved March 2, 2007, from http://www.rainn.org/programs/social-norms/index.html

Reiss, A. J., Jr., & Roth, J. A. (Eds.). (1993). *Understanding and preventing violence, volume 1. panel on the understanding and control of violent behavior*. Washington, DC: National Academy Press.

Ruback, R. B., Menard, K. S., Outlaw, M. C., & Shaffer, J. N. (1999). Normative advice to campus crime victims: Effects of gender, age, and alcohol. *Violence and Victims, 14*, 381-396.

Sable, M. R., Danis, F., Mauzy, D. L., & Gallagher, S. K. (2006). Barriers to reporting sexual assault for women and men: Perspectives of college students. *Journal of American College Health, 55*(3), 157-162.

Saltz, R. F., & Stanghetta, P. (1997). A community-wide responsible beverage service program in three communities: Early findings. *Addiction, 92*(Suppl. 2), S237-S249.

Schwartz, M. D., & Leggett, M. S. (1999). Bad dates or emotional trauma? The aftermath of campus sexual assault. *Violence Against Women, 5*(3), 251-271.

Sher, K. J., Wood, M. D., Wood, P. K., & Raskin, G. (1996). Alcohol outcome expectancies and alcohol use: A latent variable cross-lagged panel study. *Journal of Abnormal Psychology, 105*(4), 561-574.

Sims, C., Noel, N., & Maisto, S. (2007). Rape blame as a function of alcohol presence and resistance type. *Addictive Behaviors, 32*, 2766-2775.

Sochting, I., Fairbrother, N., & Koch, W. J. (2004). Sexual assault of women: Prevention efforts and risk factors. *Violence Against Women, 10*(1), 73–93.

Stewart, S. H., Zeitlin, S. B., & Samoluk, S. B. (1996). Examination of a three-dimensional drinking motives questionnaire in a young adult university student sample. *Behaviour Research and Therapy, 34*, 61-71.

Stokols, D. (1996). Translating social ecological theory into guidelines for community health promotion. *American Journal of Health Promotion, 10*, 282–298.

Testa, M. (2004). The role of substance use in male-to-female physical and sexual violence: A brief review and recommendations for future research. *Journal of Interpersonal Violence, 19*(12), 1494-1505.

Testa, M., & Livingston, J. A. (1999). Qualitative analysis of women's experiences of sexual aggression: Focus on the role of alcohol. *Psychology of Women Quarterly, 23*(3), 573-589.

Testa, M., Livingston, J. A., & Collins, R. L. (2000). The role of women's alcohol consumption in evaluation of vulnerability to sexual aggression. *Experimental and Clinical Psychopharmacology, 8*(2), 185-191.

Teter, C. J., McCabe, S. E., LaGrange, K., Cranford, J. A., & Boyd, C. J. (2006). Illicit use of specific prescription stimulants among college students: Prevalence, motives, and routes of administration. *Pharmacotherapy, 26*(10), 1501-1510.

Thompson, M., Sitterle, D., Clay, G., & Kingree, J. (2007). Reasons for not reporting victimizations to the police: Do they vary for physical and sexual incidents? *Journal of American College Health, 55*(5), 277-282.

Tjaden, P., & Thoennes, N. (1998, November). *Prevalence, incident and consequences of violence against women: Findings from the National Violence Against Women Survey.* Washington DC: National Institute of Justice and the Centers for Disease Control and Prevention.

Toomey, T. L., Lenk, K. M., & Wagenaar, A. C. (2007). Environmental policies to reduce college drinking: An update of research findings. *Journal of Studies on Alcohol and Drugs, 68*, 208-219.

U.S. Public Health Service. (1999). *The surgeon general's call to action to prevent suicide.* Washington, DC: Author.

Ullman, S. E. (1996). Social reactions, coping strategies, and self-blame attributions in adjustment to sexual assault. *Psychology of Women Quarterly, 20*(4), 505.

Ullman, S. E. (2003). A critical review of field studies on the link of alcohol and adult sexual assault in women. *Aggression and Violent Behavior, 8*, 471-486.

Ullman, S. E., & Filipas, H. H. (2001). Correlates of formal and informal support seeking in sexual assault victims. *Journal of Interpersonal Violence, 16*(10), 1028-1047.

Ullman, S. E., Karabatsos, G., & Koss, M. P. (1999a). Alcohol and sexual assault in a national sample of college men. *Psychology of Women Quarterly, 23*(4), 673-689.

Ullman, S. E., Karabatsos, G., & Koss, M. P. (1999b). Alcohol and sexual assault in a national sample of college women. *Journal of Interpersonal Violence, 14*(6), 603-625.

Wallack, L., Dorfman, L., Jernigan, D., & Themba, M. (1993). *Media advocacy and public health: Power for prevention.* Newbury Park, CA: Sage.

Warkentin, J. B., & Gidycz, C. A. (2007). The use and acceptance of sexually aggressive tactics in college men. *Journal of Interpersonal Violence, 22*(7), 829-850.

Wechsler, H., Lee, J. E., Kuo, M., Seibring, M., Nelson, T. F., & Lee, H. (2002a). Trends in college binge drinking during a period of increased prevention efforts: Findings from 4 Harvard School of Public Health College Alcohol Studies surveys 1993–2001. *Journal of American College Health, 50*(5), 203–217.

Wechsler, H., Lee, J. E., Nelson, T. F., & Kuo, M. (2002b). Underage college student's drinking behavior, access to alcohol, and the influence of deterrence policies. *Journal of American College Health, 50*(5), 223-235.

Wechsler, H., Moeykens, B., Davenport, A. E., Castillo, S., & Hansen, J. (1995). The adverse impact of heavy episodic drinkers on other college students. *Journal of Studies on Alcohol, 56*(6), 628-634.

Weitzman, E., Nelson, T., Lee, H., & Wechsler, H. (2004). Reducing drinking and related harms in college: Evaluation of the "A Matter of Degree" program. *American Journal of Preventive Medicine, 27*(3), 187-196.

Werner, M. J., Walker, L. S., & Greene, J. W. (1995). Relation of alcohol expectancies to changes in problem drinking among college students. *Archives of Pediatrics & Adolescent Medicine, 149*(7), 733-739.

White, B. P., Becker-Blease, K. A., & Grace-Bishop, K. (2006). Stimulant medication use, misuse, and abuse in an undergraduate and graduate student sample. *Journal of American College Health, 54*(5), 261-268.

Wish, E. D., Fitzelle, D. B., O'Grady, K. E., Hsu, M. H., & Arria, A. M. (2006). Evidence for significant polydrug use among ecstasy-using college students. *Journal of American College Health, 55*(2), 99-104.

Wood, M. D., & Sher, K. J. (2002). Sexual assault and relationship violence among college students: Examining the role of alcohol and other drugs. In C. Wekerle & A. M. Wall (Eds.), *The violence and addiction equation: Theoretical and clinical issues in substance abuse and relationship violence* (pp. 169-193). New York: Brunner-Routledge.

Zawacki, T., Abbey, A., Buck, P. O., McAuslan, P., & Clinton-Sherrod, A. M. (2003). Perpetrators of alcohol-involved sexual assaults: How do they differ from other sexual assault perpetrators and nonperpetrators? *Aggressive Behavior, 29*(4), 366-380.

Zimmerman, R., & DeJong, W. (2003). *Safe lanes on campus: A guide for preventing impaired driving and underage drinking*: Higher Education Center for Alcohol and Other Drug Prevention.

Zweig, J. M., Crockett, L. J., Sayer, A., & Vicary, J. R. (1999). A longitudinal examination of the consequences of sexual victimization for rural young adult women. *Journal of Sex Research, 36*(4), 396–409.

Part 2

Critical Components of a Campus Sexual Assault Response Team

Introduction: Doing the Groundwork— Research and Preparation

**by Donna M. Barry, APN, FN-CSA,
and Paul M. Cell, Chief of Police**

The development of a Sexual Assault Response Team (SART), whether community or campus based, requires a significant amount of groundwork. Comprehensive research and evaluation supplies critical information that is necessary for the creation of a campus SART. Research into all areas of need and feasibility builds a solid foundation for response that meets federal and state requirements, and integrates the unique characteristics and challenges of a particular campus. A cookie-cutter approach to campus SART development will not offer a successful and effective response.

PEARLS OF WISDOM

Several "pearls of wisdom" are offered to accomplish this task:

- *Become an expert.* Knowledge is power, and this knowledge will gain the respect of the constituencies encountered during the process of a needs assessment and feasibility study of a campus SART. These constituencies include—
  o Key campus administrators whose commitment is crucial to the success of a SART initiative;
  o Campus departments that will play a critical role in SART response; and
  o Community agencies currently available to community sexual assault victims who may be utilized in a campus SART initiative.

  The individuals that become involved will have multiple questions and concerns. The ability to offer sound information such as the principles of federal and state statutes, actual local statistics that reflect need, current response services, and best practice recommendations will instill confidence in those that have or may have a vested interest in the developmental process.

- *Develop a global perspective.* Most readers of this text will already possess an expert level of knowledge in their respective disciplines. It is now vital to formulate a more global perspective of the priorities, needs, and objectives of all key players involved in the development of the SART system. To ensure the creation of a successful program, each constituent must sense the importance and benefit to its involvement and understand the same for all professional response roles.

- *Identify the key players.* It is more than likely that many community and campus services already exist for sexual assault victims. Existing services, groups, and decision makers should be brought to the table to share ideas. Including those who are currently providing services will acknowledge the importance of their roles and avoid discrediting the work that is already being done. These groups can be a valuable and committed resource with the potential for strong and successful partnerships.

- *Learn the "language."* Effective communication is always the foundation of successful coordination of services. When various disciplines come together to achieve a common goal, each will bring to the table individual agendas and concerns. In order to integrate these pieces into a strategy to accomplish the common goal of SART development, an understanding of the focus of each agency must be gained. For instance, advocacy groups must communicate with law enforcement by recognizing the role and priorities of their responsibilities in sexual assault response and communicating ways in which the rape crisis advocate can assist in this response. Although law enforcement will have victims' needs in mind, their primary role is the safety and investigative component of the SART. Thus, communicating ways in which other disciplines will assist and improve the law enforcement response is important. Campus administrators and legal counsel will have other primary concerns such as liability issues, media reaction, and funding for the initiative, despite recognition of the importance and priority of victim needs.

- *Understand and use the principles of marketing.* Successful marketing and sales executives use some basic strategies when interacting with clients. In some respects, the concept of a coordinated SART system will need to be "sold" to the key players identified. The basics are simple: (1) know the product, (2) identify the benefits to the individual or agency, (3) acknowledge previously successful services of the group, (4) present a well-prepared plan of action, and (5) explain the role and responsibilities all agencies will play in the SART.

  It may appear harsh to approach victim services in this manner since it is assumed that most individuals involved in the SART planning process have victim needs as a priority. However, some constituencies may be resistant to improve services. These will be the groups in which basic marketing principles can be used to address the benefits of the SART for a particular campus in order to achieve a "buy in" and commitment from all disciplines.

- *Be creative, and bring practical solutions to the table.* One size does not fit all in creating a SART for any particular campus. There will be multiple variables and capabilities that are individual to each institution, some having more obstacles or more extensive preparation than others. Still others will already have the availability of quality, comprehensive services in the community, and it is only a matter of coordinating services more effectively. Whatever the scenario, creativity and "coloring outside the lines" may be necessary to discover solutions and achieve success. Campus administrators will also be more receptive to suggestions that are logical and practical, especially if this reduces funding needs.

- *Develop a constructive and objective, but critical "eye."* One of the most difficult aspects of SART development is the evaluation of current services. Querying other institutions may show that services do exist that have been serving victims for years. That does not imply that these services are adequate in the provision of a comprehensive response. Therefore, the approach taken with existing services and resources can influence their willingness to participate in the development process and be receptive to change. A validation of the importance of their current services is critical as well as obligation of an objective and constructive approach to the suggestion of how combined services and the SART would enhance their efforts.

QUESTIONS TO PONDER

To assist in determing the quality and effectiveness of existing services as well as gain knowledge of areas necessary for campus SART development, the following questions can be considered:

- *What are the federal and state statutory requirements for campuses?* In order to formulate a campus SART and appropriate sexual assault polices, it is necessary to understand both federal and state specific laws. The three major federal statutes that impact campus response include the Family Educational Rights and Privacy Act of 1974 (FERPA; Pub. L. No. 93-380 (Aug. 21, 1974)), Title IX of the Education Amendments of 1972 (Pub. L. No. 92-318 (June 23, 1972)), and the Jeanne Clery Disclosure of Campus Security Policy and Campus Crime Statistics Act (Clery Act; 20 U.S.C. § 1092(f); see also Chapter 4 and Appendix D). The Campus Sexual Assault Victims' Bill of Rights as part of the Higher Education Act of 1992 (Pub. L. No. 102-325 (July 23, 1992)) should also be a primary focus since this portion of the statute provides the additional rights of campus victims. The Health Insurance Portability and Accountability Act (HIPPA; Pub. L. No. 104-191 (Aug. 21, 1996)) must also be considered to protect the privacy and security of individually identifiable health information.

  Statutes specific to each state can provide actual definitions of sexual assault offenses, provide degrees of crime attached to the offense, determine reporting mandates for sexual offenses, and other details that must be considered when developing a framework for campus policy, response, and reporting. States can vary significantly in all of these areas. See the example in Appendix E for New Jersey.

- *What types of services are currently available on campus and in the community?* It is important to clearly identify the services available to students who are victims of sexual assault. This requires contacting all groups on campus who offer services to victims of sexual assault such as law enforcement or security officials, medical or health care providers, local prosecutor/district attorneys, and advocacy services. Are there informal or written agreements between some or all of the available services? What types of services exist, and what types of services are missing? Is there coordination and oversight, and how well does it all meet victims' needs?

- *Who are the individuals that play a role in other aspects of campus sexual assault services?* There will be individuals and departments that play a role in sexual assault issues and procedures that are nonresponders. Campus administrators, legal counsel, health educators, athletics, and Greek organization leadership, and student government representatives should be involved to determine concerns, responsibilities, and roles in SART development. Although none may be part of a formalized SART, each can assist in bringing strategies and concerns to the decision-making process.

- *What are the current campus policies and regulations regarding sexual assault?* As stated in Chapters 1 and 5, the unique culture and dynamics of a campus will have a significant impact on the incidence of sexual assault. These areas need to be taken into consideration with response development. Institutional policies and regulations vary greatly from one campus to another and establish the fundamental core of the community environment. For example, faith-based schools and public institutions may have varying regulations and codes of conduct due to the different missions of the founding organization or group.

A review of policies and regulations should determine if they meet federal compliance mandates and are based on state and local statutes that reflect the same level of seriousness for violation as do criminal codes of the state. In other words, if a state law regarding sexual assault is based on consent, campus policies and regulations should have a similar basis. In the same manner, sanctions for sexual assault code violations should also be reflective of the degree of the crime of that state. A standardization of sanctions needs to be in place, and there must be equity in the enforcement of these sanctions for all offenders and victims.

- *Is funding needed?* The unfortunate state of the world today and for many campuses is that all initiatives or projects are cost driven. A best-practice model can be created for services to victims of sexual assault and have all or part of it deferred or denied due to cost issues. Thus, determining actual costs for creating and sustaining a campus SART is a critical part of the planning initiative.

There are multiple areas to evaluate in establishing a budget (i.e., supplies, equipment, training, and salaries), and this may be where the creative juices will be needed most. Once specific line items are identified, several budget scenarios should be established until a determination of available funds has been identified. The first may be the "top-of-the-line" budget, or, in other words, the wish-list budget. It might include state-of-the art equipment, advertising and media promotion costs, and desirable salary ranges for staff. Other versions would gradually look at more modest funding, with the last being a truly bare-bones account in which only vital necessities are included.

Most often, the first question will be where is the money going to come from? Funding options include local private foundations, state agencies, and federal resources. Federal agencies, such as the Office of Victims of Crime, offer Victims of Crime Act of 1984 (VOCA; Pub. L. No. 98-473 (Oct. 12, 1984)) funding to eligible agencies in both formula and discretionary grants. Details of grant opportunities can be found at http://www.ojp.usdoj.gov/ovc/. In addition, the Violence Against Women Act of 1994 is a U.S. federal law (passed as title IV, sections 40001-40703 of the Violent Crime Control and Law Enforcement Act of 1994, H.R. 3355 and signed as Public Law 103-322 by President Bill Clinton on September 13, 1994) authorizing specific funding and initiatives to reduce violence against women including campus programs. Additional information can be obtained at http://www.ovw.usdoj.gov/.

The chapters in Part 2 offer the specifics on the critical components of a campus SART response. Using the chapter information and the questions/approaches suggested above, each of the primary response disciplines that comprise a traditional SART as well as statutory regulations compliance can be evaluated to determine strengths and weaknesses prior to development and implementation of the particular campus SART.

Chapter 3

Community Sexual Assault Response Teams—Structure, Function, and Efficacy

by Donna A. Gaffney, APRN, BC, DNSc, FAAN

Unlike the West of old, this frontier is not one of place. It is a frontier of technology, ideas and values. The new pioneers celebrate individuality over conformity . . . they compete through resilience instead of resistance, through adaptation instead of control. In a time of dizzying complexities and change, they realize that tightly drawn strategies become brittle while shared purpose endures.

—Petzinger (1999, p. 17).

NEW SOCIAL RESPONSE TO SEXUAL ASSAULT

The Sexual Assault Nurse Examiner (SANE) and the Sexual Assault Response Team (SART), they are known as today, are built out of converging historical events. In 1975, Susan Brownmiller wrote her landmark book, *Against Our Will: Men, Women and Rape* (1975). She concluded that cultural acceptance of sexual force is a pervasive process of intimidation that affects all women. Brownmiller also noted that the laws and legal system historically did not give women an equal voice. However, the 1970s brought significant reform of sexual assault laws across the United States (Cuklanz, 1996; Fairstein, 1993). These changes reflected new definitions, amended statutes, and alterations in the legal processes related to sexual assault. Linda Fairstein, the Director of the Sex Crimes Prosecution Unit in Manhattan, pointed out:

> The 1977 revision [of forcible compulsion] was marked progress, but obviously had still retained the "earnest resistance" language in the statute. It was not until 1983 that the definition was finally amended so that the focus was taken off the conduct of the survivor and placed squarely where it belonged: on the actions of the offender. (Fairstein, 1993, p. 128)

Cuklanz (1996) in her exploration of the role of the media and public opinion suggested that the understanding of sexual assault has not been

> wholly embraced by the mainstream culture, but significant changes in national level discourses may yet construe very real success. . . . The sheer number of sexual assault cases that are now receiving national attention and the magnitude of the attention they receive are signs that the subject of rape is currently important to the U.S. culture. (p. 114)

It is also important to note that SANE-SART efforts have also brought new attention to the problem of sexual assault.

The explosion of research on the effects of trauma during the Viet Nam War also influenced both public and professional understanding of sexual assault. Ann Burgess and Linda Holmstrom (1974) followed with their groundbreaking research on the psychological effects of sexual assault—specifically, rape trauma syndrome.

The women's movement served as the thread joining these significant sociopolitical events of the 1970s. Not only did the movement raise public awareness, but it initiated a new social response to victims of sexual assault—the rape crisis center and the rape care advocate (Herman, 1992). The first centers opened in 1971, and, by the end of the decade, over 1,000 centers were established to assist victims of sexual assault, abuse, and ultimately domestic violence. The role of the volunteer advocate was to offer practical, legal, and emotional support to sexual assault victims (Herman, 1992). Sometimes, the role of the volunteer advocate was to question the care provided within the medical setting and to support the victim against medical staff who were too busy caring for the medically wounded, whose needs were too often seen as more urgent than the sexual assault victim.

The impetus to improve the care of sexual assault victims within the medical setting began with nurses, other medical professionals, counselors, and advocates working with rape victims in these medical settings across the country. It was obvious to these individuals that services to sexual assault victims were inadequate and not at the same high standard of care as other emergency department clients (Holloway & Swan, 1993; O'Brien, 1992).

As a result of the goal to better meet the needs of this underserved population, the first SANE programs were established in Memphis, Tennessee, in 1976 (Speck & Aiken, 1995), in Minneapolis, Minnesota, in 1977 (Ledray & Chaignot,1980; Ledray, 1993b), and in Amarillo, Texas, in 1979 (Antognoli-Toland, 1985).

In 1992, seventy-two individuals from thirty-one SANE programs across the United States and Canada came together for the first time at a meeting hosted by the Sexual Assault Resource Service and the University of Minnesota School of Nursing in Minneapolis. It was at that meeting that the International Association of Forensic Nurses (IAFN) was formed (Lynch, 1993; Ledray & Simmelink, 1997). While the initial SANE development was slow, with only three programs operating by the end of the 1970s, development has increased exponentially. In the summer of 2006, all fifty U.S. states had at least one operating SANE program (Office for Victims of Crime, 2008).

NEED FOR COORDINATION OF SERVICES

With the evolution of new practices and new provider roles, specifically SANEs and SANE programs, it became imperative for these health care providers to coordinate their victim-centered work with others in the community, namely rape crisis programs and law enforcement. Coordination of community services for sexual assault victims, or any victims, is founded on the premise that personnel from multiple organizations collaborate and work together for the well-being of that victim (Martin, 2007). Coordination extends beyond professionals performing their individual responsibilities. A number of authors (Campbell, 1998; Campbell, Wasco, Ahrens, Sefl, & Barnes, 2001; Allen, 2005; Martin 2005) suggest that true coordination involves in-person meetings to accomplish the goals of planning, developing policies and protocols, staff training and cross-training, appearing on educational panels for the public and governmental agencies, and communicating about victims. The need to meet in each other's presence facilitates learning from and about each other, determining common objectives, and identifying best practices. Professionals also discover how to accommodate each other's roles as well as promote victims' well-being (Martin 2005).

Coordination of services facilitates the individual's transition from victim to survivor by changing the context of service delivery. Communities are better able to understand the circumstances of service delivery from the providers' perspective, and all disciplines gain an appreciation of the how sexual assault affects victims' lives (Campbell & Ahrens, 1998). The development of a common understanding, goals, and practices is essential to successful coordination (Gamache & Asmus, 1999). Finally, the number of systems that are coordinated within a community can vary depending on how many organizations have come to the table. The SART is a prime example of high-level community coordination.

COMMUNITY SART MODEL

In the early years following the initial proliferation and recognition of SANE programs across the country, communities began to create multidisciplinary teams of responders to provide support for sexual assault victims and the programs that provided services to them. These teams were called SARTs. The goals of a community multidisciplinary model are to: (1) enhance evidence collection and facilitate communication between all team members throughout the process (thus improving the likelihood of prosecution) and (2) assist sexual assault victims to recover from their experience through the provision of support systems (Girardin, 2005; Wilson & Klein, 2005). While SANEs and SANE programs offer a new and crucial resource to victims of sexual assault, this relatively new role of professional nursing cannot operate in isolation (Ledray, 2003). In fact, the best results and the best possible services for the sexual assault victim could be achieved only in the context of a team. Lang and Brockway (2001) emphasize the benefits of the SART model: a victim-focused continuum of services, improved quality of care, and minimization of the potential for secondary trauma as victims move through the medical and criminal justice systems. Lang and Brockway (2001) also hypothesize that when victims receive services that are not only more collaborative but compassionate as well, there is a greater likelihood they will participate with law enforcement and criminal justice.

While the goals of such innovative programs may be shared, the SARTs can differ in structure and in function. The acronyms SANE and SART may need clarification at this point.

- A *SANE model* is defined as a sexual assault response service in which a SANE, employed by an agency and possibly a SANE program, provides a comprehensive forensic examination and evidence collection, assessment, and treatment of the victim of sexual assault.

- A *SART model* is comprised of a multidisciplinary team. Each member of the team serves a role in the treatment, prosecution, and even prevention of sexual assault. In this model, there may be a SANE who is a member of the team, but, in many cases, there are also other health care providers who are not SANEs, such as physicians and physicians' assistants, and nurse practitioners. The SART model can vary according to the structure and responsibilities established by the community.

- A *SANE/SART model* incorporates multidisciplinary roles and responsibilities as described in the SART model. However, the SANE and/or SANE program is an integral member of the SART team. The SANE program works in conjunction with the SART.

However, there are jurisdictions where a coordinated community response is neither titled SANE nor SART. Some states recognize and even certify specialized health care providers and sexual assault response programs, for example, Forensic Nurse Examiners (FNEs), Sexual Assault Examiners (SAEs), or Sexual Assault Forensic Examiners (SAFEs).

SARTs should not be confused with a multidisciplinary or multiorganizational approach in which community groups are actively involved in initiating, planning, developing, or evaluating sexual assault services but not in their delivery (Hatmaker, Pinholster, & Saye, 2002). Many community organizing groups have used the Eight-Step Model Process developed by Boles and Patterson (1997) to launch their SART program. This model describes how to build a coordinated community service through a series of eight steps: (1) developing an inventory of existing services; (2) surveying victims to identify their experiences, both positive and negative; (3) performing a community-wide needs assessment; (4) writing the protocol; (5) formally adopting the protocol; (6) training and education of all involved; (7) monitoring; and, finally, (8) evaluating the efficacy of the coordinated response. As stated earlier, these organizations are not involved in the direct delivery of services.

HISTORY AND STATE OF THE SART

In 1975, the Memphis (Tennessee) Police Department organized a collaborative response to sexual assault. Five years later, the San Luis Obispo County General Hospital (in California) created its SART and SANE program, and it was followed by a SANE-SART program in Santa Cruz (California; Barkhurst, Fowler, Siadal, & Vokes, 2002). Over the next two decades, additional SARTs developed, as funding became available from both private and governmental sectors, and as states adopted legislation that implemented coordinated services for victims of sexual assault. However, it was not until 1994 when a *New York Times* op-ed column brought the care and treatment of the sexual assault victim to the public's attention (Quindlen, 1994). The 700-word article appeared in over 8 regional newspapers and was read by 6 million people. It did not take long for state and community governments to fund and launch a coordinated response to sexual assault in their own communities (Gaffney, 2005). In 2006, the National Sexual Violence Resource Center surveyed SARTs across the United States and U.S. territories (Zajac, 2006). The assessment resulted in a comprehensive description of coordinated multidisciplinary community sexual assault services; of the 258 teams responding to the survey, 190 teams were titled SARTs (the acronym standing for various names— Sexual Assault Response or Resource Teams, Suspected Abuse Response Teams). The teams, most of them in existence for three or more years, consisted of, at minimum, prosecutors, forensic examiners, law enforcement officers, and rape care advocates. Some communities included other disciplines from crime laboratories and administrative personnel. However, there was interest in expanding team membership and by creating new partnerships with faith-based, disability, and multicultural groups, as well as activist/advocacy organizations that could promote social change. SART administrative centers were located in health care facilities, on campuses, in law enforcement agencies, or family justice centers. Meeting frequency ranged from monthly to an as-needed basis. Policies, procedures, and protocols for SARTs were victim-centered and agency-specific. There were suggestions for meeting the needs of underserved populations and specific strategies for SARTs operating on college campuses, military installations, and in tribal communities. Cross-training among disciplines was the rule rather than the exception; yet collaborative arrangements were "generally informal" with verbal protocols, not more formal written agreements (Zajac, 2006). SART services included: victim advocacy, mental health services, such as crisis intervention, counseling, and support. Other services are: the forensic medical assessment and evaluation; assistance from law enforcement; and prosecution personnel. Prevention, media awareness, and educational programs were primarily delivered by rape crisis or victim advocacy organizations. Appraisal of SART services was accomplished through case review and case management, data collection, and monitoring convictions and incident reports. While formal evaluations have not been the norm, those that have gone through a formal process report that victims report a greater sense of safety, increased reporting to law enforcement, and consistency of evidence collection.

The National Sexual Violence Resource Center (http://www.nsvrc.org) offers an online map of the location of SARTs throughout the country and their histories (up to year 2000). They invite Web visitors to submit the history of their own SARTs to create a national backdrop of SART development.

TYPES AND STRUCTURE OF SARTS

The composition of the team can vary according to the goals established by stakeholders, professionals, and community members who initially come to the table. In addition, the framework of the funding proposals written by community leaders can also determine team membership. The make up of the team can evolve over time, as new services are added and those that may be redundant are eliminated. Most SARTs consist of health care providers, rape care advocates, and law enforcement officers, detectives, and prosecutors who assist sexual assault victims through the criminal justice process. However, the team can expand to include other disciplines such as victim witness advocates, administrators, and representatives from various community agencies. Some communities use a multidisciplinary approach in a less structured manner. Team members work with each other but not consistently and not following a set of policies or protocols to guide their actions. Ledray (2003) draws the distinction between a formal (SART) model and a network of informal collaborators. In an informal SART, team members work with each other but not consistently and not according to a set of policies or procedures. A fully functional SART model actively utilizes and coordinates the roles and responsibilities of all team members for each sexual assault.

Lonsway (2001) describes two different SART models. The Sexual Assault *Response* Team model consists of a team of individuals who respond jointly to interview the victim at the time of the sexual assault medical examination. The second model, the Sexual Assault *Resource* Team, consists of professionals who work independently on each sexual assault case. While they do not respond as a team, they do communicate with each other regularly to discuss their shared cases, and they address situations or problems in order to facilitate services for the sexual assault victim.

Sexual Assault *Response* Team

The SART model requires a formal arrangement with specific protocols, defined roles, and policies in place. These procedures govern the way each team member responds to the victim and how the team members work with each other. At minimum the three key team members are from the disciplines of law enforcement, health care, and victim advocacy. The victim accesses the system through any one of three entry points: law enforcement, a health care system, or by calling a rape crisis hotline. At that point, the SART is activated, and the team members respond, as a team, to the sexual assault event (Lonsway, 2001).

Sexual Assault *Resource* Team

Specific community needs, available personnel, and funding resources may require an adaptation of the SART concept. Lonsway (2001) describes how some communities have changed and adapted the SART model defined above (see "Sexual Assault *Response* Team"). These "teams" have a less formal, less structured approach. There is communication about cases, but the professionals do not necessarily respond simultaneously to the sexual assault victim. The multidisciplinary team members cooperate with each other, serving more as a *resource* than partners or collaborators. In the case of the resource team, either one of the other disciplines can be called when the victim presents for services.

The primary difference between the *resource* team and the *response* team is that the in-depth interview is conducted sequentially and independently by health care and law enforcement. However, in either case, the rape care advocate should be called immediately and maintain a presence with both police and forensic examiners (Lonsway, 2001).

MECHANISMS AND FUNCTIONS OF THE SART

SART models can also differ according to the function of the team, its members, and/or the administration of the team. Ledray (2003) states that interview procedures are different for two SART models: the Joint Interview SART model and the Cooperative SART model. The Joint Interview SART model, noted by Lonsway (2001), employs a single interview technique in which law enforcement personnel, the sexual assault forensic examiner, and advocacy services simultaneously meet with the victim. The Cooperative SART model, which Lonsway (2001) titles the Sexual Assault *Resource* Team model, coordinates services for sexual assault victims but does not necessarily respond at the same time. Interviews occur separately and sequentially. Ledray (2003) points out the benefits and concerns with each model. Some authors believe that a single interview in the presence of team members spares the victim the trauma of reliving the event multiple times. Retelling of a traumatic event may induce more trauma and emotional distress (Esposito, 2005). However, other researchers have found that one-time debriefing interventions recounting a traumatic event may not be useful in reducing symptoms of posttraumatic stress disorder, anxiety, and depression after psychological trauma (Sijbrandij, Olff, Reitsma, Carlier, & Gersons, 2006). In fact, a number of researchers (Friedman, 1996; Foa, Davidson, & Frances,1999) propose that retelling of the traumatic event can be useful in the healing process. Yet there is much to learn about memory and trauma. Memory of a traumatic event occurs at first on the perceptual level and then, with time, the narrative fills in (Schacter, 1996). A smooth chronological sequencing of events immediately after a traumatic event is highly unlikely and perhaps even in the days to come. Trauma distorts ones sense of time (Schacter, 1996). At first glance, a single interview can appear to insure consistent reporting by team members, as everyone hears the same account of the event at the same point in time. However, with time, the perceptions of the event can become less intense and the narrative emerges. This may occur at different time intervals after the sexual assault. In summary, the question of multiple interviewers versus multiple interviews cannot be answered without knowing the context of the interview and the manner in which it was conducted.

LOCATION OF THE SART

The word *community* implies that a specified geographic region is served by the SART. The funding and services may be generated from existing governmental or agency budget lines. The multidisciplinary team members will also share community-based roots. However, community can also mean a structure or organization within a population (e.g., a military SART or a university-based SART, an adolescent health care center, a tribal community, U.S. territory, or a prison). In such situations the organizations implementing the SART believe that there are legal, social, or population needs that are above and beyond the community at large that will better serve the victims. In many cases, these needs may be culturally determined.

EFFICACY OF SARTS

Measures of success of the SANE/SART model or the SART model have been predominantly anecdotal and offered as case reports over the past decade. In addition to limitations in research methodologies, the acronym, SART, is used in various ways and can have different meanings in studies (Smith, Holmseth, Macgregor, & Letourneau,1998). While an author may use the term SART as the mechanism by which sexual assault services are delivered, these mechanisms can vary program by program. Therefore, based on various levels of sophistication and viability, measuring the effectiveness of the SART-coordinated response across programs becomes challenging.

Zweig and Burt (2003) suggest that a comprehensive national picture of the status, needs, and sustainability of SARTs is missing. Some research addresses legal system outcomes as compared to measures that investigate victim well-being or recovery (Wiley, Sugar, Fine, & Eckert, 2003). In research done in the area of intimate partner violence services, lower repeat offenses were reported when law enforcement followed protocols developed in conjunction with other agencies (Tolman & Weisz, 1995).

Campbell and Bybee (1997) found that the presence of a SART or a coordinated community approach to sexual assault with health care providers, victim advocacy services, law enforcement, and prosecution, increased the probability that specialized services would be provided to victims. This finding underscores the importance of service coordination as one strategy that will increase access and use of such services. The presence of a community SART is positively correlated with availability of follow-up information and referrals for the physical and mental health consequences of sexual assault (Zweig & Burt, 2003). Campbell (1998) learned that the greater the coordination of services, the more positive were the victims' experiences with the legal, medical, and mental health systems compared to that of victims living in communities without coordinated services.

A study conducted by the American Prosecutors Institute and Boston College (APRI/BC; Nugent-Borakove et al., 2006) compared outcomes of SANE/SART sexual assault cases and non-SANE/SART sexual assault cases. The authors concluded that SANE/SART interventions enhanced the criminal justice system's response to adult female sexual assault cases. The most effective strategies were evidence collection and preservation. However, SANE/SART community models had a much shorter time between the sexual assault event itself and the victim's presentation to the medical or judicial system. The shortened time span may have contributed to more effective evidence collection. Additionally, the study supported previous work related to the filing of charges (Solola, Scott, Severs, & Howell, 1983; O'Brien, 1992; Crandall & Helitzer, 2003). Nugent-Borakove et al. (2006) note that this finding constitutes the first comparative evidence supporting their hypothesis that SANE/SART interventions are a valuable tool in the criminal justice system, particularly for prosecutors. Other findings indicated that in the absence of a SANE/SART intervention, there would be a decreased probability of an arrest. Although the authors theorize that a SANE/SART model would increase convictions, that hypothesis was not definitively supported.

Nugent-Borakove et al. (2006) reported one surprising result. They found that a SANE/SART response resulted in greater victim participation in the criminal justice process, as compared to cases with SANE-only interventions. The SANE-only interventions resulted in the lowest levels of victim criminal justice participation. This may be the strongest evidence to support the need for health care providers to function in the context of a team. The multidisciplinary team may indeed be greater than the sum of its parts and deserves further investigation.

UNDERSTANDING COMPETITION AND CONFLICT ON THE SART

Determining the impact of a SART program on victim outcomes is measurable. The potential findings provide the data upon which systems can make change and refine policies and procedures. However, what about the team members themselves; what outcomes relate to team functioning—both individually and collectively? As Petzinger (1999) so eloquently points out, for a revolution to occur, there has to be adaptation instead of control and resilience instead of resistance. During revolutionary change, there is competition and conflict, usually among those who have worked so diligently to bring about change. The melting pot of individuals who share a common interest also provide the most compassionate, comprehensive, expert services to victims of sexual assault. Although the majority of the team shares the overall goal, people from a variety of disciplines, with different ideas, different agendas, and different philosophies, are challenged to make the process work in a smooth, efficient manner. There may be disagreement over methods of service delivery. There may be division over who will be the best provider. This is not unusual in the sexual assault treatment and prevention field. In fact, it is apparent in nearly all victims' services, both domestic and international. These challenges are not new.

How is it that a public service that is so important is also vulnerable to such turmoil? Professionals from at least nine different disciplines (law enforcement, the justice system, medicine, social work, advocacy, nursing, psychology, sociology, political science, and more) are as committed as ever to serving the victim in the best possible way. In fact, there are more areas of agreement than conflict (Sloan, 1999). But when there is disagreement, the communication process threatens to become divisive and in danger of escalating. Umiker (1998) states the outcome can result in attacking other people or disciplines rather than the problem itself. Martin (2007) reports that there may be suspicions and fear across organizational boundaries. Case overload and ineffective communication, along with competing or conflicting values and beliefs, threaten to obstruct coordination efforts. Areas of potential concern are centered on boundary issues, role, and value conflicts. It is, however, unclear how widespread this conflict really is today. Nonetheless, it is important to address each of these concerns raised.

Conflicts on the SART

Once new roles and professional responsibilities were included in the treatment of sexual assault victims, conflicts and barriers to effective sexual assault services began to surface and continue to this day. The new role of the SANE precipitated conflict among some health care professionals, rape crisis centers, and rape care advocates (Sloan, 1999; Payne, 2007). With the advent of SART programs, it was not unreasonable to think that there would be additional role conflicts among the multiple disciplines that comprise the team. These concerns emanate from several areas: value conflicts and boundary and role conflicts.

In the 1970s, rape crisis centers went through the same conflicts with law enforcement personnel, whom they often saw as opponents, needing to advocate against them for the victim. The police then tried to avoid "those advocates," whom they saw as interfering with their investigation efforts. Unfortunately, in some areas this opposition was never truly resolved, emphasizing the need to better address the issue among all roles intrinsic to SART development today.

Value Conflicts

Reporting versus nonreporting has been an issue and source of disagreement among a number of providers who serve victims of sexual assault. Every human being has the right to make decisions about her or his care. The sexual assault victim, being no different, can decide whether to be examined, to have evidence collected, to receive prophylaxis for sexually transmitted diseases, to receive emergency contraception, or to report the sexual assault to law enforcement are personal decisions. With each decision, the victim must receive relevant information and possess decision-making capacity to make a reasonable choice regarding health care concerns (Burkardt & Nathaniel, 1998). An individual must have four qualities in order to make a decision: (1) the ability to understand all information, (2) the ability to communicate understanding and choices, (3) personal values and goals to guide the decision, and (4) the ability to reason and deliberate (Burkardt & Nathaniel,1998, p. 201).

Information is the second critical component of giving informed consent. Although there is a legal basis for informed consent, it is also an ethical imperative. "Ethically valid consent is a process of shared decision-making based upon mutual respect and participation, not a ritual to be equated with reciting the contents of a form" (President's Commission for the Study of Ethical Problems in Medicine and Biomedical Behavioral Research, 1983, p. 2). The information provided to the person is based on professional standards of practice, reasonable person standards, and subjective standards. Specifically, information includes: (1) the nature of the health concern and outcome if nothing is done; (2) a description of all options, even those the provider may not favor; and (3) the benefits, risks, and consequences of alternatives including nonintervention.

Some providers suggest there should be "no pressure to report" or "no need to explain her decision to anyone" (Sloan, 1999, p. 93) To accept, without exploration, a victim's decision might be akin to condoning nonreporting. In fact, it may even perpetuate silence. An individual's initial decision about reporting may be based on fears that may be unfounded or on expectations that may be unrealistic, or, even worse, it may be based on the misconception that the sexual contact was her fault. There is an obligation on the part of all SART members to insure that the victim understands the likely outcome of either decision in any number of circumstances.

Beginning a dialogue of exploration can initiate the healing process; this is an opportunity to talk about feelings and misconceptions, and it is an opportunity to provide correct information and support. To make the assumption that a victim does not need to talk to anyone about the decision-making process is to assume that she is informed, educated about the issues, completely clear on the processes involved, understands that what happened to her was against the law, that she is able to label the forced sexual contact a sexual assault, and that she has clearly thought through the situation. These are hardly the circumstances that surround most victims of sexual assault.

Collaborators and a History of Contradictory Philosophies?

Over forty years ago, the original reasons underlying the philosophy and goals of rape crisis centers were clearly articulated by rape care advocates and programs: the experience of sexual assault victims in the criminal justice system frequently exacerbates the trauma of the initial assault, and reporting a rape does not significantly increase convictions and imprisonment of the rapist (Sloan, 1999, p. 93). Today, it is doubtful that any advocate would directly convey such an idea to a victim; yet, there may still be vestiges of that initial premise that can present obstacles to coordination of services.

Conviction and imprisonment are not the only benefits of reporting. Other benefits include: plea bargains, increased reporting in the population at large, and holding the perpetrator accountable for his act. The greatest benefit may be that the victim has made the decision in her own mind that the sexual assault was not her fault. It is significant that she can come to the conclusion that it was a crime committed against her, and she has the right to make a police report and have the assailant questioned by law enforcement personnel. After all, it is every rapist's hope and expectation that the victim will *not* report.

Some sexual assault cases are lost to the system, and Michael Kimmel takes these "lost" cases head on. After the Anita Hill testimony before the Senate judiciary subcommittee for the Clarence Thomas Supreme Court confirmation hearings, the media collectively claimed that Ms. Hill's treatment would have a "chilling effect" on women. They asserted that women would be fearful of reporting any kind of sex crime (Kimmel, 1993). Kimmel denies the hearings had any such effect; in fact, it was quite the opposite, and "Women have come forward in record numbers to report harassment and rape" (p. 121). Novelist Mary Lee Settle eloquently wrote in her op-ed piece for the *New York Times*, "by her heroic stance, given not only me but thousands of women who have been silenced by shame, the courage and the need to speak out about what we have tried so long to bury and forget" (1991, A27). As a result of Anita Hill speaking out, Settle revealed for the first time that she had been sexually assaulted.

Boundary and Role Conflicts

Boundary and role issues can be fairly serious. Initially, there was some concern that health care providers and law enforcement professionals wanted to exclude rape care advocates, rape crisis counselors, or social service agencies from the examination room. Gaffney and Ledray (1999) point out how the literature has supported the role of the advocate as a crucial and integral member of the SART. There is concern that close collaboration with an advocate could compromise the legal case if he or she is called to testify by a defense attorney against the health care provider. While this may be a tactic that a defense attorney may try to utilize, it is highly unlikely.

Some SART team members, especially SANEs, may argue that they are trained in advocacy skills, and therefore the rape crisis advocates are not needed. Clearly, SANEs are not trained to be rape crisis advocates but use advocacy skills to address the health care needs of the victim. As unbiased clinicians who assess and treat the health care needs of the individual as well as collect evidence, practicing victim advocacy would present a serious role conflict and compromise the health care provider's position in the courtroom. However, the health care provider offers information, communicates in a sensitive manner, understands and utilizes crisis intervention techniques, supports the victim, and ensures appropriate follow-up resources.

To assume that the health care provider should not perform a supportive role because someone else in the room is specifically trained in victim advocacy and support runs the risk of reducing the provider's role to that of a mere technician. If victims of sexual assault are to be treated in a sensitive, holistic manner, it behooves all professionals responding to the sexual assault victim to utilize and maximize the overlap of roles, not to segregate the roles.

Historically the protection of the sexual assault victim has focused on "advocating against" the interventions of other disciplines so as not to revictimize the individual. The SART approach mandates a "collaborating with" philosophy for all professionals. The goal is to work together effectively and see team members as partners instead of competitors.

Coming to the Table

Conflict is a natural and expected outgrowth of multidisciplinary teams who share one underlying goal. Umiker describes the six major causes of conflict: unclear expectations, poor communication, lack of clear jurisdiction, differences of temperament and attitude, conflicts of interest, and operational changes (1997, p. 240). Resolution of the conflict is essential for effective team performance. Resolution through group decision making requires debating, negotiating, disagreeing, questioning, and probing. While there are a number of conflict-reducing strategies (avoidance, fighting, surrendering, compromising), there is only one strategy that results in a win-win situation—collaboration (p. 261). In fact, the best answer is often one that neither side originally considered.

Umiker (1998) suggests a series of questions to assist team members analyze a situation: What do we want to accomplish? What do we think the other team members want? What incorrect assumptions might other people have? Which strategy is best? What are the "hot buttons," the trigger points?

After analysis, it is time for confrontation, but *collaborative* confrontation, and it is rarely as difficult as one thinks. Although Umiker (1998) has at least twenty-five strategies for effective confrontation, there are several that are especially riveting and appropriate to professionals coordinating victim services: "be an attentive listener, be empathetic, respect the other person's feelings, let the other person know that you hear and understand-both content and feelings with validation, emphasize that you can't change the past but rather focus on the future" (p. 262).

These are the very skills offered to the sexual assault victim and the ones the SART members may have the most difficulty offering to each other.

FINAL THOUGHTS ON THE SART

A sexual assault is a complex and sensitive crime. It touches a multitude of areas in a victim's life, and, for that reason, it is impossible to rely on the services of one individual profession or a singular approach. No one "owns" the victim. Some professions may have a longer history with victims, and other disciplines should learn from them. No one role can trump the others all of the time, although the trajectory of a case may require greater or lesser involvement of different team members. The goal is the well-being of the victim, and each member of the team has a valuable and distinct but interdependent responsibility in achieving that goal (Lonsway, 2001). Collaboration is essential for the health and well-being of the victim as well as a successful investigation and prosecution, however success will be defined. Perhaps it is time to think of public policy change as the result of investigative and prosecutorial efforts. While there will be conflict and boundary issues, the long-term benefits for the victim and the community far surpass temporary obstacles. The SART model will continue to evolve, efficacy will continue to be established, and new partners will be enlisted. All professionals would do well to remember that the first and most important member of the team is the victim.

References

Allen, N. E. 2005. A multi-level analysis of community coordinating councils. *American Journal of Community Psychology, 35*(1/2, March), 49-63.

Antognoli-Toland, P. (1985) Comprehensive program for examination of sexual assault victims by nurses. A hospital-based project in Texas. *Journal of Emergency Nursing, 11,* 132-135.

Barkhurst, P., Fowler, H., Siadal, I., & Vokes, S. (2002). *Sexual Assault Response Team (SART) handbook.* Eugene, OR: Sexual Assault Task Force Staff. Retrieved February 3, 2008, from http://www.oregonsatf.org/documents/PDFVersionofSARTHandbook.pdf

Boles, A. B., & Patterson, J. C. (1997). Improving community response to crime victims: An eight-step model for developing protocol. Thousand Oaks, CA: Sage.

Brownmiller, S. (1975). *Against our will: Men, women and rape.* New York: Simon and Schuster.

Burgess, A., & Holmstrom, L. (1974). Rape trauma syndrome. *American Journal of Psychiatry, 131,* 981-986.

Burkardt, M. & Nathaniel, A. (1998) Ethics and Issues in Contemporary Nursing. Albany, NY: Delmar.

Campbell, R. (1998). The community response to the rape victim: Victims' experiences with the legal, medical, and mental health systems. *American Journal of Community Psychology, 26*(3), 355-379.

Campbell, R., & Ahrens, C. E. (1998) Innovative community services for rape victims: An application of multiple case study methodology. *American Journal of Community Psychology, 26*(4), 537-571.

Campbell, R., & Bybee, D. (1997). Emergency medical services for rape victims: Detecting the cracks in service delivery. *Women's Health: Research on Gender, Behavior, and Policy, 3*(2), 75-101.

Campbell, R. Wasco, S. M., Ahrens, C. E., Sefl, T., & Barnes, H. E. (2001). Preventing the "second rape": Rape survivors' experiences with community service providers. *Journal of Interpersonal Violence, 16*(December), 1239-1259.

Crandall, C. S., & Helitzer, D. (2003). *An impact evaluation of a Sexual Assault Nurse Examiner (SANE) program.* National Institute of Justice. Retrieved February 2, 2008, from http://www.ncjrs.org/pdffiles1/nij/grants/203276.pdf

Cuklanz, L. (1996). Rape on trial: *How the mass media construct legal reform and social change.* Philadelphia: University of Pennsylvania Press.

Esposito, N. (2005). Manifestations of enduring during interviews with sexual assault victims. *Qualitative Health Research, 15*(7), 912-927.

Fairstein, L. (1993). *Sexual violence: Our war against rape.* New York: William Morrow & Co.

Friedman, M. (1996). PTSD diagnosis and treatment for mental health clinicians. *Journal Community Mental Health Journa*l, *32*(2), 173-189.

Foa, E. B., Davidson, J. R. T., Frances, A. (1999). The expert consensus guideline series: Treatment of posttraumatic stress disorder. *Journal of Clinical Psychiatry, 60*(Suppl. 16), 4-76.

Gaffney, D. (2005). Media, government and policy: The power of the press. How one media spark ignited interest in forensic nursing. *Journal of Forensic Nursing, 1*(2), 82-83.

Gaffney, D. & Ledray, L. (1999). Sexual assault examiners and rape crisis advocates: rising to the challenge together. *Sexual Assault Report, 3*(2):17-32.

Gamache, D. & Asmus, M. (1999). Enhancing networking among service providers: Elements of Coordination Strategies. In M. R. Shepard & E. L. Pence (Eds.), *Coordinating community responses to domestic violence: Lessons from Duluth and beyond* (pp. 65-87). Thousand Oaks CA: Sage.

Girardin, B. (2005). The Sexual Assault Nurse Examiner: A win-win solution. *Topics in Emergency Medicine, 27*(2), 124-131.

Hatmaker, D. D., Pinholster, L. & Saye, J. J. (2002). A community-based approach to sexual assault. *Public Health Nursing, 19*(2),124–127.

Herman, J. (1992). *Trauma and recovery.* New York: Basic Books.

Holloway, M. & Swan, A. (1993). Assessment and evaluation management of sexual assault. *Nursing Standard, 7,* 28-34.

Kimmel, M. (1993). Clarence, William, Iron Mike, Tailhook, Senator Packwood, spur posse, magic . . . and us. In E. Buchwald, P. Fletcher, & M. Roth (Eds.), *Transforming a rape culture.* Minneapolis, MN: Milkweed Editions.

Lang, K. S., & Brockway, S. A. (2001). The response to sexual assault: Removing barriers to services and justice. In *The report of the Michigan Sexual Assault Systems Response Task Force.* Okemos, MI: Michigan Coalition Against Domestic Violence and Sexual Violence, the Michigan Department of Community Health, and the Prosecuting Attorneys Association of Michigan, Retrieved February 3, 2008, from http://www.mcadsv.org/products/sa/TASKFORCE.pdf

Ledray, L. E. (2003). *SANE development and operation guide.* National SANE-SART Web site. Office of Justice Programs, U.S. Department of Justice. Retrieved September 9, 2008, from http://www.ojp.usdoj.gov/ovc/publications/infores/sane/saneguide.pdf

Ledray, L. E. (1993). Evidence collection: An update. *Journal of Child Sexual Abuse, 2,* 1.

Ledray, L. E. (2003). SANE-SART. History and role development. In A. P. Giardino, E. M. Datner, M., & J. B. Asher (Eds.), *Sexual assault, victimization across the life span: A clinical guide* (pp. 471-475). St. Louis, MO: G. W. Medical Publishing.

Ledray, L. E., & Chaignot, M. J. (1980). Services to sexual assault victims in Hennepin County [Special issue]. *Evaluation and Change.*

Ledray, L. E., & Simmelink, K. (1997). Sexual assault: Clinical issues: Efficacy of SANE evidence collection. A Minnesota study. *Journal of Emergency Room Nursing, 23,* 175-77.

Lonsway, K. (2001). Coordinated response to sexual assault: The teamwork approach. In *Successfully investigating acquaintance sexual assault: A national training manual for law enforcement.* Harrisburg, PA: The National Center for Women & Policing, The Violence Against Women Office, Office of Justice Programs.

Lynch, V. A. (1993). Forensic nursing: Diversity in education and practice. *Journal of Psychosocial Nursing, 31,* 7-14.

Martin, P. Y. (2005). *Rape work: Victims, gender, and emotions in organizational and community context.* New York: Routledge.

Martin, P. Y. (2007). Coordinated community services for victims of violence. In L. L. O'Toole, J. R. Schiffman, & M. L. Kiter Edwards (Eds.), *Gender violence: Interdisciplinary perspectives* (2nd ed.). New York: New York University Press.

Nugent-Borakove, M. E., Fanflik, P. L., Troutman, D. Johnson, N., Burgess, A., & Lewis O'Connor, A. (2006). *Testing the efficacy of SANE/SART programs: Do they make a difference in sexual assault arrest & prosecution outcomes?* Retrieved February 4, 2008, from http://www.ncjrs.gov/pdffiles1/nij/grants/214252.pdf

O'Brien, C. (1992). Medical and forensic examination by a sexual assault nurse examiner of a 7 year-old victim of sexual assault. *Journal of Emergency Nursing, 18,* 199-204.

Office for Victims of Crime. (2008). *National SANE-SART Web site.* Office of Justice Programs, U.S. Department of Justice. Retrieved February 4, 2008, from http://www.sane-sart.com/index.php?topic=General

Payne, B. K. (2007). Victim advocates' perceptions of the role of health care workers in sexual assault cases. *Criminal Justice Policy Review, 18*(1), 81-94.

Petzinger, T. (1999). *The new pioneers: The men and women who are transforming the workplace and the marketplace.* New York: Simon and Schuster.

Presidents Commission for the Study of Ethical Problems in Medicine and Biomedical and Behavioral Research. (1983). *Making health care decisions.* Washington, DC: U.S. Government Printing Office.

Quindlen, A. (1994, October 19). Public and private: After the rape. *New York Times,* p. A23.

Schacter, D. (1996). *Searching for memory.* New York: Basic Books.

Settle, M. L. (1991, October 19). The Genteel attacker. *New York Times,* p. A27.

Solola, S., Scott, C., Severs, S., & Howell, J. (1983). Rape: Management in an institutional setting. *Obstetrics and Gynecology, 61,* 373-378.

Sijbrandij, M., Olff, M., Reitsma J. B., Carlier, I. V., Gersons, B. P. (2006). Emotional or educational debriefing after psychological trauma. Randomised controlled trial. *British Journal of Psychiatry, 189,* 150-155.

Sloan, L. (1999). Sexual Assault Nurse Examiners: The new challenges. *Sexual Assault Report, 2*(6), 81-96.

Smith K., Holmseth J., Macgregor, M., & Letourneau, M. (1998). Sexual Assault Response Team: Overcoming obstacles to program development. *Journal of Emergency Nursing, 24*(4), 365-367.

Speck, P. M., & Aiken, M. M. (1995). 20 years of community nursing service: Memphis sexual assault resource center. *Tennessee Nurse, 58*(2), 15-18.

Tolman, R. M., & Weisz, A. (1995). Coordinated community intervention for domestic violence: The effects of arrest and prosecution on recidivism of women abuse perpetrators. *Crime & Delinquency, 41*(4), 481-495.

Umiker, W. (1998). Collaborative conflict resolution. *The Health Care Supervisor, 15*(3), 70-75.

Weisz, A. N., Tolman, R. M., & Bennett, L. (1998). An ecological study of nonresidential services for battered women within a comprehensive community protocol for domestic violence. *Journal of Family Violence, 13*(4), 395-415.

Wiley, J., Sugar, N., Fine, D., & Exkert, L. (2003). Legal outcomes of sexual assault. *American Journal of Obstetrics and Gynecology, 188,* 1638-1641.

Wilson, D., & Klein, A. (2005). *An evaluation of the Rhode Island Sexual Assault Response Team (SART).* Washington, DC: National Criminal Justice Research Service, U.S.Department of Justice.

Zajac, J. J. (2006). Report on the national needs assessment of Sexual Assault Response Teams. The National SART Toolkit Advisory Committee. Enola, PA: Sexual Violence Resource Center.

Zweig, J. & Burt, M. R. (2003). Effects of interactions among community agencies on legal system responses to domestic violence and sexual assault in STOP-funded communities. *Criminal Justice Policy Review, 14*(2), 249-272.

Chapter 4

How Federal Law Applies to Cases of Campus Sexual Assault

by John Wesley Lowery, Ph.D.

The first part of this chapter focuses on cases related to sexual harassment, and the second part of the chapter focuses on federal legislation that impacts how colleges and universities respond to sexual assaults on campus. These laws include Title IX of Education Amendments of 1972 (Pub. L. No. 92-318 (June 23, 1972), which establishes requirements related to sexual harassment, the Jeanne Clery Disclosure of Campus Security Policy and Campus Crime Statistics Act (Clery Act; 20 U.S.C. § 1092; see Appendix D), and the Family Educational Rights and Privacy Act (FERPA; Pub. L. No. 93-380 (Aug. 21, 1974), which addresses how student records are handled.

TITLE IX OF THE EDUCATIONAL AMENDMENTS OF 1972

Title IX of the Educational Amendments of 1972 (Pub. L. No. 92-318 (June 23, 1972) was originally passed to address sexual discrimination in education programs. The law states: "No person in the United States shall, on the basis of sex, be excluded from participation in, be denied benefits of, or be subjected to discrimination under any education program or activity receiving federal financial assistance" (20 U.S.C. § 1681).

The Supreme Court first clearly articulated a private right of action under Title IX in *Cannon v. University of Chicago* (441 U.S. 677 (1979), which allowed plaintiffs to sue and recover monetary damages. The law is modeled after Title VII of the Civil Rights Act of 1964 (Pub. L. No. 88-352 (July 2, 1964)), which already prohibited discrimination on the basis of sex in the employment context, and much of the courts' expectations were originally developed in that context. Under Title VII, and by extension Title IX, sexual harassment is viewed as a form of sexual discrimination "because it is workplace conduct experience by an individual on the basis of his or her sex" (Kaplin & Lee, 2006, p. 414).

In *Meritor Savings Bank v. Vinson* (477 U.S. 57 (1986)), the Supreme Court first addressed quid pro quo sexual harassment in the employment context and established strict employer liability for sexual harassment when plaintiffs could demonstrate that employers "knew or should have known" about the harassment. Quid pro quo harassment in the education context refers to when "a teacher or other employee conditions an educational decision or benefit on the student's submission to unwelcome sexual conduct" (p. 5).

In *Harris v. Forklift Systems* (510 U.S. 17 (1993)), the Supreme Court extended its sexual harassment rulings to include hostile environment sexual harassment. Justice O'Connor writing for the majority in *Harris* observed,

> A [sexually] discriminatorily abusive work environment, even one that does not seriously affect employees' psychological well-being, can and often will detract from employees' job performance, discourage employees from remaining on the job, or keep them from advancing in their careers. Moreover, even without regard to these tangible effects, the very fact that the discriminatory conduct was so severe or pervasive that it created a work environment abusive to employees because of their race, gender, religion, or national origin offends Title VII's broad rule of workplace equality. (p. 22)

These categories, while helpful in understanding sexual harassment, are not rigid classifications, and cases often involve sexual harassment in both forms. In relation to sexual harassment, sexual assault is a form of sexual harassment in its most extreme form. Depending on the relationship between the survivor and the perpetrator as well as the perpetrator and the institution, sexual assault can give rise to actionable claims of both quid pro quo sexual harassment as well as hostile environment sexual harassment.

The Supreme Court specifically addressed sexual harassment in the educational context in three key cases in the 1990s, *Franklin v. Gwinnett County* (503 U.S. 60 (1992)), *Gebser v. Lago Independent School District* (524 U.S. 274 (1998)), and *Davis v. Monroe County School District* (526 U.S. 629 (1999)). Although each of these cases arose in the K-12 educational system, the principles articulated apply with equal force to colleges and universities. In *Franklin*, the Supreme Court addressed institutional liability for quid pro quo sexual harassment. In *Gebser* and *Davis*, the Supreme Court addressed hostile environment sexual harassment (as well as quid pro quo sexual harassment in *Gebser*) as a result of the actions of institutional employees and other students respectively.

SEXUAL HARASSMENT BY SCHOOL EMPLOYEES

In *Franklin v. Gwinnett County* (503 U.S. 60 (1992)), Christine Franklin was a high school student in the North Gwinnett High School in Gwinnett County, Georgia. During her sophmore and junior years at North Gwinnett High School, Christine was subjected to a pattern of sexually harassing behavior by Andrew Hill, who was employed by the school district as a teacher and coach. The behavior began with sexually suggestive comments and discussions but ultimately included three incidents in which Hill removed her from her classes and took her to his office where she was subjected to "coercive intercourse" (p. 63). While various school officials became aware of this pattern of behavior, no steps were taken to end the sexual harassment, and Franklin was discouraged from filing charges against Hill. Ultimately Hill was allowed to resign his teaching position in exchange for the sexual harassment matter being dropped. The Supreme Court ruled that the victims of sexual harassment could bring federal lawsuits and recover damages.

In *Gebser v. Lago Independent School District* (524 U.S. 274 (1998)), Alida Star Gebser was an eighth-grade middle school student when Frank Waldrop, a teacher at Lago Vista's high school, began sexually harassing her. After she enrolled in the high school, Gebser was in several classes with Waldrop, who initiated a sexual relationship with her. As a result of complaints from other parents, the principal met with Waldrop in October 1992 and warned him to be aware of his in-class comments. However, the school district did not take further action until Waldrop and Gebser were discovered by a police officer engaged in sexual intercourse in January 1993; Waldrop was terminated, and his teaching license was revoked. During this entire period, the Lago Vista School District had not implemented a sexual harassment policy or a procedure for reporting sexual harassment. Ultimately the Supreme Court upheld the decision of the U.S. Court of Appeals for the Fifth Circuit (*Doe v. Lago Vista Independent School District*, 106 F.3d 1223 (5th Cir. 1997), which ruled for the school district noting that the district did not possess actual notice until the January 1993 incident. Justice O'Connor writing for the majority articulated the Supreme Court's standard for finding for a plaintiff regarding sexual harassment claims and winning damages:

> We hold that a damages remedy will not lie under Title IX unless an official who at a minimum has authority to address the alleged discrimination and to institute corrective measures on the recipient's behalf has actual knowledge of discrimination in the recipient's programs and fails adequately to respond. We think, moreover, that the response must amount to deliberate indifference to discrimination. (Gebser, p. 290)

The Court determined "that a recipient intentionally violates Title IX, and is subject to a private damages action, where the recipient is deliberately indifferent to known acts of teacher-student discrimination" (*Davis v. Monroe County School District,* 526 U.S. 629, 643 (1999). The Court acknowledged that this was a high standard for plaintiffs to meet, but it wanted to avoid imposing liability in situations when officials did not have actual knowledge of the harassment.

STUDENT ON STUDENT SEXUAL HARASSMENT

In *Davis v. Monroe County School District* (526 U.S. 629 (1999)), the Supreme Court considered the case of LaShonda Davis who was a fifth grader at Hubbard Elementary School in Monroe Country, Georgia. She was subjected to months of repeated and serious sexual harassment at the hands of another fifth grade student. The harassment included countless sexual comments and actions toward LaShonda and other students. LaShonda repeatedly reported the student's behavior to her teachers as did her mother on multiple occasions, but the officials took no effective actions. In fact, it would be more than three months before LaShonda would even be allowed to change seats in her classroom so that she was not sitting beside her tormentor. It was also alleged that the school district had not instituted policies or trained its staff on how to respond to peer-to-peer sexual harassment. In *Davis*, the Supreme Court applied its actual notice standard articulated in *Franklin v. Gwinnett County* (503 U.S. 60 (1992)) requiring that a school official with authority to act has actual knowledge of the sexual harassment. It is also important to note that not all peer-to-peer sexual harassment will rise to a level to which the courts will demand corrective action. Justice O'Connor writing for the majority noted:

> Rather, a plaintiff must establish sexual harassment of students that is so severe, pervasive, and objectively offensive, and that so undermines and detracts from the victims' educational experience, that the victim-students are effectively denied equal access to an institution's resources and opportunities. (Davis, p. 651)

Justice O'Connor further limited institutional liability for peer-to-peer sexual harassment noting that the behavior must occur in a context in which the school "exercises substantial control over both the harasser and the context in which the known harassment occurs" (p. 645). The Court's decision in *Davis* also defined the limits of deliberate indifference, noting that this would only be applied to situations in which "the recipient's response to the harassment or lack thereof is clearly unreasonable in light of the known circumstances" (p. 648).

SEXUAL HARASSMENT IN THE HIGHER EDUCATION SETTING

Taken as a whole, *Franklin v. Gwinnett County* (503 U.S. 60 (1992)), *Gebser v. Lago Independent School District* (524 U.S. 274 (1998)), and *Davis v. Monroe County School District* (526 U.S. 629 (1999)) clearly establish the potential of institutional liability for sexual harassment by both employees and students. However, the Supreme Court has established a high standard for plaintiffs to meet in order to recover monetary damages in a civil trial. Several higher education cases help illustrate how this standard is applied. In *Liu v. Striuli* (36 F. Supp. 2d 452 (D.R.I. 1999)), Mary Liu claimed that she was repeatedly raped by Dr. Striuli, a member of the Providence College faculty and the institution's coordinator of services for international students. However, Liu's lawsuit against the college failed because she was unable to demonstrate that school officials had actual knowledge of the sexual harassment, and the court concluded that neither of the school officials whom Liu claimed had knowledge were officials with authority to take action to end the harassment.

Burtner v. Hiram College (9 F. Supp. 2d 852 (N.D. Ohio 1998)) also illustrates the difficulty in obtaining judgments against colleges and universities for sexual harassment. Amy Burtner was sexually harassed for more than two years by a Hiram College faculty member who also served as her academic advisor, Michael Emerson. Burtner's claims included both quid pro quo and hostile environment sexual harassment. During the entire period of Emerson's sexually harassing behavior towards Burtner and other female students, Hiram had a published sexual harassment policy and an identified university official to receive sexual harassment complaints. Burtner and another female student reported Emerson's sexually harassing behavior in writing to the appropriate university official on the day of their graduation. Over the summer, Hiram College investigated the complaints and with Burtner's consent sought to resolve the complaint informally. By the end of the summer, Emerson had accepted responsibility for violating the college's sexual harassment policy and was warned that any future violations could lead to his termination. In *Burtner*, the court, in applying the recently decided *Gebser* decision, concluded that the plaintiff could not demonstrate actual notice to the college of the harassment prior to filing her graduation day complaint and further that Hiram's actions in response were not deliberately indifferent. The court's comments also illustrate another reason that college students face difficulties in some of these cases:

> That case [Gebser] also involved a teacher's sexual activity with a young female, who was an eighth grader, a freshman and a sophomore during the relevant time period. In this suit, the complainant is a more mature college student and the defendant school did have a sexual harassment policy and grievance procedure. (Burtner, p. 857)

ANOTHER VIEW ON DELIBERATE INDIFFERENCE

Two appellate court cases in 2007 brought to the forefront another view on deliberate indifference (*Simpson v. University of Colorado* (500 F.3d 1170 (10th Cir. 2007) and *Williams v. Board of Regents of University of Georgia* (477 F.3d 1282 (11th Cir. 2007)). In the *Simpson* case, two plaintiffs brought a lawsuit against the University of Colorado and various institutional officials. Simpson and Gilmore claimed that they had been sexually assaulted by members of the University of Colorado football team and high-school students who were participating in a recruiting weekend. Simpson and Gilmore's primary claims were not that the University of Colorado was deliberately indifferent in responding to the sexual assault; rather they claimed that the university was deliberately indifferent in creating the recruitment program itself. The court discussed the recruitment program in the following terms,

> The CU football team recruited talented high-school players each fall by bringing them to campus. Part of the sales effort was to show recruits "a good time." To this end, recruits were paired with female "Ambassadors," who showed them around campus, and player-hosts, who were responsible for the recruits' entertainment. At least some of the recruits who came to Ms. Simpson's apartment had been promised an opportunity to have sex. (Simpson, p. 1173)

It is helpful to note that neither Simpson nor Gilmore were themselves "Ambassadors"; instead another student asked to bring a few people by their apartment, although she actually arrived with about twenty current football players and recruits. The court did not find *Davis v. Monroe County School District* (526 U.S. 629 (1999)) and *Gebser v. Lago Independent School District* (524 U.S. 274 (1998)) useful in resolving the University of Colorado case. The court instead focused on *Canton v. Harris* (489 U.S. 378 (1989)) in which the Supreme Court found a city liable for failing to properly train police officers. The court characterized the recruitment program as an official university program that involved a "serious risk of sexual harassment and assault during college-football recruiting efforts" (Simpson, p. 1184). Despite past problems with the recruitment program, "Barnett [head football coach] nevertheless maintained an unsupervised player-host program to show high-school recruits 'a good time'" (p. 1184). This led the court to conclude:

> Barnett knew, both because of incidents reported to him and because of his own unsupportive attitude, that there had been no change in atmosphere since 1997 (when the prior assault occurred) that would make such misconduct less likely in 2001. A jury could infer that "the need for more or different training [of player-hosts was] so obvious, and the inadequacy so likely to result in [Title IX violations], that [Coach Barnett could] reasonably be said to have been deliberately indifferent to the need. (pp. 1184-1185)

After the U.S. Court of Appeals for the Tenth Circuit reinstated Simpson and Gilmore's lawsuit against the university, the university settled the lawsuits for more than $2.5 million (Sander, 2007).

In *Williams,* Tiffany Williams alleged that she was sexually assaulted by multiple members of the University of Georgia men's basketball team. She filed both campus disciplinary charges and criminal charges against several individuals, but none of those individuals were found responsible. The only aspect of her lawsuit against the university that remains active is her claim that the university knowingly admitted one of those players, Cole, despite his past history of disciplinary and criminal charges relating to allegations of sexual assault at his community college. Regarding this aspect of her lawsuit, the U.S. Court of Appeals for the Eleventh Circuit noted:

> Adams, Dooley, and Harrick's decision to recruit Cole and admit him through UGA's special admission process was a form of discrimination that Williams suffered. According to Williams, Adams, Dooley, and Harrick knew at that point of the need to supervise Cole for two reasons. . . . Second, and more importantly, Williams alleges that Adams, Harrick, and Dooley knew about Cole's past sexual misconduct. Nevertheless, even with its knowledge of the need to inform its student-athletes about the applicable sexual harassment policy and of Cole's past sexual misconduct, UGA and UGAA failed to adequately supervise Cole. Williams's allegations of UGA and UGAA's failures are sufficient at this stage to establish deliberate indifference under our municipality liability precedent. But to satisfy our Title IX precedent, Williams must go further and sufficiently allege that the deliberate indifference subjected her to further discrimination. (p. 1296)

Taken together, *Simpson* and *Williams* suggest a new form of Title IX liability that originates not from how institutions respond to sexual harassment, but from their responsibility to take action to prevent sexual harassment.

JEANNE CLERY DISCLOSURE OF CAMPUS SECURITY POLICY AND CAMPUS CRIME STATISTICS ACT

Jeanne Clery was raped and murdered by a fellow student, Joseph M. Henry, in her residence hall room on April 5, 1986, at Lehigh University. After her death,

Howard and Connie Clery founded Security on Campus and began a crusade to press for legislation to require colleges and universities to address campus crime. After succeeding in passing legislation in Pennsylvania, Security on Campus and the Clerys were successful, in 1990, in passing the Student Right-to-Know and Campus Security Act (20 U.S.C. § 1092; see Appendix D), which was renamed the Jeanne Clery Disclosure of Campus Security Policy and Campus Crime Statistics Act (Clery Act) in 1998.

The primary obligation of the Clery Act is the publication and distribution, to all current students and employees, of an annual security report. The annual security report must contain various policy statements and other information:

1. The crime statistics described in 34 C.F.R. Section 668.46(c).

2. A statement of current campus policies regarding procedures for students and others to report criminal actions or other emergencies occurring on campus. This statement must include the institution's policies concerning its response to these reports, including—
   a Policies for making timely warning reports to members of the campus community regarding the occurrence of crimes described in 34 C.F.R. Section 668.46(c);
   b. Policies for preparing the annual disclosure of crime statistics; and
   c. A list of the titles of each person or organization to whom students and employees should report the criminal offenses for which statistics must be reported for the purpose of making timely warning reports and the annual statistical disclosure. This statement must also disclose whether the institution has any policies or procedures that allow victims or witnesses to report crimes on a voluntary, confidential basis for inclusion in the annual disclosure of crime statistics, and, if so, a description of those policies and procedures.

3. A statement of current policies concerning security of and access to campus facilities, including campus residences and security considerations used in the maintenance of campus facilities.

4. A statement of current policies concerning campus law enforcement that—
   a. Addresses the enforcement authority of security personnel, including their relationship with state and local police agencies and whether those security personnel have the authority to arrest individuals;
   b. Encourages accurate and prompt reporting of all crimes to the campus police and the appropriate police agencies; and
   c. Describes procedures, if any, that encourage pastoral counselors and professional counselors, if and when they deem it appropriate, to inform the persons they are counseling of any procedures to report crimes on a voluntary, confidential basis for inclusion in the annual disclosure of crime statistics.

5. A description of the type and frequency of programs designed to inform students and employees about campus security procedures and practices and to encourage students and employees to be responsible for their own security and the security of others.

6. A description of programs designed to inform students and employees about the prevention of crimes.

7. A statement of policy concerning the monitoring and recording through local police agencies of criminal activity in which students engaged at off-campus locations of student organizations officially recognized by the institution, including student organizations with off-campus housing facilities.

8. A statement of policy regarding the possession, use, and sale of alcoholic beverages and enforcement of state underage drinking laws.

9. A statement of policy regarding the possession, use, and sale of illegal drugs and enforcement of federal and state drug laws.

10. A description of any drug or alcohol-abuse education programs, as required under Section 120(a) through (d) of the Higher Education Act (HEA; Pub. L. No. 102-325 (July 23, 1992)). For the purpose of meeting this requirement, an institution may cross-reference the materials the institution uses to comply with Section 120(a) through (d) of the HEA.

11. A statement of policy regarding the institution's campus sexual assault programs to prevent sex offenses and procedures to follow when a sex offense occurs (see below).

The statistical requirements are one of the most complicated aspects of compliance with the Clery Act. Institutions are required to report statistics for offenses reported to campus security authorities who include campus and local police agencies, individuals identified in the annual security report to whom crimes should be reported, and "an official of an institution who has significant responsibility for student and campus activities, including, but not limited to, student housing, student discipline, and campus judicial proceedings" (34 C.F.R. § 668.46(a)) The crime statistics to be included in the annual security report include report occurrences for:

(i) Criminal homicide:
    (A) Murder and nonnegligent manslaughter.
    (B) Negligent manslaughter.

(ii) Sex offenses:
    (A) Forcible sex offenses.
    (B) Nonforcible sex offenses (statutory rape and incest).

(iii) Robbery.

(iv) Aggravated assault.

(v) Burglary.

(vi) Motor vehicle theft.

(vii) Arson. (34 C.F.R. § 668.46(c)(1))

Information regarding hate crimes must also be reported "by category of prejudice, any crime [listed above], and any other crime involving bodily injury reported to local police agencies or to a campus security authority, that manifest evidence that the victim was intentionally selected because of the victim's actual or perceived race, gender, religion, sexual orientation, ethnicity, or disability" (34 C.F.R. § 668.46(c)(3)). Institutions are also required to report arrests and referrals for disciplinary action for liquor law violations, drug law violations, and illegal weapons possession. In preparing statistics for the annual security report, institutions must report statistics for four geographic areas:

1. On campus;

2. Of the crimes on campus, the number of crimes that took place in dormitories or other residential facilities for students on campus;

3. In or on a noncampus building or property; and

4. On public property.

In addition to collecting annual statistics, institutions must also make timely warnings to the campus community regarding "crimes reported to a campus security authority or local police, if the institution believes a crime represents a threat to students and employees" (34 C.F.R. § 668.46((e)(1)(iii)). These timely warnings can take many forms including e-mails, flyers, and advertisements in the student newspaper.

In 1992, the Clery Act was amended to place additional obligations on institutions regarding sexual assault cases. Under the 1992 HEA amendments, institutions were required to specifically address issues related to sexual assault including:

(i)   A description of educational programs to promote the awareness of rape, acquaintance rape, and other forcible and nonforcible sex offenses;

(ii) Procedures students should follow if a sex offense occurs, including procedures concerning who should be contacted, the importance of preserving evidence for the proof of a criminal offense, and to whom the alleged offense should be reported;

(iii) Information on a student's option to notify appropriate law enforcement authorities, including on-campus and local police, and a statement that institutional personnel will assist the student in notifying these authorities, if the student requests the assistance of these personnel;

(iv) Notification to students of existing on- and off-campus counseling, mental health, or other student services for victims of sex offenses;

(v)   Notification to students that the institution will change a victim's academic and living situations after an alleged sex offense and of the options for those changes, if those changes are requested by the victim and are reasonably available;

(vi) Procedures for campus disciplinary action in cases of an alleged sex offense, including a clear statement that—
   (A) The accuser and the accused are entitled to the same opportunities to have others present during a disciplinary proceeding and
   (B) Both the accuser and the accused must be informed of the outcome of any institutional disciplinary proceeding brought alleging a sex offense. Compliance with this paragraph does not constitute a violation of the FERPA (20 U.S.C. 1232g). For the purpose of this paragraph, the outcome of a disciplinary proceeding means only the institution's final determination with respect to the alleged sex offense and any sanction that is imposed against the accused; and

(vii) Sanctions the institution may impose following a final determination of an institutional disciplinary proceeding regarding rape, acquaintance rape, or other forcible or nonforcible sex offenses. (34 C.F.R. § 668.46(b)(11))

Institutions are not allowed to place conditions upon the notification of final results. Georgetown University had a policy of requiring that the victims of sexual assault sign a nonredisclosure agreement before providing the final results. The U.S. Department of Education ruled that Georgetown had violated the Clery Act noting that an institution "cannot require an alleged sexual assault victim to execute a non-disclosure agreement as a pre-condition to accessing judicial proceedings outcomes and sanction information under the Clery Act" (http://www.securityoncampus.org/reporters/releases/degioia071604.pdf). For further discussion of institutional requirements in this area, please see Appendix C and Exhibit 4.1.

Institutions that do not comply with the Clery Act face the possibility of fines in the amount of $27,500 for each "substantial misrepresentation" of information required under the law. In recent years, the U.S. Department of Education has imposed major fines on Salem International University, which was fined $200,000, and Eastern Michigan University, which was fined $357,500 (http://www.security on campus.org/schools/cleryact/violators.html).

FAMILY EDUCATIONAL RIGHTS AND PRIVACY ACT

Originally passed in 1974, FERPA is the key federal law governing student records. The primary purpose of FERPA was two-fold—to guarantee to parents and the students themselves if they were of over eighteen years of age or a college student the:

1. "Right to Inspect and Review/Right to Access Education Records" and

2. "Right to [Written] Consent to the Disclosure of Education Records" (http://www.ed.gov/policy/gen/guid/fpco/ferpa/leg-history.html).

Education records are defined broadly as those records:

1. Directly related to the student; and

2. Maintained by educational institution or by a party acting for the institution.

Historically it has been the position of the U.S. Department of Education that student disciplinary records are part of the education records of the accused student.

The Student Right-to-Know and Campus Security Act amended FERPA in 1990 to allow the release of the final results of student disciplinary proceeding to the victim. Under the regulations, final results are defined as:

> a decision or determination, made by an honor court or council, committee, commission, or other entity authorized to resolve disciplinary matters within the institution. The disclosure of final results must include only the name of the student, the violation committed, and any sanction imposed by the institution against the student. (34 C.F.R. § 99.39)

In 1992, the Clery Act was further amended to make victim notification mandatory in sexual assault cases.

In 1998, FERPA was further amended by the Higher Education Reauthorization Act (Pub. L. No. 105-244 (Oct. 7, 1998) to allow for the release of final results of a student disciplinary proceeding to the public when the accused student was found responsible for a crime of violence, which includes forcible and nonforcible sexual offenses. FERPA did not require the release of this information to the public, but it did allow it. Therefore, under some state open records laws, the release of this information could be required under state law.

There are differing circumstances in a sexual assault that allow release of information to the alleged victim to whom results can be released regardless of whether the accused student was found responsible. However, the final results can be released to the public only if the accused student has been found responsible. This ultimately impacts the extent to which the victim may rerelease the final results. The U.S. Department of Education maintains, when the accused student is found responsible, that the victim may share the final results of disciplinary proceeding with anyone without violating FERPA because the institution could release the information to the public without violating FERPA. However, when the accused student is found not responsible, the alleged victim cannot share that information with others without violating FERPA according to the U.S. Department of Education (see Exhibit 4.1).

CONCLUSION

This chapter has sought to identify and briefly outline the key requirements in federal statutes impacting how colleges and universities prepare for and respond to sexual assaults against college students and on college campuses. Clearly, Title IX of Educational Amendments of 1972, the Clery Act, and FERPA are the primary federal laws impacting colleges and universities in this area. Institutions seeking to develop effective efforts to reduce the occurrences of sexual assaults and respond effectively to sexual assaults that occur on campus must bear these requirements in mind.

References

Kaplin, W. A., & Lee, B. A. (2006). *The law of higher education* (4th ed.). San Francisco: Jossey-Bass.

Sander, L. (2007, December 14). U. of Colorado settles lawsuit over alleged gang rapes. *Chronicle of Higher Education*, p. A20.

U.S. Department of Education, Office of Civil Rights. (2001, January), *Revised sexual harassment guidance: Harassment of students by school employees, other students, or third parties.* Washington, DC: Author.

Exhibit 4.1
Disclosure to Victims of Alleged Crimes of Violence

[Editors' note: The following material is available at the FERPA Online Library: Family Policy Compliance Office, http://www.ed.gov/policy/gen/guid/fpco/ferpa/library/carter. html.]

March 10, 2003

Mr. S. Daniel Carter
7505 Granda Drive
Knoxville, Tennessee 37909-1730

Dear Mr. Carter:

This is to respond to your October 10, 2002, letter and December 11, 2002, e-mail objecting to restrictions on the redisclosure of the final results of student disciplinary proceedings. This Office administers the Family Educational Rights and Privacy Act (FERPA), which addresses issues that relate to students' education records.

Specifically, you stated that the U.S. Department of Education should change its regulations so as to permit the victim of an alleged perpetrator of a crime of violence to redisclose the final results of a disciplinary proceeding conducted by a postsecondary educational institution with respect to that alleged crime. You also assert that the victim should be permitted to redisclose the name of the assailant, what the person was accused of, and any disciplinary action taken by the school.

FERPA is a Federal law that gives postsecondary students the right to have access to their education records, the right to seek to have the records amended, and the right to have some control over the disclosure of information from the records. The term "education records" is defined as those records that contain information directly related to a student and which are maintained by an educational agency or institution or by a party acting for the agency or institution. 34 CFR § 99.3 "Education records."

Under FERPA, a school may not generally disclose personally identifiable information from a postsecondary student's education records to a third party unless the student has provided written consent. 34 CFR § 99.30(a). However, there are several exceptions to FERPA's prohibition on nonconsensual disclosure of education records. In particular, FERPA provides specific exceptions for disclosure of disciplinary records in certain circumstances. One of the exceptions permits disclosure to an alleged victim of any crime of violence or non-forcible sex offense of the final results of any disciplinary proceeding conducted by an institution of postsecondary education against the alleged perpetrator of that crime with respect to that crime. In this circumstance, the institution may disclose the final results of the disciplinary proceeding to the individual, regardless of whether the institution concluded a violation was committed. 20 U.S.C. § 1232g(b)(6); 34 CFR § 99.31(a)(13).

Those individuals who receive information under one or more of the 15 disclosure exceptions set forth in § 99.31 may not generally redisclose that information to any other party without appropriate written consent of the student. 34 CFR § 99.33. As such, the § 99.33 redisclosure limitations apply not only to the § 99.31(a)(13) disclosure exception, but to many other of the § 99.31 exceptions as well. If an individual makes a disclosure that § 99.33 does not permit, then the educational institution may not allow that person to access personally identifiable information from education records for at least five years. 20 U.S.C. § 1232g(b)(4)(B), 34 CFR § 99.33.

A second, related disclosure exception is set forth in § 99.31(a)(14). Under this exception, an institution of postsecondary education may disclose the final results of a disciplinary proceeding, if it determines that:

1. the student is an alleged perpetrator of a crime of violence or non-forcible sex offense; and

2. with respect to the allegation made against him or her, the student has committed a violation of the institution's rules or policies.

When an institution determines that an accused student is an alleged perpetrator and has violated the institution rules, then there are no restrictions on disclosure or redisclosure of the final results of a disciplinary proceeding. In circumstances where an institution makes a determination that the accused student committed a violation, this clearly provides for much greater disclosure than is permitted by § 99.31(a)(13). In addition, the redisclosure restrictions of § 99.33 do not apply. On the other hand, § 99.31(a)(13) assures that an alleged victim can learn what the final results of a disciplinary proceeding were, even when the institution determines that the accused student did not violate its rules. When an institution discloses the final results, it must also inform the student that FERPA does not permit any redisclosure of this information.

Although we believe that the Department presently remains legally constrained to conclude that an alleged victim may not redisclose such information, we are in the process of considering what statutory or regulatory latitude there may be to permit limited redisclosures in the circumstances you described. We will be in touch with you with regard to any further developments.

Thank you for the comments you have provided on this matter.

Sincerely,

LeRoy S. Rooker
Director
Family Policy Compliance Office

Chapter 5

Navigating a Complaint of Sexual Assault Through a Campus Disciplinary Process

by Liz Baldizan, Ed.D., Linda B. Falkson, J.D., and Mary Beth Grant, J.D.

> Integrity, wisdom and empathy are among the most important character-istics necessary for the administration of student conduct standards.
>
> —The State of Student Judicial Affairs
> 1998 Tenth Anniversary of the
> Association for Student Judicial Affairs

INTRODUCTION

This chapter focuses on how a disciplinary system in an institution of higher education might approach the investigation and adjudication of a complaint of sexual assault. First the philosophical perspective of student judicial affairs is highlighted; then practical suggestions and information are provided. The chapter addresses the kinds of policy considerations and decisions that each institution must determine for itself. To illustrate the information, a hypothetical situation is developed, and questions that might come from a new professional in the Office of Student Conduct are provided, with answers provided by an experienced professional.

HYPOTHETICAL SITUATION

Cathy walks into the Office of Student Conduct on Monday at 9:00 a.m. She reports that she was victimized over the weekend and asks to meet with a judicial affairs officer as soon as possible. Max, a new judicial officer, agrees to meet with Cathy right away.

In speaking to Max, Cathy reports that on Saturday night she attended a party in a university-owned house. She was initially having fun, drinking beer, dancing, and enjoying the company of her friends. She ran into another student, Alex, who she vaguely knew from her biology class. Alex asked her to dance, and she thought they were really hitting it off. It turns out Alex was one of the hosts of the party. He told Cathy there were "jello shots" in a bedroom on the other end of the house. Cathy willingly agreed to consume shots in the bedroom with Alex and other students. After that, they returned to the main party and danced some more. The alcohol started to affect Cathy. She said that she wanted to rest, and Alex brought her back to the bedroom. By that time, they were alone. Cathy lied down, and Alex lied down next to her. Initially they kissed and Cathy said she thought that was fine. She reports that the intimacy very quickly progressed. She was unclothed, as was Alex, and she reports telling Alex she did not "want it to go any further." Nonetheless, she reports that intercourse occurred. Afterwards, she quickly dressed, walked out to the main party, and looked for her friends. She could not find them, and so she walked back to her residence hall alone. Once she was home, she found one of her friends and told her what happened. The friend told her she was raped. Cathy was not sure that is what happened, but she agreed to call the authorities. She was taken to the college health center, and she met with a Sexual Assault Nurse Examiner (SANE) and a sexual assault forensic evidence kit was completed.

Max tells Cathy that he is sorry about what happened. He explains the disciplinary process and discusses her options. While feeling a bit overwhelmed, Max is grateful that there is a campus-wide Sexual Assault Response Team (SART), which makes the process more victim-friendly. Max provides Cathy with a list of campus resources such as counseling, peer advisors, and community resources. Max asks Cathy to book another meeting, and he explains that, meanwhile, he will consult with his senior colleague. Max asks numerous questions about handling this disciplinary matter.

In answering Max's questions, his colleague refers to the university Code of Conduct (Code), which is similar to the Model Code of Conduct (Stoner & Lowery, 2004; see Appendix H).

PHILOSOPHICAL PERSPECTIVE

The real crux of my job is to enforce the Code of Conduct, right?

That is such a great question, Max! One of the largest temptations for professionals in this field is to identify ourselves as "enforcers" compared with "educators." Yes, we do look to policy in providing for consistency and fairness. But, the crux of this job is to meld together the role of ensuring compliance with our own institutional policy and the role of fostering student development.

Our positions can be such a resource for the campus community. Responding to social changes and litigation, we can help recommend and develop policy and practice on a campus. So knowledge about decisions coming from courts, the federal government, and state legislatures is important. You'll be communicating with so many people! And, it's important to be informed and prepared to respond to attorneys and civil rights organizations representing students, parents, and student organizations.

How did the role of student conduct administrator develop anyway?

Historically, the academic faculty were the primary individuals responsible for overseeing student discipline. It was integral to the *en loco parentis* standard, reflecting a parental relationship between student and teacher. Morality was central to what was taught, and live-in tutors had a tight hold (Rudoph, 1962). Student affairs as a profession in the United States can be traced back to the first dean of men at Harvard University when LeBaron Russell Briggs was appointed in 1870 (Appleton, Briggs, & Rhatigan, 1978). Deans were placed in a number of prominent institutions as a way to relieve presidents of disciplinary responsibilities and begin to guide students in academic and extracurricular matters (Nuss, 2003). As a result, student conduct as a profession was born.

The profile and context within higher education soon followed. Enrollment of women across the nation climbed exponentially, while the number of colleges and universities also grew due to federal funds from the Morrill Act of 1862 (Pub. L. No. 37-108 (July 2, 1862)). The timing of unprecedented expansion via the development of public junior colleges, teachers colleges, or normal school and technical colleges fostered a diverse student population in gender, age, ethnicity, and expectation.

Maybe in large part due to a richer student profile, the 1960s and the era of student activism fostered a social and legal environment that treated students as so-called "adults" (Lancaster & Waryold, 2008, p. 10). The central objectives of the student personnel movement were to advocate that students should be viewed holistically, that they should be encouraged to develop to their fullest potential, and that learning should be recognized as the result of a variety of rich experiences that take place both inside and outside of the classroom environment (Roberts, 2007, pp. 27-28).

In addition, there were procedural considerations for the student conduct profession. In 1961, the United States Court of Appeals for the Fifth Circuit upset more than 200 years of legal and educational theory (Bracewell, 1988). The decision in *Dixon v. Alabama State Board of Education* (294 F.2d 150 (5th Cir. 1961) paved the way for due process of law into disciplinary procedures. The general requirements of due process are establishment of a student conduct system through which cases are adjudicated; notice to students of the charge(s) they are facing; the right to know the evidence against them; and the opportunity to present their side of the story to an unbiased panel or hearing officer.

While procedural due process focuses on the process, substantive due process focuses on the nature of the institution's rules and the need to avoid the problems of vagueness and overbreadth (Lowery, 2008, p. 72). Our relationship with students has changed in tenor but not in its educational intent. Indeed, a profession has evolved dedicated to promoting growth and development in students while protecting the interests of the larger campus community (Lancaster & Waryold, 2008, p. 8).

HOW CAMPUS DISCIPLINE IS DIFFERENT FROM THE CRIMINAL JUSTICE SYSTEM

What is the difference between a campus disciplinary proceeding and the criminal arena?

We decide whether the student has committed a disciplinary violation at our university and, if so, we decide the appropriate educational sanction (including suspension or dismissal). On the other hand, the criminal court decides whether a crime has occurred and, if so, the sentence (including imprisonment).

What is the role of campus public safety law enforcement? Shouldn't they be involved?

A student can submit an incident report both through the Office of Student Conduct and through public safety. The involvement of public safety could mean that a restraining order and off-campus action would be possible. However, the public safety process rests in the criminal arena. It is up to Cathy whether she wants to file a report with public safety. So, Max, if Cathy didn't already meet with the police, please explain to her that she has the right to meet with the police and to pursue action on campus and to simultaneously pursue action through the criminal justice system. If Cathy has already met with public safety, it would be helpful to obtain any written statements that Cathy made. I can help you work with the district attorney's (DA's) office to obtain those statements. When there is a criminal charge, those statements will also be available through the court. For a lot of reasons, we do not want to make Cathy retell her story in writing. We do want to meet with her and continue to ask questions so that we have more detail about what happened that night. We should also find out what actions the DA may be taking with respect to a criminal charge. To the extent possible, we certainly do not want to interfere with the criminal process. We have a good relationship with the DA's office, which is mutually beneficial.

What is the difference if Cathy reports to public safety, student health, or the Office of Student Conduct?

A sexual assault case may be called to the attention of the authorities in any number of places. For Cathy, the first person she told was a friend who convinced her to go to the authorities. Another complainant may have felt more comfortable going to her resident advisor, which would have gotten a different entity involved. If a community is working well together, the point of entry will not matter much because, regardless of whom she asks, the complainant will learn about all the resources that can be used to address her concerns. This is a primary benefit of a system that coordinates resources on a campus-wide basis.

There are differences in the confidentiality requirements for various points of entry, though, and different degrees to which Cathy might retain control of what happens next. For example, a counselor with whom Cathy has a privileged relationship has different reporting requirements under the Jeanne Clery Disclosure of Campus Security Policy and Campus Crime Statistics Act (Clery Act; 20 U.S.C. § 1092(f); see also Chapter 4) than a residence hall advisor. Similarly, the person to whom Cathy reports the incident can impact how much control Cathy has over the "next steps." For a counselor, whose duty is primarily to Cathy, Cathy may decide not to file a police report or a disciplinary complaint. If the police are aware of a crime, however, they may be under a duty to investigate it to protect the community. Similarly, some interpret Title IX of the Education Amendment of 1972 (20 U.S.C. § 1681) to require student conduct offices to do as much as possible to protect the community, even if the complainant chooses not to go forward. So, legal issues may not allow the complainant to fully control what happens. This is why good communication and sensitivity to Cathy's needs are so important.

Why do we have a campus disciplinary process, when the behavior is an alleged criminal act?

Well, Max, there are a number of reasons. Even if it's a criminal act, the complainant may not want to go through the courts. Even if she brings it to the attention of the police, law enforcement may ultimately decide not to proceed with a criminal charge based on the high standard of proof, which is "beyond a reasonable doubt." In addition, action may be initiated criminally, but the charges may later be dismissed, reduced, or otherwise resolved in a way benefiting the accused (Stoner & Lowery, 2004, p. 35). Regardless of those outcomes, we want to make sure our campus is safe, and we have no control over the outcome of the criminal process.

If Cathy elects to proceed through the criminal court and through our campus disciplinary system, how will the two systems impact each other?

As long as we are thoughtful about it, the systems should work together. We do not necessarily want to wait for the criminal process to finish before initiating discipline. Our interest is the safety of the campus community. At the same time, we do not want to hinder the criminal prosecution. While we need to be careful about the privacy provisions covered under the law regarding what we share with the DA's office, the criminal arena is public. Therefore, the DA's office and/or the court may share information with our office. They may provide us with written statements filed in court and keep us apprised of the status of the case. Typically we will wait for police interviews before we interview witnesses. Based on the information we obtain, we can make a thoughtful decision regarding the timing of our disciplinary process. Also, Alex should be advised that he is not obligated to respond verbally to the campus allegations. In addition, both students should be advised that they may have an advisor, including an attorney, present during disciplinary proceedings. The advisor/attorney can advise but may not speak for the student.

UNDERSTANDING THE INSTITUTION'S CODE OF CONDUCT

How do I get a handle on the institution's philosophy?

The clearest statement about the institution's philosophy is its Code of Conduct. A well-written Code balances the interests of the complainant, the accused person, and the community as a whole. The Code will articulate standards that community members' behavior must meet, the processes for determining whether a community member has fallen short of those standards, and sanctions available to educate and hold accountable the community member who has not met the expected standards.

What if Cathy, the complainant, was not a student? Would we still take action against Alex, the accused?

You'll always want to refer to our campus Code of Conduct for jurisdictional questions. Our Code, like many, allows us to take action against our own student even if the complainant is a visitor. Of course, if Cathy were a visitor who lived far away, it might make it difficult for her to attend a hearing. Whenever logistical issues arise, we will try to work through them, such as allowing remote testimony via television or telephone. On the other hand, if Alex, the accused, were not a student, we would not have jurisdiction over him in our campus disciplinary process. The only option would be the criminal arena.

While this situation occurred on campus, what if the offense had occurred off campus? Would we still have jurisdiction?

Again, Max, you'll want to refer to our campus Code of Conduct for jurisdictional questions. Some Codes only permit action under the campus disciplinary system for events that occur on campus. If events occur off campus, it is up to the criminal court. Other schools, like ours, extend jurisdiction off campus. Jurisdiction will be extended off campus for conduct that "adversely affects the university community and/or the pursuit of its objectives" (Stoner & Lowery, 2004, p. 24). In this case, an allegation of sexual assault between two university students would significantly impact the school's educational mission and the well-being of the community. So, off-campus jurisdiction should be extended in this case.

Max, please keep in mind that you will review other minor allegations occurring off campus, such as disorderly behavior. In such cases, off-campus jurisdiction would not be exercised, as there is no adverse community impact from such minor incidents.

What is a "statute of limitations"?

Many Codes and laws put a time limit on bringing forward a complaint. There are a number of reasons for this: to encourage cases to be investigated when witnesses' and parties' memories are still fresh, to help preserve evidence, to maximize the availability of witnesses, and to provide fairness and closure to the accused. All these considerations must be balanced, though, with the realization that a complainant may not be ready to proceed with a case until some time after the events. Or, for some cases, the complainant may not be aware of a violation until sometime after an incident. For example, in fraud cases or cases when a victim has suppressed his/her memory, the allegations may not be known for years after the incident.

At our institution, after balancing all the competing concerns, we have decided that a complaint must be made within one year of the incident.

RECEIVING A COMPLAINT

I am a little overwhelmed. How do I start out, and exactly how do I conduct this investigation?

I know that feeling, Max! The considerations and intricacies of our role and the implications for students involved can be overwhelming. However, it is Cathy who has made this appointment with you. So, when she comes to meet with you, listen. Be objective and professional as you simply hear her story. Ask questions that are open-ended, which allow her to elaborate on the context as well as the facts as she recalls them. It takes courage to come in to even discuss an alleged violation. While still being sensitive, it is also appropriate to ask Cathy detailed questions that aid your understanding of the events in question.

I think that sometimes the frame of reference for students falls into the Law and Order perception, which can be intimidating. Focus on the Code of Conduct, the standard of proof, and determine whether Cathy's charge has merit or not. It's important not to be critical or judgmental. Take notes. Ask questions. A useful template is to follow the where, when, why, and who scenario. After this initial conversation, it is Cathy's decision whether she chooses to file a written formal complaint. If she does, at that point, your notes along with the complaint will flow into a time line of the evening. You will then generate a list of potential witnesses as you gather additional information, and your investigation will develop.

Should Cathy provide a written statement?

Yes, if she hasn't already provided one to public safety. If her statement already exists, we'll get a copy of it. Otherwise, we have a form here in the office and on the Web that guides students through fundamental questions that we need answered. And we need Cathy's signature on this document. We don't need it notarized. However, in our office, when a student submits a written statement, we are sure to date it and record it as officially accepted.

How can I be effective in interviewing Cathy but also sensitive to this type of situation?

I appreciate your awareness of the situation, Max. It can be awkward given the nature of the complaint. It will be important to set a tone for the meeting so that Cathy understands your role in treating all students with equal care, concern, honor, fairness, and dignity. As a result, Cathy will be assured of a professional and yet caring process.

Can Cathy bring an attorney or advisor when she submits this complaint?

Yes, Cathy can bring either an attorney or advisor, but the person she brings cannot speak in her place or participate in the interview. Additionally, Cathy needs to let you know in advance whether she is bringing someone or not. And she needs to make you aware whether the person is a lawyer or not. Sometimes the university prefers to have legal counsel present whenever there is an attorney involved. The attorney or advisor may help Cathy think of questions about procedure, likely outcome, and risks that she might not think of. But you need to hear from her directly about the facts.

What do you think about having a rape care advocate come with Cathy when she meets with me during the interview?

Having a friend or rape care advocate accompany Cathy is just fine. However, it is important that you explain to the friend or advocate that, just like the attorney or advisor, he/she cannot speak for Cathy. The support person can be there with Cathy, but it is important that the interview allow for only Cathy to respond to questions and provide her story to you.

How do I explain to Cathy that the university is keeping her safe?

Well, Max, frankly, we cannot guarantee safety to Cathy, but we can take substantial action to assist her. We should be vigilant in explaining Cathy's rights, including her right to pursue action in the criminal justice system. We can issue a directive to the accused to stay away from Cathy. We can move Cathy to another residence hall. We should keep Cathy abreast of our investigation, and, once we have a better sense of the evidence, discuss options with her. We should let Cathy know that, if she feels threatened or unsafe, she should immediately call public safety, which can respond to an emergency, not our office, which is not an emergency service.

Cathy should not be concerned about her name being made public by our office, as student disciplinary proceedings are private (with some exceptions) pursuant to the Family Educational Rights and Privacy Act of 1974 (FERPA; Pub. L. No. 93-380 (Aug. 21, 1974)). Again, we should explain that she has a right to be assisted by an advisor of her choosing at all phases of the case. Depending on the circumstances, we should consider an interim suspension of the accused. Finally, the Clery Act (20 U.S.C. § 1092(f)) dictates that this matter be reported as a statistic (without names) in our annual crime report to the public. Pursuant to the act, we make this report regardless of whether the accused is found in violation.

How does the stay away directive work?

The directive is a written order from the Office of Student Conduct directing Alex to have no contact with Cathy. It mandates that he not contact her in person, electronically, via third parties, or otherwise. It does not require him to withdraw from the biology class that both students are enrolled in. It does, however, require that he follow the spirit of the directive. In practical terms, this would mean sitting a reasonable distance away from Cathy and refraining from any interaction with Cathy.

The stay away directive is issued before there is a finding of a violation. Therefore, Alex should be given an opportunity to argue against the issuance of the directive. Likewise, you should find out how Cathy feels about the need for the directive. In particular, if she feels that attending the same class with Alex is a hardship, we might need to rethink the terms of the directive. Given that biology is a large lecture course, as opposed to a small seminar, there is less concern about both students attending the class. Nonetheless, we want to consider the educational needs of both students, and if Cathy feels unable to attend class, we should brainstorm about other options.

If Alex violates the order, Cathy should contact public safety immediately. A violation of this directive is a separate Code violation and may result in another sanction, including suspension.

Regardless of whether a formal stay away order is implemented, Alex should generally be directed not to have contact with Cathy. While the facts and circumstances of all cases vary, common sense suggests this advice.

Is the stay away directive the same thing as a protective or restraining order?

It's the same idea but not the same thing. We issue a stay away directive within the campus disciplinary system. It's essentially the order of a university official to stay away from another individual. On the other hand, a protective or restraining order, also called an order of protection, is a court order to stay away from another individual. If our stay away directive is violated, there are ramifications for the student within the campus judicial system, including the possibility of immediate suspension. If the protective order is violated, the court will take action against the accused, and this could include incarceration.

What if Cathy feels uncomfortable attending biology because Alex is in the class?

We can work with faculty to arrange changing class sections for the biology class in which Alex and Cathy are both enrolled. Considering the time of academic year, an independent study might also be an option. The options involve Cathy's preference, the result of the investigation, and ultimately the hearing results. The overarching decision should be premised on providing for the safety and well-being of both Alex and Cathy.

What are the factors to determine regarding an interim suspension?

This action is taken in very limited circumstances. As our Code specifies, this is for situations where we want to "ensure the safety of members of the university community." We also consider the accused "student's own physical or emotional well-being or if the student poses an ongoing threat of disruption of, or interference with, the normal operations of the university" (Stoner & Lowery, 2004, p. 59). To implement this measure, we would have to believe, based on the available evidence, that Alex is a continuing danger to our community. During the interim suspension, the accused is denied access to campus, including classes, and the other privileges enjoyed by a student. If we do this, we would want to follow up with a full hearing as soon as we have all the necessary evidence to proceed.

Why don't we always proceed with the interim suspension? We don't want to take any chances when it comes to the safety of our students, right?

Well, that is right, but, at the same time, we need to consider that an interim suspension is an administrative action taken without a hearing. In other words, it's an action taken without affording Alex the full right to tell his side and provide witnesses, a critical component of due process. We have a duty to provide for the educational rights of all of our students. Once Alex misses out on classes for a week or more, it makes it increasingly difficult for him to complete the semester. We don't want to implement the suspension based on an emotional reaction to serious allegations until we are sure the allegations are supported. If we were wrong, we would have wrongly deprived Alex of his education. So this action is taken only in limited situations.

What about relocating Alex from his campus housing on an interim basis?

While this action will not impact Alex's education as profoundly as an interim suspension, it is still an administrative action taken before the actions of the conduct board hearing. We want to be very careful before imposing it. The same standard as the interim suspension is involved, namely, consideration of "the safety of the university community as well as consideration of the student's own physical or emotional well-being or if the student poses an ongoing threat of disruption of, or interference with, the normal operations of the university" (Stoner & Lowery, 2004, p. 59).

How do I explain "due process" rights to Cathy, the complainant?

As you have explained to Cathy, she has a right to file a complaint and to consult with a student conduct professional in our office. Cathy enjoys many other rights as well, and it is important that we explain these rights. Given that she is likely feeling upset and distracted at the present time, we should repeat these rights during each meeting. We have them written on an information sheet for her too, which includes information about our system, the complainant's rights in the system, and resources for the complainant such as counseling and a victim's advocate.

As we discussed earlier, she has a right to pursue action in criminal (and/or civil) courts. At our institution, she has the right to indicate her preference regarding the educational sanction. In particular, she should let us know whether she wants the accused to remain at the school. We will consider her request as well as precedent and other factors in making a determination regarding sanction. Cathy has the right to attend all campus disciplinary hearings relevant to the case. She can also request to participate in the proceedings from an alternate location to avoid unnecessary contact with the accused or to have a screen in the hearing room to avoid seeing Alex or having him see her. She can bring a friend, support person (who is not connected to the case), advisor, or attorney to any meeting or hearing that she is entitled to attend. (These rights are parallel to the accused. In other words, if he has an attorney present, she may as well.) If she and Alex live in the same residence hall, she can request a relocation to a different residence hall. She may request a stay away order. She may generally request that evidence of sexual conduct be excluded from hearings. She may request to be informed of the resolution of the case.

While it is not a "right," per se, it is also important to make sure that Cathy knows about all of the available resources on our campus and in the area, including a rape care advocate and our university counseling center. Max, your awareness of these resources and contact information is important in regards to the student development role we provide.

INVESTIGATING A COMPLAINT

After I take the complaint, I need to investigate. Any pointers?

It is important to keep an open mind, Max, so that you are letting facts and not feelings help you figure out whether Alex violated the Code. This is the fact-finding phase. Talk to the accused student and other witnesses, draw time lines, consider forensic evidence, visit the scene of the event, speak to experts about alcohol and sexual assault—whatever it takes to gather information and to help you come to a conclusion about what happened on the night of the incident. By the way, do not assume that there are no witnesses just because no one was in the room with Alex and Cathy. People could have heard things through the door or seen or heard things before or after they went into the room that corroborate or explain either one of their perspectives.

How should I notify Alex that there is a complaint against him?

This question is very important, Max. Both the method and the timing of notifying Alex could impact not only the case, but his well-being. Regarding timing, the best practice is to contact Alex close in time to receiving the complaint from Cathy. Alex should learn of the complaint from our office instead of another party, which could happen if we talked to witnesses first. The tricky thing is that we do not want to act in ways that interfere with the criminal justice system. So, if Cathy files a criminal complaint, typically we should wait until after the police have interviewed him. This is a careful balance, because our community members could be at risk if we move too quickly or too slowly, so you and I will make this decision together, likely consulting with the police and legal counsel, too.

The other aspect of timing is that we don't want Alex to learn of the allegations at a time when there are no support services available to him. Most students would be very upset to learn of serious allegations against them, whether or not they violated the Code. It is important to make sure they have support, like counseling services. Therefore, I never notify a student late in the day, especially late in the day on a Friday or before a break.

The method of notifying Alex and what to include in the notice is also important. Our typical practice, when setting appointments with students, is to send them an e-mail indicating the date and time of the appointment and information about the allegations, including the date of the alleged incident. We do not like to put too much information in an e-mail just in case there is a breach of security. At the same time, we want to give some information so the accused student understands why he/she has to meet with the Office of Student Conduct. When we meet in person, we provide further notice both in writing and orally.

In particularly sensitive, serious cases, the tone sets a sense of urgency. If we don't hear from the student within a few hours, we attempt to reach him/her by phone too. Like other cases, when we meet with the student, we explain why we were a bit vague, and, at that time, we give more detailed notice about the allegations. Since we allow the accused student the opportunity to bring an advisor, we adjourn the meeting if he wants an advisor and has not brought one. Additionally, we provide information about our counseling center.

How do I explain to Alex, the accused student, his rights?

Just as with the complainant's rights, you need to look to our Code. Alex enjoys many procedural rights. He has a right to bring a friend, support person, advisor, or attorney to any phase of the disciplinary proceedings. If he is charged in a criminal proceeding, he may bring an attorney. He has the right to compel our office to prove the allegations by a preponderance of the evidence. At a hearing, he has the right to question witnesses, confront the allegations of the complainant, and to present evidence and witnesses on his own behalf. He has the right to appeal the hearing board decision to a higher authority.

What if Alex chooses not to speak to me or to testify during the hearing?

Alex must meet with you, Max, but he does not have to say anything regarding the events in question. When you meet, you will provide him with a full opportunity to tell his side of the events in question. It is his choice to speak or to opt to remain silent and not tell his side. You should not talk Alex into speaking or not speaking. Alex needs to know that if he remains silent, he gives up the opportunity to explain his side (Stoner & Lowery, 2004, p. 33). A violation of the Code will be based on all available evidence. If he refrains from speaking, the finder of fact will simply not consider his direct version of the events.

When it comes time to interview Alex, how do I do that?

Really, this interview is not very different from other interviews you do: you are giving the accused student an opportunity to be heard. After Alex is on notice of the allegations, ask him if he agrees with the allegations and, whether he agrees or not, if he would like to share his perspective about the incident. Generally, I let students tell their stories without interrupting, and then I go back and ask questions if something was unclear or inconsistent. Be sure to listen carefully, ask if there are other witnesses who would be able to provide further information, and keep an open mind until all the information has been gathered. I often read back from my notes to ensure that they accurately reflect the student's perspective. Sometimes, if I think the notes might be important in a hearing, I will ask the student to read them and sign them to verify their accuracy.

After you have collected all the facts that Alex offers, ask him to reflect on how he might have acted differently, even if he thinks he did not violate the Code.

Be careful not to commit to which account (Cathy's or Alex's) you believe, because you won't have full information at this point. Additionally, be careful not to commit to what sanction you will be recommending. You do not want to box yourself in too early in the process; this is fair to all the parties, and to you, Max!

I know Cathy went to the health center and that a sexual assault forensic evidence kit was administered. Shouldn't I get those records? How do I go about this?

Max, I'm glad you are thinking about forensic evidence. The forensic evidence kit will be helpful in establishing that sexual intercourse actually occurred. In the vast majority of these cases, however, consent is the real issue. Still, we can't anticipate all of the issues, and it is best to be prepared.

In addition, it is possible that the forensic records will establish a trauma suggestive of an assault. Again, it's not terribly likely from the fact pattern established, but it is best to review the actual forensic records.

To obtain the records from the hospital, you should ask Cathy to sign a release that authorizes her forensic records for the day in question be released to our office. We provide the signed release to the health center, and they provide us with the records. Of course, the records belong to Cathy, and it is entirely her choice whether to sign such a release.

Cathy acknowledges drinking alcohol, and she states that the accused drank as well. How does this factor into the analysis?

Max, alcohol is critical to the analysis of this case. Let's analyze the implications for both students. For Cathy, you should ask her how much she drank and find out from other witnesses how the alcohol appeared to affect her. If she was so intoxicated that she couldn't have consented even if she wanted to (and she states she didn't consent), that would be a powerful piece of evidence. For Alex, you should establish whether he viewed Cathy drinking and could perceive her level of intoxication. Likewise, you should try to establish Alex's level of intoxication.

For both students, there is no getting around the fact that alcohol impairs judgment and affects credibility. That's one reason we want to interview other witnesses and consider the forensic evidence before making a determination.

Max, alcohol is not "an excuse" for Alex. It is a consideration in terms of establishing what happened on the night in question.

If I learn that a witness or Cathy, the complainant, violated the Code (for example, if they were drinking when they were under the legal age), what should I do?

Max, you have hit on a critical question about relative importance of different Code violations; it's a reminder that we need to keep things in perspective. Obviously, we encourage all our students to live up to the standards articulated in the Code. But, the Code sections that we are most concerned with are those that are the most serious, which include sexual assaults. We want to encourage those who may be witnesses or complainants to come forward when the issue is serious. We don't want them to worry about getting into trouble themselves for something relatively minor. Therefore, we give immunity to complainants and witnesses for low-level violations of the Code when they are participating in the investigation of a serious allegation.

This can be tricky if the witness or the complainant engaged in a Code violation that is more serious. Suppose, for example, that your investigation reveals that a person who started out as a witness should really be another accused student because she provided alcohol to Cathy as part of a hazing ritual, causing her to get very drunk and, therefore, become more vulnerable to assault. Or, in a different context, suppose a complainant alleged he was been beaten, but it turns out he was also aggressive and used physical violence against another student. In that case, the complainant may also be an accused student.

The best thing to do is to be very honest with students when you talk to them. Let them know that we need to ask questions about alcohol because it impacts their credibility as witnesses, not that we want to get them into trouble for underage drinking. (As an aside, Max, I always give the referral information to our alcohol education program to these witnesses so they may pursue it on a voluntary basis.) But also let them know that we won't be able to ignore serious violations of the Code, and, if they have concerns, they may want to speak to an advisor first. "Transparency" can be an overused expression, but I find students appreciate the honesty and frankness that comes with being as transparent as possible.

ADJUDICATING THE CASE

Does Cathy have an option to have this case heard by an administrator rather than a full hearing board?

The short answer is yes. After you have completed your fact finding, there is the option of addressing the charges, through mutual consent of the parties involved, on a basis acceptable to us, including separation from the university. However, if both parties do not consent, we then proceed to a hearing board.

What types of forums could be available for Cathy and Alex?

Different universities might have differing options, but the most prevalent forms of resolution in use to process complaints concerning student behavior on college campuses include one-to-one disciplinary conferences, also called administrative hearings, and board or panel hearings. Board hearings vary greatly. They may include student-only boards, student and faculty boards, and boards that may include students, faculty, and staff to represent all campus constituencies. More and more campuses are also exploring various forms of alternative dispute resolutions (ADR). These may include mediation, restorative justice, and various models of ADR.

Max, my response to your question is taken directly from a chapter called "Forums and Resolution" in a book published in 2008, *Student Conduct Practice: The Complete Guide for Student Affairs Professionals* (Zdziarski & Wood, p. 98). It is a wonderful resource book that I would highly recommend. At our university, we use a board consisting of students, faculty, and staff to resolve the complain.

What do I do if Cathy or Alex feels uncomfortable or unsafe seeing each other at the hearing?

I think it's helpful to be creative in responding to students. Just so you know, we can accommodate concerns for personal safety or fear of confrontation by providing separate facilities, using a visual screen, or by allowing participation by using technology like video conferencing, videophone, or other means. This decision is typically made between you and me. It is a delicate balance, one where we want to be sensitive to genuine concerns, yet be completely fair in the process.

What sort of training do hearing board members receive?

There can be a tension created about how much time we want our volunteers to spend on training when we really need their time to hear the cases! Here's the way I look at it, Max. Training makes hearing board members more prepared to hear complicated cases, which is critical to the process. Additionally, our system is educational, and the accused student is not the only party who has an opportunity to learn. The experience of hearing board members can be an important part of their education, too, regardless of their age or affiliation.

Training can be completed in a number of different ways. At a bare minimum, before hearing his/her first case, a new member should be trained on the processes, the fundamentals of listening carefully and suspending judgment until all the information has been presented, and ideas about how to weigh information and how to deliberate. It is helpful for board members to also learn some substantive information that is not common knowledge, for example, how alcohol might impact decision making or why women become drunk faster than men of the same weight, or about Rape Trauma Syndrome, or about how students use Facebook and Instant Messenger to communicate and how the technology works.

If these types of substantive areas can't be addressed in a formal training, though, information relevant to a particular case may be presented through witnesses. Often, even if general training was given on substantive issues, witnesses will still provide detailed information relevant to the case.

How do you have a witness provide information about alcohol or Rape Trauma Syndrome to a hearing board?

You raise a good point. Up until now, we've been talking about witnesses to the alleged incident or that may shed some light on the factual aspects of the allegations (sometimes called fact witnesses). For information about medical, psychological, or technical issues that are not intuitive to a layperson, expert witnesses might be used.

For example, we have an alcohol specialist at our health center who assists in explaining to board members the physical impact of alcohol on a person. She will use information about the weight and gender of the parties, for example, to opine on memory loss and ability to make judgments. She can also speak to the importance of holding students accountable for alcohol-related violations, and she provides ideas of educational ways to do so. Similarly, we are lucky to have a faculty member who is an expert on Rape Trauma Syndrome, so she can help board members understand why a complainant may not have acted in a way a board member may expect after a sexual assault. For example, Cathy didn't initially think she had been raped, even though she reports that Alex had sexual intercourse with her after she had said she didn't want to; an expert may help explain this apparent inconsistency.

Not all technical information needs a formal expert, though. For example, if a case has information related to technology that is common among college students but less common among faculty members (like Instant Messenger and Facebook), it's important that the faculty members understand the technology, but one of the student witnesses can explain it. In essence, that student becomes an expert witness on that topic and a fact witness on the other information he/she is providing.

I am a little unclear about handling witnesses. Can Cathy cross-examine witnesses that Alex invites forward?

Both Cathy and Alex may arrange in advance through you for witnesses to present pertinent information to the hearing board, However, it is not required that either Alex or Cathy be given the opportunity to cross-examine witnesses directly. Instead, cross-examination through the hearing board is our policy. Cathy and Alex can direct their questions for either each other or witnesses to the chairperson. I think this really supports maintaining the educational role and avoids an adversarial process.

What kind of information or witnesses can Cathy and Alex request during the student conduct hearing?

We try to focus on members of the university as possible witnesses if reasonably possible. As far as records, pertinent information such as exhibits and written statements may be accepted as information for consideration at the discretion of the hearing board chairperson. As you probably recall, our Code requires that these requests be made at least two weekdays prior to the actual hearing.

Should prior sexual conduct be excluded from the hearing?

Yes. Our job is to hear this current complaint and whether it violated the Code of Conduct.

How confidential is the hearing?

The issue of confidentiality is more complicated than it may seem. For one thing, there are competing values about how confidential sexual assault matters should be. On the one hand, protecting the privacy of both parties is important, but, on the other hand, the institution may want to demonstrate that it takes these allegations seriously and treats all parties fairly. Another complicating factor is that there are a couple of federal laws that give somewhat contradictory requirements. On the one hand, FERPA (Pub. L. No. 93-380 (Aug. 21, 1974)) provides that students' educational records are private; this includes disciplinary records. On the other hand, the Clery Act (20 U.S.C. § 1092(f)) requires institutions to provide complainants with the outcome of the matter but may be interpreted to limit the ability of an institution to require confidentiality. Similarly, principles of First Amendment free speech (for public institutions) suggest that the accused student and the complainant should be able to speak about their experiences. And FERPA really only protects the documents—that is, the records—not personal observations. Additionally, FERPA makes an exception when there is an act of serious violence, allowing the institution to announce the outcome of the matter when the student is found in violation of the institutional rules.

When balancing competing values and potentially contradictory laws, a good helping of common sense goes a long way, Max. First, as always, examine our own institutional policy, which may provide additional protections over and above FERPA. If the institution's policy predates the Clery Act (20 U.S.C. § 1092(f), though, you would be well advised to seek advise from legal counsel. Second, the hearing board, witnesses, and other people who may have participated in the hearing but who are not the parties should be held to a high level of confidentiality. Any stories they would tell are not their own, and it would be gossip without a valid purpose to report the allegations Cathy made against Alex or the information Alex might provide in response. Third, with respect to the parties, Alex and Cathy, advise them that the law permits them to speak about their experiences. It might be useful, though, to advise them to evaluate the pros and cons of such speech before they do so.

You may or may not want to be the one to help talk them through the examination of those pros and cons, Max. On the one hand, as an educator you have keen insight and can help them gain insight. On the other hand, you might later be accused of biasing their decisions, which should truly be independent.

What is the standard of proof?

Whether or not you realize it, every time you hear a story, you assess whether you believe it. In your personal life, for example, you may have heard a joke that starts out like a true story; then, at some point, it becomes too absurd to be believable. Here in the office, for cases that you hear, you evaluate information from witnesses against information from the accuser and the accused that may be conflicting and, based on credibility and other factors, you determine which account you believe.

Different disciplinary systems require different levels of certainty to find an accused person responsible for a Code violation. When you evaluate facts, Max, aren't there times when you might feel completely and absolutely sure about your determination of the true facts, and, at other times, don't you feel pretty sure but still have some lingering doubts? It might take a different amount of information to get you to these different levels of certainty. For example, when one noncredible witness, who has something to gain, offers an account that differs from a credible witness, with nothing to gain, that might be enough evidence to convince you. Other times, the credibility of the witnesses might be bolstered or refuted by documentary evidence or additional witnesses. The amount of information or evidence that is needed to convince the disciplinary system that there has been a violation of the Code is referred to as the "standard of proof."

In legal and administrative settings, there are terms of art that describe the necessary standard of proof. In criminal settings, there is a very high standard of proof called "proof beyond a reasonable doubt." This would mean that there is enough evidence that jurors would have no reasonable doubt about a defendant's guilt. In our administrative settings, such a high level of proof is not used because the accused student is not facing loss of liberty or life. Some institutions use a "clear and convincing" standard of proof, which is lower than the "reasonable doubt" standard, and requires the evidence to be both clear and convincing. Other institutions use the "preponderance of the evidence" standard of proof, which is a lower standard still. For there to be a preponderance of evidence, the fact finder would have to determine that it is more likely than not that the accused student violated the Code. It allows for the possibility of other interpretations of facts, but ultimately the fact finder is saying that his/her interpretation of the facts is the most likely.

After much consideration, Max, our institution has adopted the "preponderance" standard. This seems to best balance the interests of the accused student, the complainant, and the community.

SANCTIONING

How does the sanction "fit" the violation?

Allegations of sexual assault are very serious and often include the sanction that the accused student be separated from the institution. Depending on the circumstances, this might be a time-limited separation (suspension) or a permanent separation (expulsion). As you gain experience, Max, you will start to get a feel for how we evaluate sanctions based on the violation. We follow our internal guidelines and use discretion as necessary to recognize mitigating and aggravating factors. But, even without studying our guidelines and having tons of experience, a person unfamiliar with disciplinary systems might realize that some acts are more serious than others and, therefore, will receive stricter sanctions. For example, in the area of theft, we are going to sanction differently a student who steals a package of pens from a student who steals a laptop. Of course, each case is different and must be assessed by both our office and the board.

What other sanctions are available besides separation from the university?

Separation from the institution is appropriate when we can prove that the accused student has engaged in a sexual assault or some other act of violence. We employ a number of other educational sanctions for less serious offenses. If the offense is alcohol or drug related, we require alcohol education and counseling. (We may require counseling in a suspension case as one condition for the student to ever return to the institution.) For other offenses, such as theft, we may require community service and restitution as an educational sanction. Community service is an opportunity for the student to give back to the community. For other nonviolent offenses, we also consider such sanctions as probationary periods, directed studies on a topic related to the offense, and reflection papers on an assigned topic related to the behavior in question. The objective is for the community to be safe, for the victim to be "made whole," and for the student to learn from the experience and not repeat the behavior.

What if Cathy, the complainant, does not want Alex, the accused student, to be suspended or expelled?

Sometimes a complainant expresses the wish to have the accused student understand that he did something wrong, but she states that she doesn't want the accused to be suspended or expelled. While this wish may be taken into consideration as we are making recommendations to the hearing board, it cannot be determinative. We need to consider community safety as well as the wishes of the individuals involved in a particular incident. It is important to discuss with both Cathy and Alex that it is the institution, not the complainant, who ultimately assesses any sanction.

What types of sanction(s) are appropriate for this type of violation?

Our Conduct of Code provides for categories of sanctions. Keeping in mind that the safety and well-being of all students is desired, much is dependent on the fact-finding process and the responses of both Cathy and Alex. I have been involved in cases where the student who was found in violation was remorseful and accountable for his/her actions and took proactive steps. In this situation, I have seen sanctions that involved a loss of privilege or discretionary sanction and probationary status. However, in cases where the safety of the complaining student persists and there is no remorse, stricter sanctions, such as suspension or expulsion, may be appropriate.

COMMUNICATION AND APPEALS

What is the process for informing Cathy and Alex of the resolution?

The student conduct administrator provides to Cathy, in writing, the determination of the hearing board and the sanction(s) imposed, if any. Cathy also has the option to meet with you to discuss the results. I tend to think a personal follow-up for cases like this is appropriate. Alex will hear the result at the hearing, and he will subsequently be provided the written decision.

Can Alex or Cathy appeal this?

Yes, depending on the circumstances, Alex or Cathy can appeal this sanction. Our guidelines require appeals to be received within five academic days of the decision. In order to appeal a decision, either Cathy or Alex is responsible for putting her/his appeal in writing and delivering it to our office. In the event that there is an appeal, it is important that the student understands that an appeal is not a new hearing. Appeals consider new information that is sufficient to alter a decision, determine whether the sanction(s) are appropriate for the violation, or determine whether the hearing was conducted fairly by following our own procedures or in a manner that would not significantly prejudice the results.

What if I get a telephone call from Cathy's parents? Do they have a role in the conduct process?

We can explain the process and assure them that Cathy is being heard, that we are professionals in our job, and we can provide them a copy of the Code of

Conduct. It really is an educational opportunity for us. It is best to ask Cathy to sign a release so that we can speak to her parents in greater detail. Remember, though, that without a release from Alex, you still need to follow privacy laws regarding his records.

DOCUMENTATION

How are statements of the complainant, accused student, and witnesses recorded and maintained?

In this age of improved technology and greater attention to sustainability, many institutions are reconsidering this question. Traditionally, paper copies of investigative materials, statements, exhibits and notes from hearings, and rationale of the board were all retained by our institution. At our institution we also tape record hearings and maintain those cassettes. But, Max, I am rethinking all of this. I am investigating whether we can scan the statements and important documents so we can save them on computer discs and whether we can record digitally so the proceedings will be maintained on CDs rather than on cassettes. I am considering how we can best use new technology to appropriately retain information without using so much paper and without requiring so much storage space. It is always advisable to maintain enough information so that we can demonstrate that our procedures were followed and that the process was fair, but I want to do this in better ways than having a storage room full of paper.

How long are records kept?

I consulted with legal counsel's office about this one, Max, as I was establishing our record-retention policy. For our institution, there is a university-wide policy about record retention, tied to the statute of limitations for potential lawsuits. Counsel wants to make sure that if we're sued for not providing due process (for state institutions) or for not following our procedures (for private institutions) that they have enough information to demonstrate that we did our job properly. We worked out a system where we permanently maintain records of all serious cases or cases that have historic significance; other case files are destroyed one year after the statute of limitations expires.

What is a public record?

We keep a summary of each case that goes before the hearing board, but names and identifying information have been deleted. This gives students involved in the process some idea of what has happened in other, similar cases in the past.

Can records be subpoenaed?

Yes. FERPA (Pub. L. No. 93-380 (Aug. 21, 1974)) provides for various exceptions to the privacy of a student's educational records; one such exception is a court subpoena. There are important procedures that must be followed should we receive a subpoena, Max, so legal counsel's office must be involved.

References

Appleton, J. R., Briggs, C. M., & Rhatigan, J. J. (1978). *Pieces of eight: The rites, roles and styles of the dean by eight who have been there.* Portland, OR: NASPA.

Bracewell, W. (1988). Student discipline. In M. J. Barr & Associates (Eds.), *Student services and the law* (pp. 273-283). San Francisco: Jossey-Bass.

Lancaster, J. M., & Waryold, D. M. (Eds.). (2008). *Student conduct practice: The complete guide for student affairs professionals.* Sterling, VA: Stylus Publishing.

Lowery, J. (2008). Laws, policies, and mandates. In J. M. Lancaster & D. M. Waryold (Eds.), *Student conduct practice: The complete guide for student affairs professionals.* Sterling, VA: Stylus Publishing.

Nuss, E. M. The development of student affairs. In S. R. Komives & D. B. Woodard Jr. (Eds.), *Student services: A handbook for the profession* (4th ed.). San Francisco: Jossey-Bass.

Roberts, D. (2007). *Deeper learning in leadership: Helping college students find the potential within.* San Francisco: Jossey-Bass.

Rudolph, F. (1962). *The American college and university: A history.* New York: Knopf Publications in Education.

Silverglate, H. A., & Gewolb, J. (2003). *FIRE's guide to due process and fair procedure on campus.* Philadelphia: Foundation for Individual Rights in Education.

Stoner, E. N., II, & Lowery, J. W. (2004). *Navigating past the "spirit of insubordination": A twenty-first century model student conduct code with a model hearing script. Journal of College and University Law, 31*(1), 1-78. Retrieved from http://www.asjaonline.org/

Zdziarski, E., & Wood, N. (2008). Forums for resolution. In J. M. Lancaster & D. M. Waryold (Eds.), *Student conduct practice: The complete guide for student affairs professions* (pp. 97-111). Sterling, VA: Stylus Publishing.

Chapter 6

Role of Law Enforcement in Sexual Assault Response Teams

by Paul M. Cell, Chief of Police

The role of the law enforcement agency is one of the critical components of the Sexual Assault Response Team (SART). The initial action of the responding officers sets the foundation for victim support, witness cooperation, and proper evidence gathering.

Those actions, followed by a comprehensive investigation, become the backbone for success in the prosecutorial process.

This chapter will: examine the key players and their respective roles in the law enforcement response, develop protocols for a best practice SART law enforcement response, identify specialized training needs, and discuss special considerations for acampus law enforcement response.

KEY PLAYERS

Identifying the Agency Responsible for Conducting the Criminal Investigation

The most important question that needs to be addressed is what law enforcement agency is responsible for handling criminal investigations at the particular college or university? In addition, institutional leaders should know the law enforcement resources that are available on their campus, the training the responding officers have received, and the legal authority of the agency handling sexual assault investigations.

Today many campuses have their own police agencies. There is a clear advantage in having the responding police agency as part of the community it serves. In essence, this type of "neighborhood" response provides a victim with a level of familiarity that is expected from a hometown police department, as opposed to an outside agency that may have no daily interaction with the campus community. Overall, campus law enforcement agencies tend to be more aware of the subtle nuances of college campus communities. This is especially true in a campus environment where freedom of "self" is encouraged, and institutional, fraternal, athletic rituals, and activities may appear as uncommon behaviors to an outside responding police agency. With an outside police department, these behaviors often lead to confusion or delay in identifying the key players in an incident.

When Campus Law Enforcement Is the Primary Responder

What Is the Authority of the Campus Police Department? The legal authority for most campus police agencies is set forth under individual state laws. When an institution has its own police department, there is a need to identify the agency's ability to properly investigate a reported sexual assault.

There are many campus police agencies that have full law enforcement authority but lack the specialized training, equipment, or institutional support that allows them to handle a sexual assault investigation. In some areas, municipal, county, or state agencies have created "sex crime units" that are designed to respond to all sexual assaults within their jurisdiction and have authority to take the role as the lead agency in the investigation. This is usually the result of a memorandum of understanding, a statutory law, or an institution's philosophy of how they envision the role of their campus police department. In any of these cases, the choice to use an outside agency should never be construed as an indication that the campus police department is not a professional law enforcement agency.

If the institution's campus police department is not allowed to investigate sexual assaults, the decision process that established this constraint should be researched. If there are no legal restrictions guiding this action, necessary changes need to be identified to ensure that the campus police department has the ability to investigate these crimes. The practice of choosing to have an outside law enforcement agency handle sexual assault cases on campus may give the appearance to the community that an institution does not have faith in the ability of its campus police department.

When looking at the number of unreported sexual assaults that occur every year on campuses around the nation, the importance of a comprehensively trained campus police department becomes evident.

What Is the Image of the Campus Law Enforcement Agency? The image of the campus police department can impact on a victim's willingness to report a crime. Quite often the department is judged by its ability to make community members feel they have created a safe environment to learn, work, or live. The agency needs to be viewed as a "go to" department on campus, with officers who truly have a vested interest in the well-being of the students. In addition, the campus community as a whole needs to believe that its campus police department plays an integral role in the institution's mission.

It would be remiss not to acknowledge that campus police professionals continue to work at being recognized as members of bona fide law enforcement agencies. Too often, a term like *rent-a-cop* is used by campus community members and others to perpetuate this "quasi-police" stereotype. Even many outside police agencies are still unsure of the legal authority of the campus police agency. This is more prevalent in some regions of the country, whereas in other regions, the profession is viewed the same as any other law enforcement agency. In addition, the situation is not aided by the college or university identifying its sworn police agency with nonpolice titles such as Campus Safety or Public Safety and Security. It is recommended that these departments use the police title in their department's name. A campus community's belief that their police department is a legitimate law enforcement agency is vital if the campus SART is to be a success. That is why it is important for campus police agencies to have programs, publications, and networking to educate the community on the services available and their legal authority.

Two recent tragedies on campuses have increased the recognition and acknowledgment of the legitimacy of campus police departments, which is long overdue. On April 16, 2007, a student at Virginial Technical Institute shot and killed thirty-two people and then killed himself. On February 14, 2008, a former Northern Illinois University student entered a classroom with a gun, killing six people, wounding eighteen others, and killing himself.

What Can Be Done to Enhance a Department's Image? When a campus police department is attempting to improve its image, research needs to be conducted to identify the department's current status in the community. This information serves as a foundation for growth and can help the agency recognize areas in need of improvement. Information gathering for this purpose can be done through different focus groups and campus surveys. This information can then be analyzed and disseminated to the proper departmental personnel and used as a guide to improve community image and services.

To be successful in this venture, a campus police department must take measures to ensure that its officers are highly skilled in their jobs and are willing to adopt a "community partnership" philosophy. This philosophy needs to start from the top down, and administrative officers have to believe in the mission of the institution they serve.

This can be demonstrated through officers' involvement in student programming and campus events. Their interactions with campus members send a message that the officers care about what is important to the community. At one university, the chief of police and other officers chaperoned bus trips to Broadway shows. They were not acting in their role as law enforcement officers, but rather as active community members. This is the community the police officers have sworn to protect and serve. There is no better way of serving than immersing themselves in the campus culture.

Some other examples of interactions or partnerships include:

- Attending a student vigil such as "Take Back the Night";

- Taking part in campus cultural heritage celebrations;

- Creating a residence life/dormitory liaison program;

- Working with student volunteer patrol/escorts groups;

- Creating an increased presence on bike and foot patrols in heavily traversed pedestrian areas; and

- Speaking to all new student orientation classes and ensuring that every new student knows or has spoken to at least one campus police officer.

At all times, police officers should remember they are professionals and need to maintain a positive attitude while staying within the ethical guidelines of their agency.

When a Campus Does Not Have a Law Enforcement Agency

The agency responsible for the safety of the campus must identify what law enforcement agency within its jurisdiction is responsible for the response and investigation of sexual assault reports.

When local law enforcement is the primary campus responder for sexual assault investigations, there is a significant need to ensure that the responding agency has a cooperative working relationship with the institution.

On those campuses that do not have a sworn law enforcement department, the need for collaboration, training, and response preparedness between campus safety/security departments and local law enforcement agencies becomes essential.

To help bolster these relationships, it is recommended that an institution create a law enforcement liaison position to work closely with the outside police agency. Ideally, the local police agencies should be invited to the campus on a regular basis to meet with college officials to discuss procedures for investigating reports of sexual assault, the role the college will play during that investigation, and the impact of campus internal judicial sanctions in relation to the criminal case.

It is also important that officers from the outside agency have a first-hand knowledge of the physical layout of the campus and working knowledge of where specific buildings are located and what is housed in those buildings, that is, administrative offices, information technology (IT) or access control centers, student resident life halls (dormitories), and any buildings that house large student gatherings like a student center or a library. Having a familiarity with the campus will help outside police agencies respond in a more effective and expeditious manner.

It is recommended that a coordination plan be created to identify outside police agencies and campus safety/security department responsibilities when responding to a report of a sexual assault. The plan should be developed as a collaborative effort involving campus administrators, law enforcement/security officials, and legal council to ensure governing laws and civil liabilities are properly examined and considered.

Ultimately, the onus is on the institution to ensure that guidelines are in place to help build these relationships, thus creating a foundation for planning a comprehensive SART best practice approach.

DEVELOPING PROTOCOLS FOR A BEST PRACTICE SART LAW ENFORCEMENT RESPONSE

The success of a SART response greatly depends on having effective protocols that police agency personnel can be trained in and can use as a constant reference during the handling sexual assault investigations. It is important that these protocols are reviewed on an annual basis and revised as appropriate. Below are examples of some protocols that have been have adapted in part from nationally recognized standards of the International Association of Chiefs of Police (IACP; 2005), which can be incorporated into any SART response procedure.

Dispatch/Communications Officer

The initiation of any SART response begins with a first contact to the police agency, which is usually received by the dispatcher or communications officer. The officer must obtain as much detailed information as possible to provide the victim with the proper services needed and to ensure officer and victim safety when reponding to the scene. In many cases, the dispatcher is the first contact a victim may have with the law enforcement agency and may be the determining factor if she feels comfortable enough to continue with the reporting process.

Information obtained should include:

- Victim information and location;

- Location and time the crime occurred and time reported;

- Pedigree information of the caller, to include full name, address, and contact numbers;

- The role of the caller in relation to the incident—victim, witness, or professional providing aid;

- The medical condition and needs of the victim; and

- A description of the suspect and direction/mode of travel.

If the dispatcher or communications officer is speaking directly to the victim, she should be instructed not to change clothing, shower, touch anything in the immediate area, or urinate if she displays signs of a drug-induced sexual assault. The dispatcher or communications officer should remain on the telephone with the victim to provide assistance and comfort until a patrol unit arrives on the scene. All necessary SART members on call should be contacted as determined by the victim's wishes. This can include the Sexual Assault Nurse Examiner (SANE) and detective on duty, rape care advocate, and, if the victim is a resident student, the proper director on duty for campus housing as well as the dean of students or designee.

Initial Response

Initial responding officers should be primarily concerned with the well-being of the victim and, where circumstances allow, should initiate investigative procedures that facilitate the identification and arrest of suspects.

With regard to victim assistance:

- Necessary first aid should be rendered. Emergency medical assistance, if required, should be requested.

- An attempt should be made to gain the victim's trust and confidence by showing understanding, patience, and respect for personal dignity; using language appropriate to the age, intelligence, and emotional condition of the victim; informing the victim that an officer of the same sex will be provided if desired and available; and helping the victim to locate family or friends for emotional support or to obtain outside assistance from rape care advocates. Introduction of the SART program is appropriate at this point.

With regard to initial investigation and enforcement actions:

- Investigative questioning should be limited to those matters necessary to identify the victim and to describe and locate the suspect.

- Pertinent information should be relayed to police dispatchers and the supervisor.

- The victim's emotional and physical ability to answer questions concerning the assault should be determined, and the questioning should be limited accordingly.

- Questioning should be done in private and only by one officer.

- Detailed, intimate questions regarding the assault should be avoided until a formal statement is taken by an investigator or SANE nurse.

- The crime scene should be protected, making sure to include bedding, clothing, related materials, and areas. The victim should be asked not to wash or urinate, in cases of possible drug-induced assault, until a medical examination has been performed.

- The victim's consent to undergo a medical examination should be requested, emphasizing its importance to investigative and apprehension efforts as well as to her/his physical well-being. At this point a SANE nurse should be contacted by the dispatcher who has available on-call contact information. If no SANE nurse is available to respond, the victim may be taken to a designated hospital for an examination.

- The victim should be accompanied to the campus health center without undue notice (undercover vehicle if available and officer in plain clothes) or hospital, when no SANE nurse is available for response. Pertinent information concerning the assault should be relayed to the nurse examiner.

- The officer should remain on hand at the medical facility (but not witness the examination) until family members, support service personnel, or the detective on duty arrive.

- The officer should also ensure that evidence is properly stored and identified; the detective or officer will retain custody of all evidence and submit it to the evidence "officer."

- Arrangements should be made for the victim to provide a statement to investigative officers whether a medical examination was conducted.

Follow-Up

An investigative officer will be assigned to the follow-up investigation as soon as possible after the initial complaint and will remain responsible for the case until it is closed or removed from his/her responsibility. This officer shall:

1. Compile the basic investigative information contained in the initial interview, criminal complaint, and medical examination.

2. Conduct an initial interview that will allow the victim to describe the incident without interruption.

3. Determine the victim's emotional and physical ability to submit to an in-depth interview and schedule the interview as soon as these factors will allow following the incident, during which the investigator shall—
    a. Employ a comfortable setting that affords privacy and freedom from distractions, attempting to obtain all necessary information at this time;
    b. Explain the need for obtaining detailed information concerning the crime to include details of the sex act, the suspect's modus operandi, clothing, means of restraining the victim, and the use or availability of weapons; any words used or instructions given to the victim; marks, scars, tattoos, deformities, or other unusual physical features or body odors of the suspect; and any witnesses, participants, or accomplices that may be described or identified by the victim;
    c. Note victim's behavior during the assault, to include the type and degree of any resistance offered, the nature of any acquaintance with the suspect to include any prior intimate relationships and the state of mind of the victim during the attack, being careful not to make judgmental statements that could hinder the victim's willingness to cooperate;
    d. Determine the degree to which the victim has received support services from family, friends, and victim advocacy groups, and encourage/facilitate these interactions where necessary;
    e. Detail the events, in cases in which a drug-induced assault is probable, prior to the victim's blackout or period of amnesia and upon awakening; determine what physical effects the victim usually experiences when she ingests alcohol, what other drugs she may have taken voluntarily, and unusual side effects experienced the day after the assault;
    f. If victim consents, request the interview be videotaped for preservation.

4. Review the victim's account of the event in order to clarify any discrepancies with earlier accounts and to elaborate on issues of significance to the prosecution.

5. Encourage the victim to prosecute the case should she hesitate to do so, emphasizing the importance of prosecution for public safety. Respect the victim's wishes in all cases.

6. Solicit the victim's continued support in the investigation, apprising the victim of future investigative and prosecutorial activities that will or may require involvement and cooperation;

7. Work with the prosecutor's office to develop the case, to familiarize the victim with the types of inquiries that may be faced during cross-examination, and to ensure that requests for victim protection orders are made where indicated.

8. Maintain continued contact with the victim to ensure that appropriate mental health and other support services are readily available.

9. Maintain appropriate contact with university officials such as the dean of students (if student involved), the director of campus housing, the vice president of human resources (if employee is involved), and through the chain of command within the campus law enforcement agency.

10. Maintain contact and make recommendations to the coordinator of student conduct for matters of student disciplinary proceedings and advise the victim that alternate living arrangements and class assignments may be made through the dean of students.

11. Refer an on-campus victim to on-campus services, for example, the Center for Nonviolence and Prevention Programs, the Women's Center, the Dean of Students Office, and Counseling and Psychological Services.[1]

IDENTIFYING SPECIAL TRAINING NEEDS

What Training Have They Received?

There needs to be continuous professional development throughout a law enforcement officer's career. This training needs to be more than the mandatory yearly training updates set forth by state statute. It is highly recommended that a departmental training committee be created and put in place to develop a needs assessment training tool, to evaluate the relevancy of the training offered, and to select skilled instructors to provide the training. This committee should also be responsible for identifying the officers most appropriate to receive the training. It is also good to have in place a posttraining evaluation to measure the practicality and feasible implementation of the information learned. There should be a department training log developed to keep a written record of all officers' training and certifications. It is not hyperbole to equate having an officer untrained in sexual assault investigations interviewing a victim to an officer untrained in firearms carrying a gun; both are inevitably on their way to doing more irreversible harm than good.

---

[1]For a sample in-depth state protocol, see http://www.state.nj.us/OAG/DCJ/AGGuide/Standards/standardssartsane.pdf (NJ Division of Criminal Justice, 2004).

Identifying Training Disciplines

With regard to sexual assault investigations, officers should receive advance training in several different subject disciplines. It is important that officers are crossed-trained so that they can provide a more comprehensive response. Officers who are assigned to investigate sexual assaults should receive training in various areas related to sexual assault response and investigation, crime scene investigation, and interview/interrogation techniques.

Below are other training suggestions that will enhance officers' abilities, including:

- Victim psychology and behaviors;
- Campus cultures and dynamics, and the impact on reporting;
- Offender psychology and profiling;
- Sexual assault victim/suspect interview and interrogation techniques;
- SART development and operations; and
- Federal laws that protect sexual assault victim's rights.

All officers should be well versed in their institution's rules and regulations as they relate to victims of sexual assault. They also need to have a working knowledge of the state statutes that govern their legal options.

SPECIAL CONSIDERATIONS

"Nonstranger" Sexual Assault on Campus

The most common type of sexual assault on a college campus is "nonstranger sexual assault." A recent study done at both two- and four-year colleges found 35 rapes per 1,000 female students over a seven-month period, and 90 percent of those victims knew their assailant (Fisher, Cullen, & Turner, 2000). This type of crime also becomes one of the hardest to investigate and prosecute. The law enforcement agency handling the investigation must be able to identify legal "speed bumps" that may be encountered in the investigative and prosecutorial procedures in order to properly ensure an effective victim centered response.

Example—Anatomy of a Sexual Assault: Leslie, a nineteen-year-old freshman, visited the campus health center services to request emergency contraception. While speaking with the nurse, she broke down and explained what had occurred the previous night. Leslie stated she had gone to the university basketball game on campus with her girlfriends. There she sat next to Steve, a student who was well known on campus. The two talked throughout the game about "hanging out" later that night. After the game was over, Leslie left her girlfriends and went with Steve to his campus dormitory room, where he had invited her to come and watch a movie. As they walked through the campus, it began raining very hard and both their clothes became soaked. At Steve's room, he gave Leslie a large "jersey" style shirt to wear. Leslie went into the bathroom, removed her wet clothes, and came out wearing the jersey and her underwear. Steve put on a tee shirt and shorts. During the next few hours they watched television and drank alcoholic beverages that Steve already had in his room. Throughout the night Steve made advances towards her; some kissing and light touching occurred. Leslie made it clear she wanted it to go no further. Steve suggested she spend the night with him. She fell asleep in his arms only to wake up several hours later with him on top of her starting to penetrate her vagina with his penis. Leslie told Steve to stop, and he did for a minute; then he held her arms down and told her he knew she really wanted it. When Steve was finished, he fell back asleep. Leslie then got up and left the room. She returned to her room and told her roommates what had happened. Leslie refused to report the incident or acknowledge it as an actual "rape." She blamed herself for getting in bed with Steve. Her roommates told her that they have heard that Steve is a player, and it is rumored he has done this before. They encouraged her to report the incident as a crime. Leslie continued to refuse to report the assault as a crime. Days later, after speaking with the university health center staff several times, Leslie decided to report the crime to the police.

Too often cases like this are common within campus communities nationwide. The majority of these cases are also never reported. Throughout this section, the scenario described above, based on an actual case, will be referenced to examine different responses, techniques, and strategies that could be used to ensure a proper "victim-centered" police response. The names and minor details have been changed to protect all involved.

Law Enforcement Response to Campus Cultures and Dynamics. As the police agency responding to this type of report, it is important that the officers understand the unique dynamics and culture of college campuses and the impact they have on reporting to law enforcement. The officer/investigator must realize that the traditional reporting channels and question responses may be contradictory to reactions from victims of other types of crime.

These distinctive mores play an intricate part of a police investigation. Some of the most prevalent differences will challenge traditional ways of thinking in relation to the reporting of a crime.

The successful investigation of any crime begins with two key elements: the victim's willingness to report and the ability to identify the perpetrator. Yet, unlike other crimes, most victims of nonstranger sexual assault on college campuses know or can easily identify their assailants. This information allows the law enforcement officer to have an advantage in investigating these types of crimes. But the victim must believe that a support system is in place throughout the campus, if she is going to cooperate and move forward with filing disciplinary or legal action against her attacker.

For the law enforcement officer responding to the report of a sexual assault on campus, many of these campus distinctions will play a major role in the investigation.

A good example of this distinction is "when a bed is not a bed?" Often, when dealing with students who live in a dormitory environment, the bed serves many purposes. Beds are used for a variety of reasons beyond sleeping or having sex, including: a couch or sitting area, a work station, a table to eat on, or even an ironing board. It is important to recognize that being on a bed with another person in a dormitory environment does not equate to intimacy. This is important to remember when responding to the scene or investigating the case. It will help the officer not fall into the trap of forming opinions or misinterpreting a crime scene. Being able to articulate this type of distinction will also aid in the prosecution of the case and help jury members and court officials understand "when a bed is not a bed."

Understanding and identifying some of these unique nuances will aid in a more effective law enforcement response.

Reporting Concerns. One of the major reasons for a victim to be unwilling to file a report is that the perpetrator is "everywhere" in her campus life. She may see the perpetrator in classes, in the dormitory, where she eats or socializes. This additional pressure and fear of constantly seeing the attacker will affect the victim's willingness to continue cooperating with authorities. In the case of Leslie, in our earlier example, Steve was a fraternity brother to the sorority she was pledging. She knew that she would be seeing Steve in most of her social circles. Unlike a stranger sexual assault, where the victim may never see her attacker again, Steve would be around Leslie throughout her college years.

Another concern in victim reporting, just like with Leslie, is that the perpetrator was not seen as a "rapist." The stereotypical image of a rapist is that of either a stranger hiding in the dark alley or the act of a violent psychotic person, but not of a well-known campus student like Steve. Leslie could not bring herself to see Steve as a rapist even though she knew what he had done was wrong. Too often, a victim blames herself for her role leading up to the assault. The victim questions if she led on the attacker or sent the "wrong message." Leslie's difficulty categorizing what type of perpetrator Steve was led to confusion about what action she should take. That is why it is important for police agencies to educate community members on what constitutes a sexual assault and what a person can do if she becomes a victim.

The victim's worry about reputation and social status being damaged in a non-stranger sexual assault is paramount in the reporting process. Leslie knew there would be a direct impact on her getting into and accepted by the sorority she was pledging if she was to have a fraternity brother arrested. In addition, Steve was well known on campus, and she was afraid that she would be labeled as a person who caused problems, and her actions would cause her to be ostracized by her peers. This is a serious concern for many victims, and law enforcement investigators need to recognize these issues in advance and help create strategies that would minimize victim exposure. In many incidents, this will be the first time the victim will be in a position to have another arrested or face internal disciplinary action. That is why it is important that the law enforcement officers ensure that the victim is aware and understands the criminal laws and court procedures along with the internal disciplinary actions that are available to her. In addition, the victim should be aware of both state and federal statutes that are in place to protect her. It is important that comprehensive programs are established on a campus to ensure information is available for all community members. In addition, it is important that a system for measuring the success of these programs is created, monitored, and updated on a regular basis.

Reporting Process. A very common response in these types of crimes involves delayed reporting. There are many reasons why this occurs. Too often, key factors play a role in delayed reporting, including social status, understanding legal and campus judicial systems, or fear of victim blaming. Statistical data show that many of the nonstranger sexual assault victims on campus report the crime to someone other than campus law enforcement. The majority of times, victims first report the assault to a friend or a peer. Other individuals who are notified include housing staff, professors, athletic coaches, and other campus officials who play a pivotal role in the victim's campus life. In addition, many students are unaware of the role of campus law enforcement, and they report the assault to an outside police agency. The statistical data support the need for a comprehensive training program that educates campus community members on sexual assault response awareness and protocols. Campus law enforcement should also work closely with the surrounding police agencies to inform them of the services available on the campus. This collaboration will also aid in a more effective monitoring of campus crime statistics.

Identifying Investigative "Speed Bumps." The investigative processes of these types of crimes are often counterintuitive to standard police investigative procedures. Officers who are involved in the investigations will need to recognize the "speed bumps" that are associated with victim reporting of nonstranger sexual assault.

A major speed bump is the victim's inability to legitimately recount the incident to a law enforcement officer. Victims give inconsistent statements in their reports in attempt to make all the pieces fit. There are a variety of reasons why victims react this way. In some cases, victims have been under the influence of drugs or alcohol and may not accurately be able to recall their or the perpetrators' actions leading up to and during the assaults. In other cases, the inability to recall details may be attributed to traumatic memory loss. That is why it is important that responding officers conduct extensive investigations, which include interviewing other people who were with the victims prior to and after the assaults. In cases where the victim cannot recount her actions due to a drug- or alcohol-induced state, proper evidence collection may be the only key to a successful prosecution.

Societal attitudes also influence how a victim may relate the sequence of events of the assault. Having knowledge of how her actions will be perceived will affect the accuracy of the details in her report. The law enforcement officer may also find that the victim will create a scenario that sounds like a "real rape" but is contrary to the evidence provided. This tends to create the feeling that the victim is purposely trying to misdirect the investigation. Officers interviewing a victim must remember that this is a defense mechanism that only time, trust, and good interview techniques will overcome.

An additional speed bump in the investigation is going to be victim credibility and reputation. This includes if there is a history of the victim reporting unsubstantiated incidents or if she has a reputation on campus as a "partier" or frequently "hooking up" with different partners. In these cases, the investigator needs to have the ability to be able to accurately recreate the scenario of the assault and weed out any victim, accused, and witness statements that cannot be substantiated. This not only effects the criminal investigation, but will also play a crucial role in the judicial process.

Victims also omit details of the assault because they fear exposing themselves as violators of an illegal act. A good example is that Leslie, in the earlier example, failed to mention her alcohol use to the police when she reported the assault because she was under the legal age to consume alcoholic beverages in this state. During subsequent interviews, she admitted she had consumed beer and was feeling the effects of it before falling asleep. When this happens, law enforcement officers may find themselves questioning the validity of the assault due to the inconsistencies in the report. This is especially true when the officers have other evidence contrary to the information being provided by the victim. But being able to recognize these various speed bumps will help ensure a more comprehensive investigation.

When interviewing victims, frequently investigators' speed bumps will include victims being uncomfortable with discussing their own or the perpetrator's sexual actions. The investigators should anticipate and be prepared with an alternate method of having victims relate what occurred. Quite often the victims' stories will either be very vague or extremely detailed. In many cases, like with Leslie, victims are comfortable describing the perpetrators' physical features and actions, but they are uneasy discussing their own body and reactions during the assault.

Nonstranger Sexual Assault Perpetrators. When perpetrators of these crimes are identified, they can be placed in basically two categories: "opportunist offender" or "serial offender."

The fact is that most college students eighteen to twenty-four years old will attend some type of party on or off campus during their college experience. At those parties, alcoholic beverages and or drugs will be available for consumption and use. There will be attendees who go to the parties with the desire to "hook up" (be with) with another. It is at that almost unmeasurable point when the natural desire of someone looking to be with another turns to intent, and, when that intent is acted upon, the actor becomes what is referred to as the "opportunist offender." The "opportunist offender" is the person who takes advantage of a situation when it arises. This is the offender that many campus law enforcement officials are likely to encounter and adds to why the numbers of nonstranger attempted or actual sexual assaults are so high on campuses nationwide.

The serial offender, as indentified by David Lisak (2002), is the person who in essence is setting the stage to commit sexual assault. An example of this behavior involves actions that include recruiting a young underage female student to a party he is hosting and setting up a bedroom in advance with the anticipation of engaging in and/or filming of sex with an intoxicated female. In addition, the serial offender will only consume "watered down" drinks with little or no alcohol in them, while providing the female guest with full-strength drinks.

The investigation of the "opportunist offender" is often more difficult because there was no initial intent to commit an assault, which may limit the availability of obtaining evidence and witnesses to the crime. This is opposed to the "serial offender" who has planned to commit an assault and more often has involved others in the arrangements, which may aid in providing witnesses in the case.

Both types of offenders are equally capable of committing the act of sexual assault. Their actions are motivated by the desire of the male to maintain control over the female. The officer should remember that the act of control is a key element in all sexual assault cases. In either case, the law enforcement officer must conduct a thorough investigation, canvass and recanvass the crime scene area and perimeter for other witnesses or evidence, and get into the habit of interviewing and reinterviewing witnesses and potential suspects until all leads in the case are exhausted. Having knowledge of the differences in the offenders' "methods of operations" will help guide the law enforcement officer in the criminal investigation.

It is inevitable that the "opportunist offender," if not stopped immediately, will become the "serial offender."

Stranger Sexual Assault

Victims of stranger sexual assault tend to respond and are often treated differently than those of a nonstranger sexual assault. One of the main differences is that the victims are more apt to report the assault immediately. The victims also appear to be more credible because they tend not to change their statements. In addition, more often the victim has injuries and displays more of the behaviors of the stereotypical sexual assault victim. Sometimes, responders tend to fall into the trap of treating victims of stranger sexual assault more seriously than those of a nonstranger assault. Both groups are true victims of the crime, and the response should never differ.

In the campus environment the Jeanne Clery Disclosure of Campus Security Policy and Campus Crime Statistics Act (Clery Act; 20 U.S.C. § 1092(f); see also Chapter 4 and Appendix D) requires colleges and universities to disclose certain timely and annual information about campus crime and security policies (Security on Campus, 2008). The act of stranger sexual assault would fall under this federal law, and the campus law enforcement or security agency is responsible for notifying community members of the threat on campus. That is why a system for timely notification must be incorporated into the department's regulations and periodically tested for its ability to reach a majority of community members. This system could include mass e-mail or text messaging notification.

When any serious crime occurs on a college campus, community members experience a certain amount of fear and anxiety. This is especially true with stranger sexual assault. The law enforcement or security agency must work diligently to keep community members feeling safe and informed without compromising the criminal investigation.

CONCLUSION

The law enforcement officer must work to maintain a victim-centered approach when responding to and investigating the report of any sexual assault. The officer can expect that no two victims will respond the same way when reporting or being interviewed about the assault. But, if the officer is well trained in dealing with victims of assault and can identify the nuances involved with this type of investigation when it occurs in a campus setting, there will be a much better chance of a successful outcome of the criminal case. It is imperative to remember that the victim's physical and psychological well-being and wishes are always the priority during the SART response.

References

Fisher, B. S., Cullen, F. T., & Turner, M. G. (2000, December). *The sexual victimization of college women.* Washington, DC: National Institute of Justice.

International Association of Chiefs of Police. (2005). *Model Policy on investigating sexual assaults.* Retrieved January 24, 2008, from http://www.iacp.org/research/VAWPoliceResponse.html# assault

Lisak, D. (2002, March). *The undetected rapist.* Boston: University of Massachusetts.

New Jersey Division of Criminal Justice. (2004, December). *Standards for providing services for survivors of sexual assault.* Retrieved September 14, 2008, from http://www.state.nj.us/ OAD/DCJ/AGGuide/standards/standardssartane.pdf

Security on Campus. The Jeanne Clery Act. Retrieved March 15, 2008, from http://www.security oncampus.org/schools/cleryact/index.html

Chapter 7

Role of the Rape Care Advocate

by Roberta Gibbons, M.A.

INTRODUCTION

No two victims of sexual assault are impacted in exactly the same way. As each person has her own upbringing, her own cultural background, and her own personal belief system, so too does each person have her own response to the experience of sexual assault. It is important to recognize this fact in a chapter on sexual assault advocacy because writing about a rape care advocate's or advocacy organization's (see Exhibit 7.1) response to sexual assault, one must generalize about what is needed by and what is helpful to victims of sexual assault. This does not mean that on-campus sexual assault organizations use a one-size fits all model of advocacy. Quite the contrary. Because advocates give options and not advice, there is plenty of room for taking into account differences in religion, race, ethnicity, sexual orientation, and ability status when working with victims. It is the job of the advocate to ensure that the victim has full knowledge of the available options and a chance to discuss what the possible consequences of pursuing (or not pursuing) each option may be. Advocates do not judge victims or push them into hasty decisions. Rather, it is the role of the advocate to answer the victim's question: "What can I do now?" Only the victim can determine what she *should* do now, and that "should" will probably be different from one victim to the next.

Although the experience of sexual assault and the road to recovery is an individual experience, there are some common feelings that victims report regardless of background and culture. Attending to these feelings, above all other goals, is one of the principle roles of the advocate as a part of a Sexual Assault Response Team (SART) and one of things that sets the advocate apart from other members of the SART. Other factors unique to advocates are confidentiality, an *a priori* belief that the victim is telling the truth, and an open-ended working relationship and time line for service.

The remainder of this chapter will discuss the unique characteristics of the advocate and how they impact her role on a SART. A general model of advocacy will be presented, and the factors specific to advocacy on a college campus will be delineated and explained, including the importance of on-campus partnerships. The chapter concludes with brief discussions of primary prevention on a college campus and evaluation of campus programming.

ROLE AND DISTINGUISHING CHARACTERISTICS OF THE RAPE CARE ADVOCATE

The rape care advocate may be the first person to meet with the victim, or she may be the last. The role of the advocate in general can change depending on whether the victim chooses to have an evidentiary exam and/or make a police report. As a member of the SART, the advocate is in a supportive role during a police report or evidentiary exam. The advocate does not speak for the victim or in any way become involved in the chain of custody of the evidence. Yet the advocate is present, supporting the victim with her presence, and ensuring that the victim understands what is happening and why. The advocate has a thorough knowledge of evidentiary exams, police investigations, and the criminal justice process. An on-campus advocate also understands the adjudication system at the university as well as rules about academics, credit load, and financial aid.

Confidentiality

It is impossible to overstate the importance of confidentiality to a successful campus advocacy program, and the promise of such confidentiality is one factor that sets apart the rape care advocate from other members of the SART. Victims of sexual assault are often very concerned about keeping their experience private. When a program guarantees confidentiality, within the limits of the law,[1] it increases the likelihood that victims will come forward and ask for help (Karjane, Fisher, & Cullen, 2005). For victims who choose not report their assault to the police and thus do not work with all members of the SART, their contact with an advocacy program is usually to attend to their own health and recovery. Knowing that they can receive information about their choices and at the same time keep complete control of their own experience/case encourages victims to seek help and learn about their options. The choice not to make an official report is respected by the advocate who will continue to offer support, counsel, and information to the victim.

Of course, if a victim has first contact with another member of the SART, the fact that she was assaulted will not be confidential because she will have already reported the assault to either law enforcement or a Sexual Assault Nurse Examiner (SANE). In these cases, it can still be comforting for the victim to have someone that she knows she can speak with confidentially. Interestingly, although the rate of reporting campus assaults to law enforcement is extremely low, less than 5 percent according to a study by National Institute of Justice (Fisher, Cullen, & Turner, 2000), a study of one well-established campus advocacy program in the Midwest found that a relatively large percentage of the victims it served made police reports (Gibbons, 2005). From 2001-2005, 31 percent of victims who had a single contact with the advocacy program made a police report, and 43 percent of victims who had multiple contacts with the advocacy program made police reports. This was true even though the advocacy program operates under a strict model of allowing victims to make their own choices These data seem to suggest that although victims may be drawn to an advocacy program because of its confidentiality, working with a supportive advocate and gaining a clear understanding of the criminal justice process may increase the likelihood of making a police report.

Finally, confidentiality is of special concern to college student victims because many of them are terribly afraid that their parents will find out about their assault. They fear that their parents will be disappointed, worried, angry, or tempted to "bring them home." Of course, talking about the assault with a parent is a great way for some victims to get the support and care they need. But the option of disclosing the assault to one's parents is certainly not right for everyone. A confidential advocacy program will not discuss the assault or anything else about a victim with anyone, parents included, unless the organization has written permission from the victim.

The need for confidentiality does not dictate that campus advocacy programs forego keeping records about how many people they serve, why those people sought services, and how representative their clients are of the population from which they are drawn (i.e., demographic information). Such information, when presented in the aggregate, should not violate confidentiality, and it helps to establish a continued need for such services as well as provide information to the program about what communities may not be accessing its services. Many universities are quite diverse, and since sexual assault knows no demographic bounds, information about who is and who is not being served can inform decision making about outreach and training on cultural competency.

The Campus Right to Know and Campus Security Act (adopted in 1990 and renamed the Jeanne Clery Disclosure of Campus Security Policy and Campus Crime Statistics Act (Clery Act; 20 U.S.C. § 1092(f); see also Chapter 4 and Appendix D) in 1998)

---

[1]There are limits placed on the confidentiality of advocates just as there are limits placed on the confidentiality of other helping professions. For example, if a person makes a serious threat that she is going to harm herself or another person, the advocate is required by law to report this information.

requires college campuses to report the number of *reported* sexual assaults that occur on campus (and within specified geographic bounds near campus). However, this law does *not* require the inclusion of those assaults that are "reported" only to a campus advocacy group (and not to the police or any university official). Despite this lack of requirement, some schools choose to include the number of assault victims seen by the advocacy program in their Clery numbers in order to give a more accurate representation of what is happening on campus. For these schools, record keeping takes on an added purpose.

Despite the importance of data, a balance must be struck between record keeping, confidentiality, and competent service. Victims who feel too much is being asked about them by their advocate may be hesitant to continue seeking services for fear of loss of privacy. Service for the victim always comes first, and questions about demographics and details can follow if appropriate.

A *Priori* Belief in the Truth of the Victim's Statement

Unlike the police and SANE nurses, rape care advocates do not have to be unbiased. In fact, it is the advocate's job to believe the victim and use language such as "I believe you" and "It was not your fault." Advocates are not part of the chain of evidence nor can they be called to testify except in the rarest of cases. An advocate's role is to offer counsel, support, assistance, and options, each with the assumption that the victim is telling the truth. The presence of an advocacy program that is confidential and offers support has been identified as a "promising practice" for universities nationwide (Karjane et al., 2005).

Open-Ended Working Relationship and Time Line

Because the needs of victims are different from one person to the next, the role of the rape care advocate can change from client to client. One person may need to be connected with counseling, another may want to pursue crime victim's reparations, and a third may desire a restraining order. The job of the advocate is to fulfill each of these needs or find someone who can. This is not to say that an advocate works without boundaries. In fact, boundaries are extremely important in advocacy because it is easy for a victim to begin to think of her advocate as a friend or as her main support person. The advocate should be neither. As important as friends and a support system are to victims of sexual assault, it is the advocate's duty to help navigate systems and give support throughout the process.

Some victims work with the advocate for only a brief time. They may receive initial crisis counseling and then pursue no further contact. Others can have a much longer working relationship with their advocates. Even after the close of a criminal case, difficult feelings about the assault can remain. Advocates are in a position to follow up with clients and to continue to offer assistance if, for example, a client has a new partner and is struggling with intimacy. Additionally, some victims feel they have come to a point of closure around their assault and then a year later find themselves dealing with nightmares again. Advocates discuss possibilities such as this with victims so that they feel comfortable reaching out for help—even a year (or two or three) later.

Attending to Feelings

Rape care advocates are in a unique position to spend more time with clients, offer support, and help to sort through feelings. Although each person responds differently to sexual assault, some feelings are quite common among victims. These include:

- Feelings of guilt, shame or self-blame;
- Shock, anger, and fear;
- Concern about intimacy and sexual relationships; inability to trust;
- Loss of control;
- Concern about the assailant; and
- Disruption of their daily life.

Many victims feel ashamed and guilty about the assault. The shame can lead victims to feel that they do not deserve help. They worry that they did not do enough to avoid being raped or that they made a bad decision that directly caused them to be raped. Some of these feelings are the result of society's myths about rape and sexuality. Sometimes blaming oneself helps a victim to feel less helpless, because she can then still retain the belief that she can avoid a future assault if she wants to.

Another common set of feelings is shock, anger, and fear. Victims are often in shock, disbelief, or even denial right after an assault. They may feel detached and isolated, unsure of what to do to get through the day (much less plan for tomorrow). These feelings may give way, in time, to anger about what happened and questions of "why me?" Finally, many victims experience a period of feeling afraid: afraid of their assailant; afraid people will be able to look at them and know that they were raped; afraid that it will happen again.

There are several sexual concerns that may worry victims. Right after an attack, victims may fear pregnancy or sexually transmitted diseases. Some may have a difficult time with intimacy or avoid it altogether; or perhaps certain sexual acts may trigger memories of the assault. Other victims may turn to sex for comfort and use it as a way to cope with their pain. Additionally, victims often have difficulty trusting others. They are unsure, too, of their own ability to make good decisions about whom to trust.

Perhaps more than anything else, a victim feels a loss of control. A sexual assault can really change one's perception of the world, and victims often feel disoriented and anxious. They may feel unsure about themselves and lack their usual self-confidence, even when making the smallest decisions. Finally, some victims may suffer acutely from diagnosable mental health disorders such as depression or posttraumatic stress disorder (PTSD).

All of the feelings mentioned above can result in a severe disruption to the daily life and routine of a victim. The victim may experience nightmares, shaking, inability to concentrate, and acute sadness. Her sleeping and eating patterns may change. She may wonder if her life will ever be normal again. Even though these are all normal reactions to an assault, they can make her feel like she is "losing it." Having one's life disrupted with such feelings can lead to difficulty at work or school and/or problems with one's family. It is the role of the advocate to attend to these feelings and to validate the concerns of the victim. The advocate can talk the victim through the difficult feelings and, if necessary, refer the victim to long-term counseling or a support group. The advocate can also address some of the concerns with information. For example, some victims may be anxious about and misunderstand the criminal justice process. Perhaps they believe that they are responsible for pressing charges against their assailant. It is the role of the advocate to explain that while the victim makes the report, it is the state that will "press charges" should there be the evidence to do so. This information may allay some of the anxiety of the victim, and she then may be more interested in making a report to the police.

MODEL OF ADVOCACY

Advocacy on a college campus in many ways mirrors advocacy in the broader community. Models of advocacy generally are built upon the ideas that (1) sexual assault is never the fault of the victim, and supporting victims is the most important job of the rape care advocate; (2) knowledge is power and, after support, sharing information is the principle task of the advocate; and (3) victims are the best equipped to make their own choices about what options they will pursue including if and when they will access available resources (such as the criminal justice system).

Only a small percentage of schools currently have on-campus advocacy programs, and another small number partner with community agencies to offer services on campus (Karjane, Fisher, & Cullen, 2002). Much like community-based organizations, university advocacy agencies seek to assist victims through any avenue that they choose to pursue and offer information about the possible consequences of the decisions they make regarding accessing health care, undergoing an evidentiary exam, making a police report, seeking counseling or a support group, or simply whom to tell about the assault. Thus, for example, a campus-based program may offer the following services that may also be available at community-based agencies:

- *24-hour crisis line, operational 7 days/week, 365 days/year.* This service enables access to an advocate whenever the victim needs one.

- *Walk-in crisis counseling during business hours.* Many victims choose to talk with someone in person, and drop-in hours allow for such a meeting without an appointment.

- *Telephone or walk-in referral services for victims seeking long-term counseling, therapy, TANF assistance, etc.* Some victims have needs that a sexual assault agency may not be able to meet. Many sexual assault agencies have a comprehensive list of referrals and will assist the victim in finding what she needs.

- *Accompaniment for an evidentiary exam.* Victims may want to have evidence of their assault collected for the purpose of prosecution. This option provides for the inclusion of another SART member, the SANE, who provides this service; and hospitals and campus health centers will also attend to the health care needs of the victim in addition to the collection of evidence. Advocates are sometimes present during these exams, supporting and comforting the victim through the process.

- *Accompaniment to hospital emergency room or health clinic for health care concerns.* Some victims do not want to undergo an evidentiary exam or are not candidates for such an exam (if, e.g., the assault took place more than three days prior[2] to the victim coming forward). These victims may still need health care, and an advocate can help to locate such care and offer support and comfort to the victim.

- *Arrange for alternate safe housing.* Most victims of sexual assault are attacked by someone they know and often in their own homes. Victims need to feel safe

---

[2]There is some disagreement about how much time can pass before an evidentiary exam becomes irrelevant. Many SANE programs follow the seventy-two-hour model, some use a shorter time frame, and still others consider exams on a case-by-case basis (e.g., there may still be tearing and bruising for many days after the seventy-two-hour window).

in their homes in order to work towards a healthy recovery. Advocates can assist the victim to locate safe housing and to work through whatever is necessary to terminate a lease and find a sublettor.

- *Act as a liaison.* Advocates can act as a liaison between victims and professionals in the criminal justice system including the police and prosecuting attorney. The criminal justice process can be confusing, intimidating, or even scary for victims. Many choose not to report their assault, and this choice is their absolute prerogative. However, should a victim choose to report, advocates can explain the process, provide support during a police interview, expedite communication between the victim and criminal justice professionals, and see to it that the victim has full information about her case as it makes it way through the criminal justice system. Advocates can also accompany the victim to court if the case is prosecuted.

- *Provide support groups.* Many agencies have in-house support groups for victims. Support groups allow victims to hear the stories of other victims and work together toward recovery. Some support groups may be specific to a certain age group, ethnicity, sexual orientation, or religion.

- *Provide legal advocacy.* Those victims who are assaulted by someone with whom they have a prior (or current) intimate relationship are eligible to request a restraining order. Additionally, in some states, a single sexual assault meets the criteria for obtaining a restraining order against one's assailant. Agencies that provide legal advocacy: (1) assist victims with writing the affidavit for an order of protection or harassment restraining order, (2) file the order in the appropriate county, and (3) accompany the victim to court for any required hearings. Some agencies also provide transportation to and from court for the victim.

- *Assist with crime victim reparations and restitution.* If a victim chooses to make a police report, she will most likely be eligible to apply for crime victims' reparations. Although laws differ from state to state, often these funds can help to defray the cost of medical bills, counseling services, lost wages, funerals, and child care. Victims can also apply for restitution to cover other costs such as damage to property. Crime victims' reparations are funded by the state or county, and restitution is paid by the offender, if convicted. Advocates can aid victims in learning about these options and filling out the necessary paperwork.

This list of available services through campus programs or community-based agencies is not exhaustive. Many community-based agencies offer a broader range of services including long-term therapy, housing, child care, employment advocacy, culturally specific services, health care, and a host of other options that will assist a victim to her full recovery. Still, this list of options is a fair representation of the help available to a victim of sexual assault in the broader community.

SEXUAL ASSAULT ON THE COLLEGE CAMPUS

The advocacy services listed above are helpful to victims of sexual assault regardless of where the crime occurred. However, the experience of sexual assault victims on a college campus can be different from the experience of a victim not affiliated with a college or university. The concerns of and options available to victims of sexual assault on a college campus are shaped by factors unique to a university setting. Advocacy on the college campus is designed to address the specific concerns that arise from these factors in addition to the more general concerns of victims.

> *Example:* Shawna was sexually assaulted. She feels afraid and is unsure whom to trust. She is having nightmares and having trouble concentrating. She fears leaving her home and is concerned about pregnancy and sexually transmitted diseases. Sometimes she feels sick and cannot explain it. She is angry, sad, and confused. She wonders if she will ever be able to have a "normal" intimate relationship. She sometimes blames herself.

There is nothing surprising in Shawna's reactions to her assault. Thus far, Shawna could be a victim of sexual assault anywhere in the world. But, in addition to the challenging emotional and physical reactions to sexual assault that Shawna experiences, there are situational factors on a college campus that can complicate her recovery. Shawna may live in the same residence hall as her attacker. He may sit next to her in class. Shawna's friends may also be friends with the person who raped her. Especially if she is a new student, Shawna may have no support network to turn to for comfort. These additional variables can complicate an experience of sexual assault, exacerbate the negative feelings that accompany an assault, and hinder recovery from such an assault. Each of these factors is discussed in detail below.

The first of these situational factors is a shared social group. An overwhelming majority of sexual assaults, and, of course, all dating/relationship violence, occur between two people who know each other (Fisher et al., 2000). In a campus environment, the victim and perpetrator often share the same group of friends. Additionally, many students on campus who experience interpersonal violence share a cocurricular activity in a student group (such as band, dance, athletics, or Pan-Hellenic membership) with their perpetrator. This common network of friends and support people complicates a victim's decision to report the crime to police or even to tell any of her friends about the experience. Victims fear that they will not be believed and that they will be "dropped" by their group of friends if they accuse someone within that group of hurting them. Attending college away from their hometown and traditional support network can exacerbate this problem even further.

If they previously had a close relationship with the perpetrator, victims are often concerned that they will "ruin the perpetrators life" if they tell anyone, especially the police. Many victims do not want to force their friends to take sides, and they fear that this is what would happen if their experience became public. When victims share a cocurricular activity with their perpetrator, they are often forced to face that perpetrator every day as they pursue their interest in that group/activity. This can impact a victim's ability to classify the experience as "violence" because the offensive act was committed by someone that not only the victim, but many of her friends, has interactions with on a regular basis. A shared social group is one of the many reasons why victims of interpersonal violence on campus have an astonishingly low rate of reporting the crimes against them to the police.

A second complicating factor of campus sexual assaults is shared living space. Some victims of interpersonal violence on campus share a residence hall or other living quarters with their perpetrator. This fact can increase their danger, fear, and confusion about the violence. If the student is a victim of relationship violence, all of the dangers associated with cohabitating with the abuser apply. More unique to colleges is the likelihood that victims of *sexual assault* will share living space with their perpetrator. In both cases, the victim may have concerns about seeing the perpetrator in the dining hall, the stairway, or the lounge area. Shared living quarters can increase a feeling of vulnerability and can have real implications for the safety of victims of campus violence.

Third, many, undergraduate students are financially dependent on their parents. For these students, this often includes subscribing to their parents' health insurance. If students need to access medical care due to a sexual assault or injury relating from a violent relationship, they may have concerns about a parent finding out about what happened. They view their victimization as a failure on their own part and are concerned that they may anger, disappoint, or be blamed by their parents. For this reason, some victims of interpersonal violence on campus do not seek medical attention nor, for cases of sexual assault, do they seek to have an evidentiary exam performed. Again, the unique circumstances of campus violence negatively affect the likelihood of reporting and prosecution of interpersonal violence.

Fourth, excessive alcohol consumption is generally considered a risk factor for perpetrating sexual assault, and it can also be a risk factor for becoming a victim of sexual assault. Alcohol is often used by perpetrators to (1) render their victims more vulnerable through intoxication and (2) excuse their own behavior. Although many college students do not drink and, of those who do, most do not abuse alcohol, it remains true that alcohol is a complicating factor in a significant portion of campus violence incidents. Those victims who were drinking or using other drugs prior to their assault are often reticent to make a police report because they fear they will be cited (if they are underage or the drug use is illegal) or they blame themselves for their assault because they were too under the influence to deter their assault.

INSTITUTIONAL FACTORS

Universities have an interest in appearing to be safe. They must recruit students, please parents, and win donations. However, the reality of campus violence can lead potential stakeholders to question the safety of the campus. Some universities unintentionally discourage reporting and help-seeking by victims (see Exhibit 7.2). For example, they may distribute materials about self-defense and other risk reduction measures without balancing them with a message to perpetrators regarding their sole responsibility for committing the crime. Such materials can influence victims to blame themselves because they did not stop the crime from happening, and victims who blame themselves are much less likely to make a report. In an effort to show concern for safety, some universities have also invested in "blue lights" and safety call boxes, which do not address the fact that most sexual assaults occur in the home of either the victim or perpetrator.

These situational factors can be addressed, some to a greater extent than others, through options and advocacy services that are specific to the college campus, including:

- Academic advocacy;
- Housing/residential life advocacy;
- Financial aid advocacy;
- Student judicial affairs advocacy;
- On-campus support groups;

- On-campus legal advocacy; and

- University systems and policy advocacy.

These are all discussed in the following sections.

Academic Advocacy

Most campus-specific services require strong partnerships between campus advocates and other university offices (see "On-Campus Partnerships" below).

Imagine that Shawna, in the example above (see "Sexual Assault on the College Campus"), is having trouble sleeping and concentrating. These common responses to an assault could affect her performance in classes. *Academic advocacy* involves working with Shawna and her professors/instructors to ensure that the effects of the assault do not detrimentally affect her status as a student in good standing. Academic advocacy involves talking with the victim about what she needs to successfully complete her classes and then contacting her professors on her behalf (and only with her permission) to request accommodation.

Academic advocacy can include requests for extensions on deadlines for homework, exam accommodations such as requesting extra time, retaking an examine that may have been administered only a few days after the assault, or having a private space in which to take the exam. If the victim shares a class with her perpetrator, the first choice is always to have the offending student change classes (through some institutional mechanism such as the student judicial affairs system). However, if the victim does not wish to report the assault to the institution, or if the institution's adjudication process moves slowly, the victim may wish to move to a different section of the class or change classes altogether. As a motion of last resort, the victim may want to request an incomplete for the course or withdraw from the course. This final option, a course withdrawal, must be handled with great care as it may affect a students financial aid status, and some schools place a limit on the number of "W's" (withdrawals) that can appear on a student's transcript.

Most professors are understanding about extreme circumstances such as those that are presented when a student is a victim of sexual assault. Academic advocacy is really a practice whereby the rape care advocate works to help the victim communicate with her professors about a personal and painful experience. Unless a school has a specific policy about how its professors deal with the requests of sexual assault victims and that policy states that requests will be fulfilled, the success of requests for academic accommodations should not be promised to victims like Shawna. Rather, academic advocacy is presented as an option with a good track record of securing some relief for victims of sexual assault, as long as they agree to disclose to their professors that they are working with a campus sexual assault program.

Housing/Residential Life Advocacy

If the victim lives in a residence hall or other campus-sponsored housing, there are several reasons why there may be a need to arrange for safe, alternate on-campus housing. First, the assault may have occurred in the victim's place of residence. She may feel unsafe remaining there; or, the living quarters may serve as a constant reminder of her victimization. Second, the perpetrator may share her residence hall or apartment building, thus increasing the chance that she will see him on a regular basis. Third, the "story" of her assault may be circulating throughout her place of residence, and this can increase the stress and discomfort she feels. In any of these situations, it is the role of the rape care advocate to work closely with the housing and residential life staff to ensure a quick and quiet change of address for the victim if she so requests. Some universities have a policy of moving accused perpetrators when a report is made either to the police or to student judicial affairs (and the perpetrator shares a residence hall or apartment building with the victim). School policies differ on whether a student accused of sexual assault is automatically moved if he shares the same residence as the victim.[3]

The option of changing rooms should be offered to the victim as well, especially if she was assaulted in her room or if the assault has become public information. This option is perhaps easier for some universities than others. Large universities with a significant on-campus population often have an empty space into which the victim can move. Smaller universities may have a more difficult time finding space quickly and may need to investigate other possibilities. The task of the advocate is to work with whatever system response is available and make sure that the victim has complete knowledge of her options.

Housing advocacy can aid victims regardless of the school's policy on perpetrator relocation. Housing advocacy involves working with the university's housing authorities to find a space for the victim to relocate should she choose to do so. As previously mentioned, a victim may want to move because she shares living space with her attacker. She may also seek relocation because she was assaulted in her room or apartment, and it is not a safe space for her (regardless of where the perpetrator lives). Finally, some victims may want to move because friends of the perpetrator may share her living space, or the "rumor mill" may be very active at her place of residence. Many victims who live on campus will request to stay on campus, and it is this type of relocation that requires a strong partnership between campus advocates and the university's office of housing and residential life. If a victim wishes to move off campus, the search for appropriate housing would mirror the type of work done by off-campus, community-based advocacy agencies.

Financial Aid Advocacy

If a student withdraws from a class after the university's tuition refund deadline, she may be able to petition for a retroactive tuition refund. This process differs from school to school, but it nearly always involves paperwork and tenacity—two things that a rape care advocate can help with if the victim is in need of assistance. Additionally, if a student wishes to withdraw from one or more classes, this may trigger the need for *financial aid advocacy*. Loans and grants almost always carry with them a minimum credit load requirement. If a student drops below this level, she may be faced with losing her award or having to pay a portion of it back. Financial aid advocacy involves working with the financial aid office and the victim to make sure that the student has a clear understanding of what the financial consequences will be if there is any change

---

[3]Many schools that require a student accused of sexual assault to be moved also have requirements of relocation regarding students accused of other serious crimes. Relocation refers to finding the accused student a comparable living space in another university-sponsored housing facility. Unless the nonnegotiable conditions are delineated beforehand, accused students generally will not have their housing contract completely cancelled without some sort of adjudication process.

in her student status (i.e., from full time to part time) and, if possible, to work with the loan- or grant-making authority directly to request that the victim not incur a penalty for dropping below the credit minimum.

Student Judicial Affairs Advocacy

Another type of advocacy specific to college campuses is *student judicial affairs (SJA) advocacy*. Colleges and universities have specific rules and standards of behavior for their students. Some of these rules and standards mirror state law (i.e., rules about theft and underage drinking), and some are specific to the context of the university (i.e., prohibitions of waterbeds in the residence halls, rules about cheating). Although university rules and standards for student conduct differ from school to school, the student conduct code of many universities specifically addresses and defines sexual assault.[4] The Office of Student Judicial Affairs is the campus body that adjudicates violations of a university's student conduct code (see Chapter 5 of this volume for more information on SJA).

Although making a report to SJA is an option for victims, most of them do not understand the process or what will be required of them as a complainant. Victims are often nervous about telling their story to another person and the possibility of facing the perpetrator in a hearing. SJA advocacy involves explaining the process to the victim, accompanying the victim to the SJA office, giving support to the victim throughout the process, including at a hearing if necessary, and serving as a liaison between the office and the victim if the victim so requests. For example, perhaps the victim mentions to her rape care advocate that she fears seeing her perpetrator and is very anxious about spending hours with him in the same room. If a hearing is scheduled, the victim may wish to request to be in a separate room and participate by videotape. The advocate can make this request on behalf of the victim. Furthermore, if the victim makes a police report, the advocate can help her understand the boundaries around these separate systems of adjudication. SJA protocols differ from one university to another. It is the role of campus advocates to make sure that the victim has full knowledge of both the process of SJA and expectations that will be placed on her, so that she can make an informed choice about whether or not to report her assault to that office.

Both SJA and the criminal justice system give the victim the opportunity to hold her perpetrator accountable. These systems of adjudication are a good option for some victims, but not for all. For example, some victims feel so much shame that they do not want anyone to find out about their assault. Some victims fear their attacker and are afraid to "set him off" with an official report. Many victims are concerned they will not be believed or they are worried about being hurt, rather than helped, by "the system." Still other victims think they can handle their experience, and they do not even tell a friend or an advocacy organization about their assault until a month or a year after it happened, making their assaults unlikely candidates for adjudication or prosecution. For these victims, the main concern is for a healthy recovery from the assault. An on-campus support group can be a good option for such victims.

---

[4]Four-year colleges and private nonprofit schools are the most likely to have a written sexual assault policy; and of those schools with policies, about half delineate specific goals of the policy (Karjane et al., 2005).

On-Campus Support Groups

On-campus support group*s* give victims a safe space to tell their stories and receive validation and support from others who have had similar experiences. Although many community agencies have support groups, holding a group on campus for students gives college victims both convenience and the knowledge that the others in the group will share some basic similarity to them. For those with a primary focus on recovery rather than accountability for the perpetrator, on-campus support groups can create a circle of understanding and affirmation. Of course, these groups can be very helpful to victims who make police reports and/or seek accountability through SJA as well.

On-Campus Legal Advocacy

Legal advocacy refers to assisting victims in their interactions with the civil and/ or criminal justice system. There are two types of legal advocacy: civil court legal advocacy and criminal court legal advocacy. In most states, if a victim is assaulted by someone with whom she has an intimate relationship, she can pursue a civil restraining order against her perpetrator. Some states also allow victims to request restraining orders against their perpetrators regardless of the prior relationship (or lack thereof) between the two. On-campus *civil court legal advocacy* includes writing restraining orders for victims, filing the orders in the appropriate county (or other designated jurisdiction), and accompanying the victim to court should the perpetrator (identified as the "respondent" on the affidavit for the order) request a hearing. The legal advocate does not represent the victim and thus cannot speak for her in court. However, the advocate can sit with the victim, explain the process and what to expect, and offer support for the victim.

By providing the writing of orders on campus, civil court legal advocates are able to meet with the victim in a safe, nonintimidating environment and take the time necessary to explain the process and possible consequences of applying for an order. Of course, civil court legal advocates need special training beyond crisis advocacy training in order to learn the intricacies of writing orders, presenting the order to a judge for signing, and filing the order. Such advocates also need to walk a fine line between sharing knowledge and insight about the legal system and giving legal advice.

Criminal court legal advocacy refers to helping victims understand and maneuver through the processes of investigation and prosecution. Because these systems can be confusing and intimidating, the advocate's role is to explain the process and offer support throughout it, including going to court with the victim should the case make it to trial. Advocates can also assist victims with filing for reparations or restitution. Victims often benefit from having someone confidential to talk with who also has significant knowledge about the criminal justice system and their rights as victims within that system.

University Systems and Policy Advocacy

Many universities have made great strides in their policies and procedures regarding how sexual assault cases are handled on campus. However, there is still much work left to done to ensure that victims encounter a supportive system when and if they report their assault to campus authorities. University *systems advocacy* refers to the work of advocates on behalf of victims at the policy and protocol level. For example, if a campus decides to allocate some money for sexual assault prevention, sexual violence advocates would work to ensure that the money is directed to effective services and/or outreach. In other words, advocates would request that financial backing be given to primary prevention programs or direct victims' services rather than "blue lights" or self-defense courses for women, both of which address stranger rape much more than acquaintance rape. Systems advocacy can be tricky, especially on a college campus where sexual assault programs are often funded by the very institution that advocates are trying to change or improve. Despite this challenge, systems advocacy is an important part of campus advocacy for sexual assault victims because the outcomes of systems advocacy affect many, if not all, victims of sexual assault on campus.

PARTNERSHIPS

Just as a successful SART requires strong collaboration between nurses, law enforcement, prosecutors, and rape care advocates, so too does advocacy on a college campus require partnerships with campus departments. Two of the most important partnerships are with university housing/residential life and the Office of SJA. This section briefly describes the working relationships between advocates, police, and SANE programs, and then turns to the on-campus partnerships with housing and SJA.

Partnership Between Rape Care Advocates, Police, and SANEs

There are two basic models of collaboration between on-campus rape care advocates, the police, and SANE programs. Some universities have their own police force, health centers, and emergency rooms. On campuses as such, the advocate will work with others familiar with the university and its policies. Where the police and health providers are not directly on campus, the advocate will need to make sure that university policies are conveyed to these vital partners. Examples of policies that may be significant to off-campus police and SANE partners include (1) the requirement that any case of sexual assault reported to the police must also be adjudicated through the university's system or (2) the option of changing the on-campus residence of either the perpetrator and/or the victim. In addition to sharing information on university policies and protocol, the on-campus advocate works as part of the SART much the same way that a community advocate would. The advocate may be present during a police interview and/or a SANE exam, act as a liaison between the police and the victim, and provide follow-up care and support after forensic evidence collection. In both police interviews and evidentiary exams, the role of the advocate is one of support. The advocate does not speak for the victim at any time (in order to avoid becoming part of the chain of evidence).

On-Campus Partnerships

The department of housing is an important partner because the staff members who live with the students (on the same floor or in the same building) often have a good pulse on what is happening in the residence hall. A resident or community advisor is sometimes the first person to whom a victim discloses her assault. It is imperative that housing staff knows how to respond to a disclosure and what the available resources are for the victim; yet, a recent study found that only 40 percent of schools offer any sexual assault training (Karjane et al., 2005). Some campuses require their resident advisors (RAs) to share information about a sexual assault with their supervisor and/ or the housing judicial officer. In such cases, the victim does not have control of what happens with her case once she tells her RA. Other schools grant confidentiality to their RAs about this issue. Regardless of school policy on confidentiality, an RA should not be expected to handle the sexual assault of a student on his/her own. One of the first calls an RA should make is to on-campus rape care advocates (or community advocates) who are trained to deal with crisis situations.

In addition to working together to respond to the immediate crisis of a sexual assault, residence life staff and the advocate often work together if the victim needs a change in her living situation in order to feel safe and hasten moves when needed to ensure a smooth transition to new living quarters for the victim.

When a student sexually assaults another student, the option to pursue action through SJA is available to the victim. The SJA may depend on the advocate to explain the university's adjudication process to the victim and to offer such adjudication as one of the options for the victim to pursue. The advocate and the SJA officer(s) work together to ensure that the victim receives and understands all necessary communication about her case as well as to do what they can to make the process as smooth as possible for the victim. There are several things that a university can do to make its process of adjudication more "victim friendly" such as requiring that hearing board members receive adequate training on sexual assault dynamics and myths and offering the option of a video-conferenced hearing for victims fearful of sharing a hearing room with their attackers.

In addition to the partnerships with housing and residential life and SJA, campus advocates also have collaborations or at least interaction with several other units including: student counseling centers, the women's center, the gay, lesbian, bisexual, transgender (GLBT) programs office, diversity units, disability services, academic affairs, the department of athletics, the student health center, faith-based groups, and Greek life.

EVALUATING SERVICES FOR VICTIMS

Rape care advocates exist to serve and support victims in their recovery. On a college campus, in addition to reaching a healthy emotional state, a "successful recovery" probably includes aspects of continuing one's education as planned, passing classes to the best of one's ability, and finding a supportive social network. The attainment of these additional goals of a campus advocacy program can be a challenge to measure.

Evaluating advocacy services, in general, has proven to be complicated (Zweig and Burt, 2002), and assessing how well campus advocates serve victims of sexual assault is no less difficult. First, there is not an easily accessible comparison group. That is, it is difficult to find and speak with victims who experienced sexual assault while attending college but who did not seek the assistance of an advocate. Such a task may be accomplished through a large-scale research effort, but most campus advocacy organizations do not have the resources or time to undertake such a project. Second, although there is anecdotal evidence about individuals who left school because they were sexually assaulted, it is nearly impossible to track all students who leave the university and question them about the reason(s) for their departure. However, because universities are concerned with academic performance and retention, as well as the healthy emotional lives of their students, it makes sense for campus advocacy programs to make some efforts at evaluating the impact of their services on academic performance and retention, as well as on a victim's emotional recovery.

One relatively simple way to demonstrate process and outcome successes is to keep careful count of services provided, numbers of victims (and other clients[5]) served, and time spent with each victim. These measures help to demonstrate the need that is being filled by campus advocates. A second evaluative undertaking that will help to document impact is to ask victims to rate how the services received affected their recovery in several areas including emotional health, social support network, academic success, and the decision to remain in school. Victims who volunteer to answer such questions (in survey form, for example) may not be entirely representative of those served, but asking such questions can result in responses that are both informative and illuminating. This method, although not scientific, is one way to document personal stories of service impact. For example, one campus advocacy program serving a large urban campus in the Midwest used this method and was able to report:

> The Center has an impact on students' academic achievement as well as the decision to continue as a student at the University. About one third (35.3 percent) of responding clients reported that "The Center's services helped me to stay in school." Clients also reported that the concerns that brought them to the Center negatively affected their grades (35.3 percent), academic work (64.7 percent) and plans to continue enrollment (29.4 percent). Finally, it was reported that working with the Center positively affected students' grades (23.5 percent), academic work (41.2 percent) and plans to continue enrollment (29.4 percent). (Gibbons, 2007)

PRIMARY PREVENTION

Advocacy for victims of sexual assault aims to decrease the negative consequences of a sexual assault and hastens a healthy recovery. Obviously, this is an important service for individual victims; yet, as a tactic of prevention, advocacy is best categorized as *tertiary* prevention, that is, the focus of advocacy as the prevention of further damaging effects. Some campuses with advocacy programs also have initiatives that address only *primary* prevention, where the focus is on preventing the problematic behavior before it occurs. Primary prevention thus concentrates on tools, methods, and curricula that view the problem of sexual violence as an issue of perpetrators making the bad choice to sexually assault someone.[6] As opposed to risk reduction for potential victims (which is secondary prevention), primary prevention focuses on the risk factors associated with being a perpetrator of a sexual assault (at all ecological levels including the individual, relational, social, and community). This focus sends a

---

[5]Many campus programs serve both victims of sexual assault as well as people concerned about a friend or loved one who is a victim. These "concerned persons" can thus also be clients at an on-campus sexual assault advocacy program.

[6]See Katz (1995) for further discussion of primary prevention ally behavior.

message that sexual assault is never the fault of the victim and thus can help to create a climate where victims are less likely to blame themselves and more likely to report their assault to law enforcement or at least seek advocacy services.

Some universities are currently using a bystander approach to sexual violence prevention, which has been called a "best practices model" by the U.S. Department of Justice (Karjane et al., 2005). This model defines sexual assault as both a men's and women's issue and calls on all students to be a part of the solution to the high incidence of sexual violence on campus. Students are encouraged to consider sexual violence on a continuum and given the tools to do something—rather than nothing—when they are bystanders to violence, whether it be on the less severe end of the continuum (e.g., cat calling, rape jokes) or the more serious end (e.g., witnessing someone leading a very drunk woman into a room at a party).

SUMMARY

This chapter has provided a comprehensive description of the role of the rape care advocate in response to sexual assault victims. On campuses, the traditional role is further expanded to assist in addressing the unique needs of campus victims. These include advocacy for academic accommodations, housing financial aid, and judicial affairs. Through extensive partnerships with campus departments and community resources, the rape care advocate is an essential component of the SART response and a primary factor in meeting the needs of campus victims as well as supporting primary prevention initiatives for the college community.

References

Fisher, B. S., Cullen, F. T., &Turner, M. G. (2000, December). *The sexual victimization of college women.* Washington, DC: National Institute of Justice.

Gibbons, R. E. (2005). *Police reports of clients: 2001-2005.* Unpublished report, Aurora Center for Advocacy and Education, University of Minnesota.

Gibbons, R. E. (2007). *Assessment brief: 2007 client satisfaction survey.* Unpublished report, Aurora Center for Advocacy and Education, University of Minnesota.

Karjane, H. M., Fisher, B. S., & Cullen, F. T. (2005, December). *Sexual assault on campus:What colleges and universities are doing about it.* Washington, DC: U.S. Department of Justice, National Criminal Justice Reference Service.

Karjane, H. M., Fisher, B. S., & Cullen, F. T. (2002). *Campus sexual assault: How America's institutions of higher education respond.* Final report. Newton, MA: Education Development Center.

Katz, J. (1995). Reconstructing masculinity in the locker room: The Mentors in Violence Prevention Project. *Harvard Educational Review, 65*(2), 163-174.

Zweig, J. M. & Burt, M. R. (2002). *The complexities of victim research: Implementation lessons from the Victim Impact Evaluation of Nonprofit Victim Services in the STOP Program.* Washington, DC: National Institute of Justice.

Exhibit 7.1
What Is a Rape Care Advocate

Sometimes victims have questions about what a rape care advocate is and what she/he can do. The following information is a summary of information commonly seen in brochures given to clients when they access services at a campus-based program.

An advocate is a person who talks with you and gives you options so that you can make the best choices. Advocates are trained crisis counselors who are knowledgeable about health care, victims' rights, the criminal justice system, and the resources available. They can answer questions about your options and how things work. They also understand that you may not want to make a decision right now. Advocates will not pressure you towards one choice or another. You will make your own decisions.

Advocates want to help.

People become advocates because they want to help other people. Oftentimes, a person who experiences a crisis can use the help of someone who is caring, compassionate, and knowledgeable. An advocate can be that "someone."

You will make your own decisions.

Any decision you make now belongs to you. Your advocate will not pressure you to choose one option over another. Advocates will explain your options and help you to sort through them, but they will not make decisions for you. For example, if you decide that you do not want to make a police report, the advocate will support that decision. If you change your mind and choose to make a police report in the future, the advocate will support you, help you to make the necessary contacts, and be present with you when you make the report, if you so choose.

It was not your fault.

The advocate knows that a rape, relationship violence, and stalking are never the fault of the victim. Even if you place some of the blame on yourself right now, the advocate will never say or believe that it was your fault. Never.

Any information you share with an advocate is confidential.

Confidentiality is the foundation of our work. We will not discuss any information you give us with anyone, unless you ask us to do so and give us permission in writing. Even if someone says that she/he just wants to know how you are doing, we tell him/her that we cannot affirm or deny whether you are working with us. Simply put—we will not tell anyone—not the police, not your family, not your friends—that you are working with us, unless you ask us to.

Limits: For your protection and the protection of others, most states have laws that place limits on confidentiality. If you state that you seriously intend to harm yourself or another person, we are mandated by law to report such intent. We also must report if: there is suspicion of child or elder abuse or neglect; you are pregnant and using illegal drugs; and/or if you were abused by a psychologist or psychiatrist.

Advocates will believe you.

Unlike the police or medical professionals, it is *not* the role of the advocate to be "unbiased." *It is the advocate's job to believe you*, to support you, and to help you get connected to the resources that you need.

An advocate is different than a friend.

Lots of people need a friend when they are hurting, and friends can assist in a person's journey towards recovery. However, an advocate is different than a friend in many ways. Sometimes people turn to a friend for advice, but an advocate will never tell you what to do. Instead, the advocate will help you to understand the choices that you have, and what the consequences of those choices may be. Some friendships last a lifetime, but an advocate's job is time-limited. It is the advocate's role to support you through your immediate crisis and to make sure that you're connected with the resources you need. The advocate's knowledge of resources will help you to make the best choice for yourself.

Advocates will never judge you or your decisions.

The right decision for one person may not be the right decision for the next. An advocate understands that there are as many "right" ways to do things as there are people. Even if you feel you have made some "bad" decisions, you can trust the advocate not to blame or judge you. Even if you decide you don't want to "do anything" now, the advocate will support that decision. No matter what you've done or decide to do in the future, the advocate will respect you and the decisions you make.

Exhibit 7.2
Encouraging and Discouraging Reporting on Campus

The following information is adapted from Karjane, Fisher, & Cullen (2005).

Discouraging practices:

- *Policies on drug and alcohol use.* In and of themselves, these policies seek to curb unhealthy and illegal behavior by students. However, victims of sexual assault who were drinking or using other drugs before they were assaulted may be less likely to report for fear of criminal repercussions for their own behavior. Schools that have such policies should be clear about what victims can expect when reporting their sexual assault.

- *The requirement that victims participate in adjudication.* If a victim is forced to participate in on campus adjudication (or criminal prosecution) when she makes a report, then "making a report" is a much more significant decision than if a victim knows that she can make a report and decide at another time in which processes she does and does not wish to participate.

- *Messages that stress victim responsibility.* Messages about self-defense and risk reduction must be balanced with the messages about the perpetrator's responsibility for committing a crime. If all a victim is exposed to are messages that intimate that she could have stopped the rape if she had tried hard enough, she may be less likely to report her assault.

- *Trauma response.* High levels of psychological distress and trauma may lead to underreporting.

- *Stigma of being "a victim."* Victims often desire to avoid the perceived—and real—stigma of being labeled a "rape victim."

Practices that promote reporting:

- *Services for victims.* An on-campus or community-based sexual assault advocacy program—that is known and trusted by the students—can promote reporting.

- *Written law enforcement response protocols.* Law enforcement that follows consistent and publicized procedures (i.e., not ticketing for underage drinking when someone reports an assault) can encourage reporting.

- *Information sharing at new student orientation.* Students only know about policies and services if they are told about them. Including information on available advocacy services as well as policies on consequences for perpetrators in new student orientation may promote reporting.

- *Policies on confidential and anonymous reporting.* Universities that allow victims to make a report confidentially and/or anonymously may experience higher rates of reporting.

- *Violence prevention program/peer educator program.* Educational programs that include information on rape awareness, available services, and primary prevention can help to remind students throughout the course of their college careers that the perpetrator is responsible for a sexual assault and what to do if they or someone they know experiences sexual assault.

Chapter 8

Forensic Medical Examination of the Sexual Assault Victim

by Donna M. Barry, APN, FN-CSA

A timely, well-done medical forensic examination can potentially validate and address sexual assault patients concerns, minimize the trauma they may experience, and promote their healing. At the same time, it can increase the likelihood that evidence collected will aid in criminal case investigation, resulting in perpetrators being held accountable and further sexual violence prevented. (United States Department of Justice Office on Violence Against Women [U.S. DOJ], 2004)

HISTORY OF MEDICAL TREATMENT AND FORENSIC EVIDENCE COLLECTION IN SEXUAL ASSAULTS

Historically, medical care and forensic evidence collection for sexual assault victims was accomplished within an emergency room environment, with both interventions done by existing emergency room personnel. Victims frequently endured long hours in waiting rooms amidst other patients needing care that was often prioritized over their needs. Emergency room staff dreaded having to examine sexual assault victims, and, even more so, they dreaded doing an evidentiary exam. It was a time-consuming and uncomfortable process for the untrained professional who was also responsible for other critically ill patients. Most had minimal competency in completing a sexual assault forensic evidence kit and were unfamiliar with the standards of medical care necessary for victims. Care and kit completion would be interrupted due to other emergency situations, compromising the integrity of evidence, and extending significantly the time victims spent in this environment. In addition, staff worried about the possibility of having to testify in court. When medical care was offered, it was inadequate at best, and many times the care was provided in a judgmental manner. Patient teaching, referral services, advisement about follow-up care, and advocacy support was not a standard part of the services.

The outcome of these experiences typically resulted in retraumatization and a delay in the healing process for victims. Discouraged, exhausted, and overwhelmed at times with self-blame, the experience impacted negatively on victims' desire and commitment to file criminal charges. A validation of their victimization seldom occurred. Inaccurate and/or cursory histories, unskilled evidence collection techniques, and frequent breaches in chain of custody procedures made prosecution of offenders extremely difficult for those victims who did remain committed to seeking justice. The ability of the criminal justice system to successfully hold an offender accountable for the assault and achieve a conviction was severely impeded.

HISTORY AND ROLE OF THE SEXUAL ASSAULT NURSE EXAMINER

The type of services described in "History of Medical Treatment and Forensic Evidence Collection in Sexual Assaults," above, changed dramatically in the mid 1970s with the inception of the role of the Sexual Assault Nurse Examiner (SANE). Recognition of the inadequacy of these response areas by a multidisciplinary group of professionals initiated specialized training for health care professionals in Minneapolis, Minnesota, followed by programs in Amarillo, Texas, Memphis, Tennessee, Tulsa, Oklahoma, and Tampa, Florida. Acknowledgment of the need to improve victim services by the U.S. Department of Justice (DOJ) Office of Victims of Crimes (OVC) and endorsement of SANE programs occurred shortly afterward:

> OVC believes that an informed, effective response to violence in America transcends the criminal justice system, and builds on many disciplines, including the health care sector. We know that victims of sexual assault suffer psychological trauma and, all too frequently, long-term health consequences as a result of their victimization. Therefore, providing sensitive health care to victims is critically important in the aftermath of a sexual assault. . . . The services of trained, experienced SANE practitioners help to preserve the victim's dignity, enhance medical evidence collection for

better prosecution, and promote community involvement and concern with crime victims and their families. (Ledray, 1998)

The number of SANE programs has expanded rapidly throughout the United States since then, and today the number continues to grow, establishing a benchmark for best practice in the medical and forensic examination of sexual assault victims.

The Albuquerque SANE Collaborative demonstrated the impact of SANE programs in a study done in 2003 in which it concluded

> that a SANE unit greatly enhances the healthcare quality of women who have been sexually assaulted, improves the quality of forensic evidence, improves law enforcement's ability to collect information and to file charges, and increases the likelihood of successful prosecution. (Crandall & Helitzer, 2003)

Comparing the experiences of victims for two years prior to the initiation of SANE services with post-SANE victims' feedback, the results showed that post-SANE victims received more medical services including treatment for sexually transmitted infections (STIs), pregnancy testing and prophylaxis, and more comprehensives victim service referrals. Reports to police increased by 22 percent, with the collection of evidence kits increasing from 30 percent to 88 percent. Conviction rates also increased by 12 percent, and the average sentence lengthened from 1.2 to 5.1 years (Crandall & Helitzer, 2003)

In 1996, the International Association of Forensic Nurses (IAFN) created a conceptual framework describing the role of the SANE using accepted roles and responsibilities of the registered nurse and establishing a certification/training curriculum to standardize the practice of SANE practitioners and programs (International Association of Forensic Nurses, 1996). In 2005, the National Standards for Sexual Assault Forensic Examiners (SAFEs) were established through the U.S. DOJ and the president's DNA Initiative (Justice for All Act of 2004, Pub. L. No. 108-405 (Oct. 30, 2004)). That same year, curriculum standards for SAFE training programs were created (U.S. DOJ, 2006). The specific goals, responsibilities, and format of the forensic medical examination, as described through the National Standards, are used in this chapter.

Prior to the chapter's detailed description of a forensic medical examination, clarification of several acronyms commonly used to identify professionals in this role needs to be provided. The terms Sexual Assault Forensic Examiner (SAFE), Sexual Assault Nurse Examiner (SANE), Forensic Nurse Examiner (FNE), Sexual Assault Nurse Clinician (SANC) and Forensic Nurse Certified in Sexual Assault (FN-CSA) are primarily interchangeable. SANE, FNE, SANC, and FN-CSA are registered nurses or nurse practitioners who possess specialized training to perform the medical forensic exam. SAFE may refer to these providers as well but also includes physicians and physician's assistants who have received the same training. The term SANE is used in this chapter for simplicity but acknowledges all clinicians who have been trained and are committed to providing a victim-centered, comprehensive examination in support of victims and the criminal justice system.

MISSION OF SANE PROGRAMS

As referenced in the OVC publication, *Sexual Assault Nurse Examiner (SANE) Development and Operation Guide*, "the primary mission of a SANE program is to meet the needs of the sexual assault victim by providing immediate, compassionate, culturally sensitive and comprehensive forensic evaluation and treatment by trained professional(s)" (Ledray, 1998). The SANE role is also based on the belief that

> all sexual assault victims have a right to report the crime of rape . . . a right to know what her options are and what to expect if she does or does not decide to report . . . those who report have a right to sensitive and knowledgeable support without bias . . . (and) those who do not report still have a right to expert health care. (Ledray, 1998)

The SANE most often works as a key member of a coordinated Sexual Assault Response Team (SART) and strives to achieve several goals:

- To protect the sexual assault victim from further harm;
- To provide crisis intervention;
- To provide timely, thorough, and professional forensic evidence collection, documentation, and preservation of evidence;
- To evaluate and treat prophylactically for STIs;
- To evaluate pregnancy risk and offer prevention;
- To assess, document, and seek care for injuries;
- To appropriately refer victims for immediate and follow-up medical care and follow-up counseling; and
- To enhance the ability of law enforcement agencies to obtain evidence and successfully prosecute sexual assault cases. (Ledray, 1998, pp. 8-9).

In addition, SANE services are victim centered; the needs of the victim take precedent, and the decisions regarding services are made primarily by the victim. The fundamental premise of victim-centered services is to offer care and interventions that are compassionate, nonjudgmental, thorough, and confidential in which the victim is informed of her options and allowed the freedom to make choices. Research has demonstrated for decades that a large component of rape trauma revolves around a feeling of loss of control in what has happened. Keeping a victim informed at all times and providing the opportunity to make decisions initiates the healing process and allows victims to regain a sense of control in their lives.

Ensuring confidentiality to a victim can be a key factor in a victim's decisions. Many express grave concerns about not wanting family or friends to know about the assault. A fear that informing law enforcement will allow others to know what happened often becomes a barrier to filing a police report. By ensuring that victims will be protected to the highest extent possible and explaining their right to confidentiality, victims frequently decide to report the incident to police and agree to an evidence examination. Thus, valuable evidence is preserved that will increase the potential for offenders to be held accountable for the assault and reduce the risk of a repeat offense.

SANE RESPONSIBILITIES

The individual details of the medical care and methodology of the evidentiary exam will vary from state to state and sometimes within state jurisdictions. Some states, such as California and New Jersey, have created standard protocols and procedures for the role of the SANE based on their individual statutes and state SART systems. All however, include standardized components based on the current national guidelines (Ledray, 1998; U.S. DOJ, 2004). Those components are:

- Care of injuries;
- Crisis intervention;
- STI evaluation and preventive care;
- Pregnancy risk evaluation and prevention;
- Forensic evidence collection and documentation, including photography;
- Evaluation for drug-facilitated sexual assault (DFSA);
- Discharge and follow-up; and
- SANE court appearances.

A general description of the overall process of the medical forensic examination, inclusive of these components, follows. More comprehensive details can be obtained from the resources listed in Appendix F as well as individual state protocols that may be in place.

It is important to keep in mind some key concepts. In the collection of evidence process, the SANE is required to be an objective investigator of a living crime scene—that being the victim. The process is not intended to determine if an assault occurred, but rather to gather and document injuries and evidence without bias based on the victim's statement and what is seen, heard, and observed. The assessment includes findings that may, or may not, be consistent with sexual assault and findings that may be related to disease, infection, or normal anatomical variations.

It is also not the role of the SANE to provide medical care for significant injuries or provide medical diagnosis or treatment of an identified condition. Typically, victims will be evaluated medically by emergency room staff for significant injuries and treated by that facility prior to clearance for an evidentiary examination. The SANE is responsible for making every attempt to preserve evidence during any needed interventions. She may also confer with facility staff if, during her assessment, she determines further injuries that require more than superficial wound care or signs and symptoms of disease or infection that have not been identified. The actual diagnosis and treatment of those findings are done by the medical staff of the facility where care is provided.

GENERAL FORMAT OF SANE EXAMINATION

The SANE examination should always be victim driven. Since every victim is unique, every assault is different, and victim reactions to events will vary significantly, the SANE is responsible for recognizing and addressing these variations and coordinating care and evidence collection based on the informed consent of the victim.

The overall format of the exam does not vary in its process, but the format is always individualized to the specific circumstance. The general areas of responsibility and intervention include:

- Assessment;
- Evidence collection;
- Preventive health measures; and
- Discharge and follow-up instructions.

Assessment

A thorough assessment of a sexual assault victim includes safety concerns, health history, history of the reported incident, physical examination, assessment of injury, and assessment of psychological/social risk factors and needs.

Safety Assessment. The first priority in the assessment of a sexual assault victim is to determine safety needs. Usually a SANE will work with victims in an emergency room or clinic environment that removes the victim from the location of the assault. However, many victims are brought to the SANE site by family members who may know or be the suspect. Victims may have concerns that the offender will come to the site to prevent the examination or police report. The additional fear that family members or children will be harmed may also be present. Sexual assault occurs most often by someone known to the victim and frequently is a component of domestic violence. These safety concerns, whether initiated by the victim or SANE, need to be addressed prior to the medical forensic examination. Minimal assistance and cooperation will occur from a victim if she has underlying fears for herself or her family, and her needs cannot be effectively met until a sense of safety and security is present.

The safety of the SANE is an important consideration prior to the exam. Victims who have willingly used drugs and alcohol or were possibly drugged during the assault may exhibit unpredictable and sometimes aggressive behaviors. The trauma of an assault may also trigger behaviors that can jeopardize the safety of the SANE in individuals with a history of mental illness.

College students are not exempt from the fears and safety risks of community victims including the prevalence of violence, drugs and alcohol, and domestic abuse. Therefore, it is prudent for all individuals responding to victims of sexual assault to use sound judgment in evaluating the safety of both responders and victims.

Health History. A thorough health history is the fundamental basis of any nursing assessment. Traditionally, patients seeking all forms of health care tend to reveal only the information asked of them. Many are unwilling to share behaviors or disease history that may reflect negatively on lifestyle choices. This factor is exacerbated by the trauma a sexual assault victim experiences and the normal feelings of self-blame about the assault. Victims fear that some of their past history may affect the credibility of their statements and omit vital information. Thus, obtaining an accurate and thorough health history can be difficult but achievable with the use of specific strategies.

Acknowledgment of the victim's experience in a compassionate and nonjudgmental manner is key to the establishment of an effective rapport with victims and initiates the beginning of a trust-based patient/provider relationship. An explanation of the aspects of informed consent and confidentiality gives victims a sense of protection and security, and reestablishes feelings of self-control in all aspects of care. A simple statement such as "I'm sorry this has happened to you" can break down barriers and begin an honest and thorough dialogue. An explanation as to why specific information is needed and its importance in evidence collection will again reduce barriers and assist to gather accurate information. The following statement is an example:

> Information about your menstrual cycle is important in order for me to determine your risk for pregnancy from the assault. If bleeding is found in your vagina or at the opening of your cervix when the forensic

examination is done, it helps to determine whether it is menstrual flow or bleeding from an injury. This information greatly helps the crime laboratory when the evidence is evaluated.

Nurses are trained to use observational and therapeutic listening skills with all patient interactions. These actions can be used effectively in obtaining thorough histories by observing facial expressions and body language, and adjusting questions and phrasing to assure comfort and understanding. Reflective responses validate and clarify patient statements to enhance patient trust and improve accuracy of information.

History of Reported Incident. The SANE obtains detailed information of the incident, most often gathering a narrative of the assault using the victim's own words and then asking specific, evidence oriented questions. The information is used for investigative purposes by the criminal justice system and by the SANE to direct the focus of evidence collection. The format may vary based on jurisdictional policies and state protocols. It is important to recognize that the documentation of the incident done by the SANE is not considered a police statement, but rather a recollection of the event by the victim.

Victims want to be believed when they report an assault, but they are also wary of punishment for their own potential behaviors such as the use of illegal drugs or underage drinking. Trauma secondary to the assault and drugs or alcohol may impact the victim's memory of events. As a result, many victims "fill in the gaps" of what they cannot recall, embellish the actions of the offender to influence believability, and omit victim behaviors that may be illegal. SANEs are often the first individuals to do a detailed interview with the victim, or they may do the interview jointly with law enforcement officers. Unless handled effectively, the victim's account of the incident will be different with each interview and may change over time as the investigative process is completed. Damage to the victim's credibility is the potential outcome as the "story changes" over time.

In order to obtain an accurate history, the SANE can preface questions with specific instructions such as:

1. It is important for you to tell me only what *you* recall, not what you've been told by others who may have been present.

2. Describe exactly what happened only as you remember it, not as you imagine it. This information doesn't determine whether an assault did or did not occur. It is only a part of the investigative process.

3. It is normal for you to have gaps in what you remember right now. If you aren't sure of the answer to a question, it is OK to say you are unsure or can't recall.

4. If you were involved in any potentially illegal behaviors either before or during the assault, it is important for you to be honest. The investigation will focus on the seriousness of the crime of sexual assault and not your actions.

5. If you don't understand a question or a word that is used, don't be afraid to ask for an explanation.

6. Things may have happened to you that are so offensive it can be extremely difficult to talk about them. There isn't anything you will say that may cause us to think differently about you, and everything you tell us always remains private. It is important that you tell us everything that you remember so we can provide you with the best possible services.

The recall of details of a sexual assault is one of the most difficult actions for a victim. These simple techniques can objectively and gently guide the victim through the process of "reliving" the experience and increase the likelihood of obtaining accurate and thorough information.

Physical Examination. Victims are evaluated for serious or life-threatening injuries prior to the forensic medical examination. This action is to assure that a victim is medically stable to undergo the SANE examination. The examination done by a SANE does not repeat this evaluation, and it does not contain traditional physical assessment techniques. The focus of the examination is to strategically examine the victim from head to toe for evidence that should be collected or injuries that need to be photographed and documented. It also documents normal variations or abnormalities that cannot be attributed to sexual assault and prior injuries.

Similar to a problem-focused examination, the SANE uses the victim's description of the incident to assess areas of the body that may have been involved but also inspects other areas based on her judgment and experience. For example, a vaginal speculum exam may not be done if the victim is sure that she was only forced to have oral sex. However, if the victim has little memory of the event or is unsure, the SANE will most likely choose to do a comprehensive examination to ensure that all possible evidence has been collected. This approach is used to avoid unnecessary procedures for the victim and avoid retraumatization.

The use of an alternative light source is a common procedure during the physical examination process. It allows for visualization of dried secretions, such as saliva and semen, to be seen that cannot be observed with the naked eye. It can also reveal bruising that may not be evident with standard visualization.

Many SANE programs require examination of certain areas such as the perineum or oral cavity with a magnifying instrument such as a colposcope. This allows for the identification of microscopic tears that may have occurred and would not be noticed without the use of magnification. Some SANE protocols also use Toluidine blue and Gentian violet dye to assess for genital injuries not visible through gross visualization.

Assessment of Injury. SANEs are trained to look for injury patterns based on a victim's statement as well as to identify injuries that may have occurred prior to the assault. Bruising or petecchiae present on the roof of the mouth or broken skin on the lips from a tooth puncture are common findings in victims who have been forced to have oral sex. Bilateral, symmetrical bruising of the upper extremities may be seen in someone who was restrained. Basically, the SANE looks for evidence that may (or may not) substantiate a victim's statement. It is important to remember that the majority of sexual assaults result in minimal, if any, injuries. Therefore, lack of injuries does not necessarily indicate that an assault did not occur.

The SANE distinguishes injuries that most likely occurred during the assault from those that may have happened prior to the incident. A common finding in domestic abuse victims who report sexual assault is past injuries, which are recognized by different coloring of bruised areas and/or the stage of healing of a wound or laceration.

It is through the trained, objective eye of the SANE that the pieces of the puzzle begin to come together. Injury assessment can be a key component in assisting the criminal justice system to prosecute and convict offenders.

Assessment of Psychological/Social Risk Factors and Needs. Victim behaviors when reporting an assault vary dramatically. Some appear nonchalant and matter-of-fact while others are angry, tearful, and frightened. What should be noted is that all of the observed behaviors of victims are considered normal and are usually found in coping mechanisms developed from their life experiences. That being said, the SANE assesses and observes victim behaviors and then considers information gained from the health history to determine whether the victim is in need of additional interventions or is at risk for future concerns.

Most individuals in our society today have unresolved issues within their life that remain buried in the subconscious in the misguided belief that forgetting a traumatic event or negative experience will eventually force these experiences and the subsequent emotions to disappear. Many individuals also have a history of mental illness that may or may not have been treated and stabilized. None of these necessarily indicate an individual is unstable. In fact, most lead grounded, productive lives. However, the trauma of a sexual assault can significantly impact on this stability and cause illness, past experiences, and buried emotions to resurface.

The SANE will make an assessment whether a victim is currently in need of additional psychological interventions, beyond the scope of the SANE examination, based on the victim's health history and observed behaviors. If a victim is in need of immediate intervention, the medical forensic examination will be deferred until further evaluation can be done. This decision is based on the inability of the victim to provide informed consent and to prevent revictimization.

Evidence Collection

Nursing professionals are highly trained to accurately and comprehensively document patient findings and interactions. They are highly skilled at specimen collection especially in protection of specimens from contamination. Nurses also use critical thinking and problem-solving skills daily in their professional roles. These three abilities are a prominent part of the evidence collection process and provide sound rationale behind the success of the SANE in assisting the criminal justice process.

The details of evidence collection requirements and techniques may be different from state to state. However, certain commonalities exist:

- Timing of the forensic examination;

- Written documentation;

- Specimen collection and preservation;

- Photo documentation; and

- Evaluation for DFSA.

This section will offer an overview of each area and again emphasize that details within each component will vary from state to state and/or jurisdiction.

Timing of the Forensic Examination. The timing of the forensic examination must be considered in the care of the sexual assault victim. Each program, jurisdiction, or state will set the policy regarding the time frame in which evidence can be collected. When SANE programs were first developed, examinations were not done if thirty-six hours had passed since the assault. With the advancement of laboratory technology to identify DNA, these parameters have been extended in most areas and vary from thirty-six hours up to seven days.

The U.S. DOJ National Standards for SANEs recommend specific interventions regardless of the time that has elapsed since an assault:

- Whether or not evidence is collected for the sexual assault evidence collection kit, examiners should obtain the medical forensic history, examine patients, and document findings (with patient consent).

- Patients should be examined promptly to minimize loss of evidence and identify medical needs and concerns.

- Decisions about whether to collect evidence and what to collect should be made on a case-by-case basis, guided by knowledge that outside time limits for obtaining evidence vary.

- Responders should seek education and resources to aid them in making well-informed decisions about evidence collection. (U.S.DOJ, 2004, p. 67)

Written Documentation. Three areas of written documentation are standard in the medical forensic examination: (1) patient consent forms, (2) the medical record, and (3) the forensic record.

Written, informed consents should always be obtained from a victim. The number and type of consent varies based on local SANE protocols. A consent to render medical care is obtained from the facility where the examination occurs and becomes a part of the permanent medical record but not necessarily the forensic record. Another consent is obtained by the SANE to do the medical forensic examination. This documentation remains with the forensic record and does not typically become a part of the facility's medical record. Other consents are usually obtained to photograph injuries, release specific evidence to law enforcement, and obtain blood and urine specimens, especially in the case of a suspected DFSA.

The medical record of the victim's visit to the care facility should not be a part of the forensic record. This should remain a record of medical treatment only, which was provided by the facility or clinic with minimal documentation of sexual assault information. Unless the SANE is on staff at that facility, and also provides the medical evaluation to release a victim for the SANE examination, the SANE should not document information in the medical record. Although discoverable, this record should remain completely separate from the forensic record and not be released to law enforcement with the forensic record.

The forensic record is the written component of the SANE's findings. It should be a standardized form to capture all aspects of the examination. The SANE uses this record to provide written, objective documentation of all findings including anatomical diagrams. The record also lists the photographic component of the exam, use of special equipment such as the colposcope, and a list of evidence contained in the examination kit. When specimens are packaged and sealed in an evidence kit, a copy of the record is included. A copy of the record is also given to law enforcement officers if they are involved in the response, and a copy is usually kept with the coordinating authority of the SANE program. The copy of the forensic record should never become a part of the facility's medical record.

Specimen Collection and Preservation. The image of a television-show–type mechanism to collect evidence is not an accurate picture of the specimen collection process. Most evidence kits simply contain swabs, microscope slides, containers and envelopes for packaging, blood and urine collection containers, and labels. It is the collection process and preservation of specimens only that mimics today's media image of crime scene evidence collection. The sexual assault victim is considered a "living crime scene" in which evidence is identified, collected, preserved for laboratory evaluation, and secured through a "chain of custody" process.

It is important that kits be standardized. Each jurisdiction determines the contents of an evidence kit, often based on the methodology used by the jurisdiction's specific crime laboratory. How evidence is gathered and the process for preservation and protection are also standardized regardless of the items in a kit.

Although sterile technique is not used, the SANE will gather evidence without contamination from other sources and allow it to dry prior to being packaged. Each item is carefully labeled to identify the source of the specimen and the victim. Once dried, the specimen is packaged and labeled again. The SANE then seals the package and initials the sealed area.

Once all evidence is processed, it is placed in the evidence kit with the written documentation of the examination, and the kit is sealed and again initialed over that area. The outside of the kit often provides a list of other evidence gathered, such as clothing, which will also be submitted to law enforcement.

Chain of custody refers to the procedure for turning evidence over to another individual. In order to ensure the integrity of evidence specimens, the SANE always remains with the evidence gathered from the examination. Initials and seals on specimens and the kit indicate that the evidence has remained in her custody and not been compromised or touched by another individual since it was collected by the SANE. To continue the protective process, the individual accepting the kit from the SANE will review the contents and its integrity and then sign the kit. This signature indicates the individual has now taken custody of and responsibility for the evidence.

Photo Documentation. The advancement of photo technology in recent years has simplified this process and increased the availability of high quality, visual images of injuries improving the accuracy of evidence for the criminal justice system. Many programs use a high-quality 35mm or digital camera with magnification capabilities. Digital cameras need to be used with caution since the ability to alter images is available and can hinder prosecution efforts.

The use of photography can cause victim distress. There should be a mechanism in place for the victim to decline some or all of the use of photos as well as the ability to withhold photographs as evidence in a protected way until they are requested by the court system. This provides some assurance to the victim that the photos will not be viewed by others unless necessary for investigative purposes and allows decision-making opportunities for areas of the body that the victim may not want recorded on film. Victim comfort and privacy should be considered at all times when taking photos. Draping areas not to be filmed is important to the dignity and comfort of the victim.

A detailed description of recommended procedures for sexual assault photography is available in the *National Protocol for Sexual Assault Medical Forensic Examinations: Adult/Adolescent* (U.S. DOJ, 2004).

Evaluation for Drug-Facilitated Sexual Assault. SANEs are trained to recognize indicators in both victim behavior and statements that reflect the possibility that a victim may have been unwillingly drugged for the purpose of a sexual assault. Every victim is considered for this possibility, and blood and urine specimens are obtained when a DFSA is suspected.

Standard guidelines for specimen collection exist based on crime laboratory recommendations and overall knowledge of the length of time certain drugs and alcohol can be detected in blood and urine. Most drugs known to be used such as Rohypnol and gamma hydroxybutyrate (GHB), as well as alcohol, are rapidly processed in the human body and often leave no evidence of ingestion past twenty-four hours. This is complicated by the fact that victims frequently delay reporting sexual assaults past twenty-four hours, making it very difficult to gather evidence of a possible DFSA. Although Rohypnol and GHB are widely publicized as date rape drugs, alcohol is the drug of choice for most offenders especially on college campuses.

Preventive Health Measures

SANEs have the responsibilities to offer and provide health interventions for the screening and prevention of STIs, including human immunodeficiency virus (HIV), and pregnancy. This is frequently a significant concern for victims.

Most programs follow either the Centers for Disease Control (CDC) or American College of Emergency Physicians (ACEP) recommendations. Both state that sexual assault victims should not be tested for STIs at the time of the examination. This is based on the knowledge that exposure to an STI from a recent assault cannot be detected until at least two weeks has passed as well as the knowledge that preexisting disease could be detrimental to a victim's case.

Prophylaxis through antimicrobial treatment or immunization against most STIs is recommended. For infections such as the herpes simplex virus (HSV) and HIV, patient teaching and follow-up care or testing is recommended to the victim. If there is a concern of high-risk exposure to HIV secondary to the assault, immediate HIV prophylaxis is recommended.

Victims who are not pregnant at the time of the examination should be offered the option to receive preventive medication against pregnancy at the time of care. The use of emergency contraception (also known as the morning after pill or Plan B) has been a controversial issue due to individual religious and cultural beliefs. Despite this concern, many faith-based institutions now routinely prescribe emergency contraception or at least provide referral information to victims. Since emergency contraception in the form of Plan B is currently available without a prescription, victims have easy access to pregnancy prevention. They should be informed of its availability if not provided by the facility conducting the examination.

Other needs identified by the SANE during the assessment and examination process are addressed through a referral process at the conclusion of the exam, including referral for emergency medical treatment and referral for continuing care for psychosocial needs.

Discharge and Follow-Up Instructions

The days that follow an assault can sometimes be the most difficult. When the victim leaves the care of the SANE, it is important that there is a support system in place to meet the victim's needs whether or not she chooses to report the assault and work with the criminal justice system.

When the forensic medical examination is completed, the victim is often emotionally drained from the incident and having to relive the experience during the examination. If she has not showered or changed clothing since the assault, the desire for cleanliness can be overwhelming. Many SANE programs will offer a cosmetic kit and a place to shower or wash, including replacement clothing such as a sweat suit, to wear home.

A primary concern for victims returning to their living environment is the presence of any future safety risks. Although immediately addressed at the time of the assessment, support and safety plans need to be considered for the victim.

Campus victims are considered a population with unique needs and additional options from community victims. At a minimum, these victims should be given a copy of the Campus Sexual Assault Victims' Bill of Rights (20 U.S.C. § 1092(f)(8)). In best practice, the SANE will have a working relationship with campus resources and can refer the victim directly to these individuals for academic or housing accommodations and access to the judicial process.

Instructions will be provided to the victim regarding medication received during the examination, follow-up testing and care for sexually transmitted diseases and pregnancy, contact information for law enforcement and advocacy services, and victim witness offices. Much of the information and recommendations that are given to victims will not be retained unless all referrals and instructions are provided in writing. The victim then has easy access to accurate information in the days ahead and hopefully will utilize services that may be needed.

CONCLUSION

The forensic medical examination is a critical component in providing comprehensive services to sexual assault victims. SANEs have significantly improved the quality of this care through compassionate, comprehensive, victim-centered services. By using their investigative tools, SANEs have also assisted the criminal justice system in holding offenders accountable and reducing repeat offenses. Yet, it is the victims who have benefited most through the commitment and dedication of these professionals, which enables victims to regain their dignity and begin the healing process.

> People often ask me why I became a SANE. It is the most challenging and difficult job I have ever had as a nurse. Sometimes I'm called out in the middle of the night, and the process can take four to six hours. When the exam is over I'm usually exhausted and emotionally drained. And yet, when a victim tells me thank you with tears in her eyes I know why I do it. It can't be expressed in words. The reward is what is felt in your heart.
>
> —Anonymous

References

Crandall, C. S. & Helitzer, D. (2003). *Impact and evaluation of SANE programs* (National Institute of Justice Grant #98-WT-VX-0027). Albuquerque, NM: SANE Collaborative and University of New Mexico School of Medicine.

International Association of Forensic Nurses. (1996). *Sexual assault nurse examiner standards of practice.* Arnold, MD: Author.

Ledray, L. (1998). *Sexual assault nurse examiner (SANE) development and operation guide.* Washington, DC: Sexual Assault Resource Service and the U.S. Department of Justice, Office of Justice Programs, Office for Victims of Crime.

United States Department of Justice Office on Violence Against Women. (2004, September). *National protocols for sexual assault medical forensic examinations: Adults/adolescents* (Publication NCJ206554). Washington, DC: Author.

United States Department of Justice Office on Violence Against Women. (2006, June). *National training standards for sexual assault medical forensic examiners* (Publication NCJ213827). Washington, DC: Author.

Part 3

Training and Implementation

Introduction:
A Team Approach

by Donna M. Barry, APN, FN-CSA,
and Paul M. Cell, Chief of Police

The SART model recognizes that the victim of sexual assault and the criminal justice system have distinctive sets of needs. Sometimes there are inherent conflicts between these two sets of needs and goals. These conflicts, however, do not have to polarize individuals and agencies. Through professional collaboration between rape crisis centers, health care providers, and the criminal justice system, both sets of needs can be accommodated. (California Coalition Against Sexual Assault, 2000)

Utilization of a team approach in the form of a Sexual Assault Response Team (SART) is a recommended practice for both community and campus response. How it is structured and carries out its functions, however, will determine whether it effectively will meet the needs of victims.

The needs of any victim are:

- Easy access to care;
- Early emotional support and advocacy;
- Compassionate and sensitive interventions;
- Accessible medical care for evaluation of injuries and prophylaxis against pregnancy and sexually transmitted infections;
- Accessible, timely, and skilled forensic examination;
- Information and access to criminal justice procedures; and
- Follow-up medical care and resource referrals.

Campus sexual assault victims have additional needs that have been identified:

- Access to care and reporting procedures without judgment or punitive action;
- Accommodations for housing and/or academic schedules to reduce the risk of further trauma;
- Ability to receive care through anonymous or blind reporting;
- Information and assistance in reporting to campus authorities, law enforcement, and the judicial affairs process;
- Availability of follow-up counseling and other campus/community resources; and
- Cooperation and assistance from campus officials in all aspects of victim needs and services.

Provision of the above options and services is a complex task but can be accomplished if all SART members work together in a coordinated manner and truly function as a team.

Team building begins with the establishment of a team mission statement, created from input of all SART constituents and reflective of the collective vision of the team. This promotes a joint team commitment and acknowledges each discipline's vested interest in the team's success in meeting victim needs. Mutual understanding and respect of each member's roles and responsibilities can improve team member communication, strengthen the connection between responders, enhance commitment to the providing effective service, and support the criminal justice process.

A coordinated, team approach to victim response promotes consistency and continuity of comprehensive services. However, any team success requires some form of leadership to assure the quality of these services and to determine areas for improved response. The identification of an individual to oversee the SART operation is critical since the leadership role requires extensive knowledge and experience in understanding victim needs *and* the criminal justice process. Specific responsibilities will include: (1) in-depth cross-training of all members; (2) oversight and coordination of all SART activations; (3) management of systematic, multidisciplinary review and evaluation; and (4) implementation of changes for improvement.

The department or agency that fulfills the leadership role varies significantly, especially within a campus environment. Specific recommendations as to the "best" area for oversight cannot be provided since each institution has different variables to consider in developing a SART. What is most important in the determination of the best location is that the department, agency, or individual possesses the above abilities and does not have a conflict of interest. For example, at many universities, the dean of students is the supervisor and/or decision maker regarding disciplinary actions and conduct code violations. If this individual is designated as the coordinator of the SART system, it may be difficult to make objective decisions regarding evaluation of a case's SART response as well as judicial decisions for the same case. Thus, the administrative leadership must be in a position that does not pose potential conflicts.

An additional consideration for coordination of services is to factor in actual coordination within other SART systems that may exist. In order to effectively meet the needs of a campus victim who may seek services outside of a campus SART, other SARTs need training and education regarding the additional needs of campus victims. Most community responders are unaware of the specific needs and options of college victims resulting in a return to school without knowledge of available accommodations and services. Educating other SART systems to provide this information and coordinate referrals to campus resources is an ideal way in which to reach all campus victims in an effective manner.

As Chapter 9 states, extensive cross-training of all SART members is imperative to strengthen the SART approach. It provides an in-depth review of each member's purpose and responsibilities and enhances team functioning by offering a better understanding of each individual's team role.

An example of an ideal practice between two SART systems can be demonstrated in a recent case. A nineteen-year-old college female went to the local emergency room to report that she had been assaulted a few hours before at a house party off campus. The following coordinated steps were taken:

- The county SART was activated and municipal police, a rape crisis advocate, and a Sexual Assault Nurse Examiner (SANE) responded and provided quality, comprehensive care.

- The SANE advised the victim of available accommodations and resources on campus.

- With the victim's permission the campus SART coordinator was contacted, and arrangements were made to meet with the victim and provide the assistance requested. The alleged offender was not a university student, so academic and housing accommodations were not needed, and there was no need to access the judicial affairs process. Arrangements were made for counseling services and follow-up medical care on campus.

- Municipal police notified campus law enforcement of the report, including a court-mandated no-contact order for the offender.

- With the victim's permission, a campus law enforcement representative contacted the victim to offer services as a "liaison" between the victim and the municipal agency.

- Advocacy services continued throughout all interventions.

In the chapters that follow, specific information is provided for consideration in the final aspect of campus SART formation. However the pieces are "put together," an effective SART takes skilled leadership, synchronous and shared team interventions, extensive trainings, and communication with additional responders and services.

References

California Coalition Against Sexual Assault. (2000). *California sexual assault response team manual*. Sacramento, CA: Author.

Chapter 9

Training Considerations

by Kieran Barrett, Police Lieutenant

INTRODUCTION

Under normal circumstances, a law enforcement officer, a rape care advocate, and a specimen-collecting nurse walk separate professional paths. In the Sexual Assault Response Team (SART) model, it is essential for this triad to work seamlessly and without conflict; however, this seems to be rare if not impossible. The sad reality is that individuals working in each area are professionals in their own right, but misunderstandings and misgivings about past experiences have left each numb about the others' role in the criminal justice system. For a team to be both proactive and successful in a victim-centered approach, the walls must be broken down by understanding each other better through cross-training and case evaluation.

All SART members, be they law enforcement officers, medical professionals, or advocates, have a story to tell about the other discipline's lack of professionalism. Similar frustrations are felt by many community constituents involved in the assault reporting process. The fault does not lie entirely with the team members however; it squarely reflects a lack of focused training and coordination on the part of the police agency, community administration, and community stakeholders. This chapter focuses on training considerations for all SART components (law enforcement officers, Sexual Assault Nurse Examiners (SANEs), advocates, mental health professionals, and community members) and the specific topics that should be covered in the training.

TRAINING POLICY: TEAM CONCEPT

Every component of the SART model plays a role in the training of the other parts of the model. The SART coordinator delineates the training required for each component and identifies the partners who will cross-train. A policy of training that is both exhaustive and flexible is the rule.

In a campus setting, many departments in the area of student services should be included. The SART training policy should designate the various departments that will present the training, the goals of the training, and the expected outcome of the training. The policy should be distributed among SART members as a guide and remain effective to address employee turnover and refresher training.

In basic law enforcement, for example, training focuses primarily on response techniques, tactical response, and legal remedies, and the training also provides the officers with a good dose of fear that they are always a target. While this training plays a major role in the formation of complete police officers, victims' concerns and fears are left to the rape care advocates and caregivers; conversely caregivers feel certain that the police are too insensitive to help victims find their way back from their assaults. A well-rounded investigation and case involves the cooperation and support of the victim; likewise, a successful prosecution can occur with the sole testimony of a cooperative police officer or caregiver who has done his/her job well. The role of caregivers in health and advocacy is crucial to the well-being of victims and is in no way less important than the role of the police officer for successful case resolution.

The team concept, innate in the SART, provides the balance that both the victim and the prosecution so richly deserve. So why is training undervalued in favor of simply handing out protocols, directives, and mutual aid concerns? Why are initial responses and investigative techniques ignored when it comes to sexual assault? Why does the police officer not see the difference between a robbery victim and a sexual assault victim? Why does the officer not value the role and expertise of the caregivers and visa versa? Effective and comprehensive training for field officers, investigative staff, command-level officers, health care providers, advocates, and community members that is specific to the most violent crime of sexual assault is essential to the success of an educational environment willing to acknowledge the biggest problem facing college age women today. Training within the SART model must be extraordinarily inclusive and multidisciplinary so that each functional unit understands and recognizes the value of the other.

LAW ENFORCEMENT TRAINING

One of the greatest issues facing police agencies, campuses, and communities across the United States is that there are few procedures that differentiate between crimes of violence against women and any other crime. Effective policies and procedures provide the most basic of resources and training available to the police officer responding to a sexual assault incident. Within the police agency, there must be a specific policy in order to properly conduct sensitive investigations. Included in this policy should be a designation of specific training that officers must undergo. The training should be comprehensive and victim centered in its model. Within the campus or community hierarchy, there should also be a system of checks and balances designating who is responsible for what and defining the specifics. The various SART components must work together to formulate a comprehensive training initiative to meet the needs of all team members.

Police Agency Training Policy

A general and specific training policy can be achieved simply by addressing the needs of the department and identifying:

1. Mandatory goals of the training;
2. Who will be trained; and
3. Who is performing the training and his/her qualifications to do so.

The policy need not include the content of the training, as recommended procedures change regularly, and there should be some leeway for the instructor to develop a training strategy to meet the goals.

Goals of Training. With respect to sexual assault investigations and operations' training goals, it is essential to set out a course of action. The goals must be liberal in their focus but specific in their topic. The policy should be simple and not confuse its intended audience. In law enforcement, direction is desirous but seldom sought for fear of inadequacy. Goals should include training of all officers in sexual assault typology, related criminal law, initial officer response, investigation techniques, contact requirements, evidence collection, and other responsibilities required as a member of the SART.

Who Will Be Trained? Within the SART model and in police department policy, the various titles and persons that must be trained in the numerous topics of the system should be identified. Essential personnel that must be trained include: command personnel, investigations staff, and communications officers/dispatchers, as well as non-police personnel including first responders, SANEs (see "SANE Training"), rape care advocates (see "Rape Care Advocates and Mental Health Professionals Training"), victim services, prosecutors or legal services, community leaders, campus executive administrators, and any other essential personnel that may fit the particular model (see "Community Training and Programs"). It is wise to designate one coordinator from the SART model to facilitate training to ensure an organized order.

Who Will Provide Training? It is an enormous mistake to assume that just anyone can cross-train members of the SART model. Each component may have to look at its staff to ensure that the right person with the right credentials is doing the training. A surly police officer should not train rape care advocates in initial police investigations; and an advocate who has had negative police interactions should not train new officers. An effective team that creates cross-training at all levels within the SART model should be created. Experience has shown that training can be well received by most and poorly received by others; what has been the most consistent positive factor has been the motivation of trainers and speakers. There is a growing need for dynamic presenters with energetic skills to challenge audience members and provide interactive learning and role playing. The experience and credentials of trainers should be enough for them to be legitimately accepted by the audience. Police personnel, in particular, are wary of those who view them negatively and will shut down fast when this is perceived.

Levels of Those Being Trained

Training of police officers can be trying, even training conducted by fellow police officers. Each discipline within the SART mechanism presents training issues; however, many outsiders are uncomfortable at the thought of presenting to police officers. There can be a group mentality that undermines the role of the expert presenter, and there can be topics that are of little concern to the officers' daily routines. There are three levels of police personnel that are trained for participation on the SART: the entry-level officer, the in-service officer, and the seasoned administrative officer. What is important for all participating police officers is that they be recognized as professionals within the SART protocol; this will go a long way toward engaging them in the team concept.

Entry-Level Police Officer Training. The entry-level police officer may be considered the most moldable character within the agency. This officer has undergone rigorous testing and training at the police academy and is a virtual machine of information and respect. If the police academy has done its job, the entry-officer is easy to train on such a victim-centered team concept, assuming the trainer develops a strong bond with the police officer and clearly demonstrates expectations. The entry-level officer is seeking guidance and discipline but may not realize his/her role as caregiver. For those agencies with a county- or state-led SART program, the police academy is the perfect time to introduce protocol and team members. Many police academies do a tremendous job of teaching recruits how to fight crime; it is important to focus on the role of service provider as well. Recruits undergo rigorous training in body, mind, and spirit, and there is no greater time to reach an officer than when he/she is in the police academy. If academy training is not appropriate, officers normally undergo field training once they graduate from the academy, and this may also be an appropriate time to introduce appropriate standards regarding response to crimes of sexual violence.

In-Service Police and Administrative Officer Training. One of the greatest fears nonpolice trainers have is training the in-service and seasoned police officer. Police officers loathe in-service training for a variety of reasons: it may disturb their schedules, as they would normally work overnight; instructors are many times less experienced in law enforcement; it keeps them from enforcing the law; and they feel that the training is more liability geared than education motivated. For nonlaw police trainers, working with this audience may be difficult; however, when approached with empathetic resources and police officer "fish" stories, the trainer can achieve great success. Fish stories are those rehashed stories that are mostly true but are trumped up for emphasis and credibility—the greater the story teller's credibility, the more the audience is engaged.

SANE TRAINING

SANE professionals and other medical team members are vital components of the training model. For training purposes, if the SANEs have taken the required certification program, most will not require a rehashing of the medical intricacies of a sexual assault exam process or the evidentiary rules. The SANEs will need background information on their legal authority and background on the other topics of the SART model, particularly the law enforcement end. Key areas of training should include: areas of common understanding among the key players, chain of custody, case management, legal implications, testimony, and prosecution. SANES should provide needed information to other team members on their objectives and how they can assist the other team members with their goals.

RAPE CARE ADVOCATES AND MENTAL HEALTH PROFESSIONALS TRAINING

Rape care advocates and mental health professionals do not provide the same service, but their goals are the same—to help the victim become whole again in mind and spirit. As with health care providers, advocates and mental health professionals should have the prerequisite credentials to provide the services needed to a victim of sexual assault. An advocate will be the guiding resource and champion the rights of the victim; a mental health care provider will be a counseling resource for healing, and he/she can also help guide others on the team in understanding the course of the victim's revival. It is important to recognize both advocates and mental health providers as separate and equally pivotal to the success of services to the victim as well as a successful prosecution of the suspect. Cross-training for law enforcement and SANEs should include how the advocates will work with the other professions to assist victims in a progressive and case-managed model, and presentations on how this will assist the roles of SART professionals.

COMMUNITY TRAINING AND PROGRAMS

Community partners who are not directly involved in the immediate services related to the SART mechanism are often overlooked. On most campuses, there is a wide variety of student services, faculty, and peer groups that can assist with the mission of a SART program. Training should be provided to the dean of students office, Greek life, residence life, campus ministries, women's centers, judicial affairs, athletics, emergency medical services, victim-oriented organizations, student government, and peer advocacy groups. Essentially, all campus partners who may be first contacts with victims are part of the response hierarchy and should be included in long-range training and outreach programs. It is imperative as well to present to diverse organizations of women's groups, lesbian, gay, bisexual, and transgender communities, minority and religious student organizations, and staff organizations. In addition to introducing, or reinvigorating, the SART program to the community, SART services should be advertised to a wide variety of campus constituencies. While it may not be necessary to provide the formal SART mechanism and protocols, it may be beneficial to provide programming from one or two areas to introduce the program in the general sense. In an effort to reach as many victims as possible, programming on many levels can enhance access to care.

On a college campus, in particular, the role of faculty and first contacts is crucial in the reporting and service cycle. A 2005 U.S. Department of Justice research study found that students who are sexually assaulted are most likely to tell friends first. "Research shows that social support from friends—and other 'first responders'—can help the victim recognize what happened as a violation of the school's sexual misconduct policy and potentially a crime and encourage the victim to report it to the authorities" (United States Department of Justice, 2005, p. 6). Faculty in particular have an enormous stake in the care of victims given their frequent contact with students; to ignore this would be a critical error in training planning. In addition, it is prudent to reach out and formally train other local police agencies and emergency care personnel that may respond so they may better understand the campus environment, recognize the needs of college students, understand the role of campus administrators in areas pertaining to sexual assault, and provide appropriate referrals and follow-up care for campus victims.

ESSENTIAL TOPICS IN SART TRAINING

There are several obvious topics involved in training the entire SART model. Once training polices are in place and the various components are advised, the topics should be discussed. As with the training policy, the scope can be flexible, but the goals of the policy should always be maintained. By examining the chain of victim services, a clear picture emerges of the order of the presentations. Sexual assaults can be reported to any member of the SART, and who actually gets the report is unpredictable at best. While each component has an essential role to play, the health and safety of the victim is the overall goal, so the general outlook should begin there.

History of SARTs and SANEs

An understanding of the history of the SART and SANE provides a basis for all being trained, whether they are police officers, rape care advocates, or health professionals. Within this area of training, it is important to stress the response to crimes of sexual violence in a historical context to see how far society has actually come from the "boys will be boys" era. The SANE program, according to Dr. Linda Ledray, had its origins in the metropolitan cities of Amarillo, Texas, Minneapolis, Minnesota, and

Memphis, Tennessee, in the early 1970s and was largely unnoticed until the late 1980s. It was when nurse examiners began working in a more national network that the idea of an interconnected SART program took root (Ledray, 2001). The idea was simply to improve law enforcement investigations, enhance access to advocacy, and provide victims with a less intrusive and less restrictive sexual assault exam. The added benefit would be to improve the chain of evidence custody and the integrity of evidence collection. The overall goal was to improve an extraordinarily evidence-based exam and investigation as well as providing comprehensive victims' services. This goal has not changed; however, the implementation of SART programs across the country and training available to team members has been greatly enhanced over the last twenty years.

Individual SART Protocols

Every SART team, while similar in its function and composition has different protocols; some may be dictated by state statute, others by internal preference, and still others by best practice. The SART coordinator should outline the many steps and methods necessary to activate the SART process. This is an opportunity to discuss responsibilities when a victim reports a sexual assault to one of the components of the SART. Introduction of the protocols, in effect, also introduces the agencies that will be working together to meet the victims' needs, and the introduction is a good opportunity to discuss who will be providing the training.

The SART coordinator should begin by discussing who can activate the team, what the "order" of services can be, and what some typical outcomes may be. The order of SART services is important, as this is a victim-centered approach, and should the trust of the victim be lost at any point along the process, it is very difficult to regain. So this would be a great time to mention, respectfully, that all professional egos should be checked at the door; this is a group effort with a common goal—to help a person traumatized by a violent crime.

Victims' Options

Victims' options should be discussed at length. These include Jane Doe reporting, the choice of any or all of the SART functions in the process, and the goal of moving forward for the victim. The victim must understand that using the SART services does not mean that someone is going to be arrested, have to go to court, have certain medical procedures performed, or utilize advocacy services—if this is implied, it may cause a victim to rethink SART services and shun professionals trained to help her. This is also a good time to distribute contact and on-call lists that may be applicable to the SART.

Improvements to Evidence Collection

Improvements to the accuracy of evidence collection by a SANE are a key element for all parties to understand. Cases are often made on the collection of evidence, and the SANE's role has become essential not only to the prosecution, but also to the appeals process as well. While policies may differ, there should be a discussion about the importance of the chain of evidentiary custody between the health care facility and the law enforcement agency. Evidence packing supplies and procedures are of great concern to the judicial process, and custody must be carried out in an efficient and organized manner, which indicates responsibility by the SANE and the law enforcement officer taking receipt of evidence. Policies from the law enforcement agency as well as internal SANE evidence protocols should be discussed and put in writing so that there is always a resource when a question arises.

Law and Guidelines

It is important to review the actual legal language of the particular state's reference to sexual assault. While most are similar, there are subtle differences within statutory code that may limit or give latitude to each component's individual role within the SARTs (see Appendices A and B). Working with the district attorney or prosecuting attorney ensures that all SART members are aware of the law pertaining to sexual assault; it may help to distribute this in writing with definitions. Each state has enacted legislation that both defines sexual crimes and delineates who may be a victim and what constitutes a violation of the law. While the text of a law can be convoluted, it is important to stress the law as a resource to continue with providing services. For example, the New Jersey defines sexual penetration as

> vaginal intercourse, cunnilingus, fellatio or anal intercourse between persons or insertion of the hand, finger or object into the anus or vagina either by the actor or upon the actors instruction. The depth of insertion shall not be relevant as to the question of commission of the crime. (N.J. Code of Criminal Justice § 2C:14-1c (2008)

In addition, many states have written statutes for the creation of SARTs and SANEs that include their scope and functions. All members may have to abide by guidelines to provide services to sexual assault victims, and victim services programs may be statutory as well. This area can be difficult to navigate but must be addressed so that everyone has general understanding of the legal basis of their goals and responsibilities.

Dynamics of Sexual Assault and Effects of Trauma

This topic is often overlooked, as it may be assumed that most components of the SART have a grasp of these concepts. Prior to the training, many SART members have little understanding of the role each plays in the SART model. It should not be assumed that something that is intrinsic to one professional area is not vital to the professional growth of other SART members. Included in this topic should be the following:

- The varied types of sexual assault as defined not only by the law, but by victims as well;
- The effects of trauma, both immediate and long lasting;
- Various responses victims may go through during and after the assault;
- The absence of trauma and "unusual" responses;
- Victim reluctance to come forward;

- Biases law enforcement, medical professionals, and rape care advocates have about each other, biases towards sexual assault victims, and biases sexual assault victims have about themselves and the SART members; and

- Language, physical, emotional, and cultural barriers that exist in recognizing and reporting sexual crimes.

Advocacy Component

When the SART mechanism is activated by any team or community member, the advocacy component should be the first area to respond to assist the victim. All team members provide essential services; however, it is the role of the rape care advocate that guides the victim through the entire process. If a victim reports a sexual assault to either law enforcement or a medical facility, it is essential that advocacy services are summoned. To begin the healing process, victims of sexual assault should, in every case, be afforded the right to have the support of a trained advocate during all medical and legal proceedings.

Rape Care Advocate Role and Experience. The rape care advocate role is one of compassion and emotional support for the victim. The advocate trainer is a person who can bridge the varied assumptions that law enforcement and medical profession-als may have of the profession. It is important to stress that the advocate is not there to interfere with any team member's job; rather the advocate is attempting to provide guidance to a victim who has been severely traumatized by a violent sexual crime. Case studies can be a great way to emphasize the decision-making process for some victims. It is the role of the advocate to introduce the SART program to the victim and to ask how she wishes to proceed. The advocate trainer should illustrate the emotional spectrum victims may follow and further discuss posttraumatic stress. The joint devel-opment of safety measures between police and advocacy is a great training tool that can highlight the goals of the advocacy role.

Case Management and Follow-Up Care. It is the rape care advocate who will give the most comprehensive support to the victim after the incident is reported. Case man-agement for all team members is essential; however, it is good practice for the advo-cate trainer to really show team members the amount of work put into a single case. Other team members should know about the difficult and varied tasks an advocate must fulfill. The SART training module is a great opportunity to exemplify the ardu-ous road to successful prosecution. One final area to cover during training is to discuss the importance of follow-up care from all team members. This includes preparation for court proceedings, follow-up medical care, follow-up referral, and any other areas that the advocate trainer feels are essential for other SART members to follow up on in order provide comprehensive and complete services.

Medical Component

SANEs are perhaps the backbone of the SART model and the driving force in the United States for perfection of SART implementation. The medical and health compo-nent of the SART model should always be at the forefront of victim treatment. If the person comes forward to police first, the officer should instinctively be thinking of the health of the victim. The SANEs that are presenting on their roles within the SART system should emphasize some generalities as well as some specifics that are involved in their function within the team approach.

SANE Role. By virtue of their training in the field, SANEs have demonstrated that they have a comprehensive view of victim services. SANEs do not take this job because of the money or perks involved. The role of the SANE is pivotal to the success of the comprehensive SART program and, ultimately, the successful prosecution. When discussing the role, it is important to discuss the training required in order to be certified as a SANE and how that specific training is geared toward helping both the law enforcement and advocacy components. Other team members may be less interested in medical jargon; however, it is always useful to gain insight into the complexity of the SANE role. It would be wise to select a very outgoing and experienced SANE to introduce, or reintroduce as the case might be, the role of this profession in the SART model, to allay the fear of ineptness or inadequacy that each member may have of the other's role. Team members do not have to prove their credentials or training, but walking into a room full of police officers and lawyers is not for the meek.

Forensic Medical Exam and Equipment. The forensic medical examination is perhaps where the genesis of SANE and SART is located. A review of all state requirements for the exam should be discussed at length. Forms to be used, essentials of the exam, time frames of when an exam can and cannot be performed, conditions of the exam, and internal protocol considerations are imperative for all team members. All members present at the training are professionals, so the SANE trainer should be as frank and honest as needed; case studies are an excellent idea. A visit to the medical facility where exams are to be conducted is perhaps the best training method to illustrate the exam process. Police officers are strongly impressed by the evidentiary skills of SANEs, and bringing the police officers into this world will do wonders for team interaction and professional reciprocity. The most important topics to discuss are the right to privacy, reactive and proactive medical care, documentation, and patient education.

Evidence Collection and Storage. The SANE trainer should specifically discuss the practices and methods of evidence collection and packaging, particularly for law enforcement. The sexual assault exam evidence kit should be a standard kit that includes the DNA collections and any other evidence collected by the SANE. A demonstration using an actual kit can show the contents as the kit is sealed following the exam. The chain of evidence custody and evidence storage protocols should be discussed so there is no confusion as to expected roles. The SANE training module can include any other items of interest for the particular team; however, the essentials must be covered so the members can fully appreciate the role, and the SANE members can express their goals and expectations.

Law Enforcement Component

Training by law enforcement should be left as the last SART topic. This helps to identify law enforcement as being the last, but certainly not the least, component of the SART model. Any SART program should emphasize the advocacy and medical care as the most immediate of services to a victim of sexual assault; law enforcement should, until all immediate victim care is complete, remain a supportive and guiding team member that will also provide comprehensive services when requested by a victim. For training the SART model, it is essential that police officers not provide separate and exclusive training for their officers; the involved officers are now part of a team for this purpose, and training should be no exception. Police officers are often xenophobic when it comes to those in the mental health, legal, or medical fields, and this is not acceptable in the SART model. To successfully integrate the SART mentality, the police trainer needs to open the lines of communication and relax the atmosphere to gain real and supportive insight into services. The interview with a sexual assault victim should be considered different in the sense that an officer's mannerisms, tone of voice, and question framing can greatly affect the victim's confidence and trust factors. Law enforcement officers are typically trained to follow statements that seem confusing or misleading; trauma from an act of violence can greatly impede perception or memory, so care should be given to root out what may be important to prosecution. Rape care advocates and prosecutors can often facilitate training in interview techniques by elaborating the victim's and judiciary's points of view, and it should be considered as vital training for the law enforcement component's success.

Law Enforcement Role. The law enforcement role in a sexual assault investigation has been unfairly treated in both the news media and movies. To emphasize this, the police trainer may show some of the stereotypes that have been portrayed of uncaring and misguided police officers in relation to victims of sexual assault. The role of the law enforcement officer must be stressed as one that is crucial to comprehensive and victim-centered services. The trainer should discuss the role of the responding officer, the investigating officer, the supervisor, the crime scene investigation, and the victim services function of the agency. The important feature of this module is to stress that law enforcement, like any profession, is not without its problems; however, any agency committed to the goals of a SART program is indeed a forward-thinking agency. There will be many outside the law enforcement agency attending the training that will have preconceived notions based on a past negative experience. The trainer, as if this was not difficult already, must never minimize the importance of the role of the law enforcement component.

Training and Experience. Law enforcement training and experience is unique among the SART members because it involves a broad range rather than the sometimes narrow focus of some other team members. While the focused view of both rape care advocates and medical team members will serve victims well with individual services, police officers must have varied skills to be efficient in their role. Training in crime scene management, statement analysis, patrol techniques, interview skills, and photography are essential for the responding and investigating officers. The police trainer must describe the professional expertise of some officers within their agency so other team members can recognize the skills of the agency with which they are serving. Police officers take their jobs very seriously, and, when recognized as professionals in their own right, they can be a vital tool for the entire SART program in many areas. The relative experience of the officers should be emphasized; rookie officers have much to learn of a victim-centered approach, but the SART model can become a critical element in their early experience. It is the seasoned officers with twenty plus years on the job who may be the toughest officers to bring into the SART fold, as they may be jaded to the team concept and are less trusting of other professionals. The police trainer and other trainers must gain the mutual respect of these seasoned officers and work to overcome the obstacles of being on the job; their life experience is great, and seasoned officers can become critical members of the team.

Law Enforcement Investigation. The police trainer should always emphasize the very misunderstood world of law enforcement investigations. Again, popular media does not serve the function of law enforcement well. Today's police officer is well educated and well trained to provide the most comprehensive investigation to meet both victim and court standards. The police trainer should stress the overall investigative model within the SART model. The chain of command within an agency should be explained, and the varied functions from the chief of police, to the responding officer, to the supervisor and the investigating officer as well should also be explained. Crime scene management techniques should be emphasized as essential. Taking members through a crime scene case file can help illustrate this as can actual evidence from prior cases. Interview skills of the police investigator can be stressed as essential to successful prosecution; it should also be strongly suggested that victims should not have to continually recount the incident during initial reporting and throughout the entire investigation.

Prosecution. The prosecution area of training may be handled by the police trainer with, perhaps, the help of the SART's legal advisors. An explanation of court procedures and court schedules is an essential element. To demonstrate the difficult nature of prosecution and court testimony, it is strongly recommended that the entire team witness and participate in a mock court case where team members are on the witness stand being grilled by defense attorneys questioning their role in the SART model. While the overall goal of all SART services is to provide comprehensive and equal services to victims of sexual assault, an underlying goal is also successful prosecution of those committing such offenses. A review of case files will also help demonstrate the prosecution phase of a sexual assault. This may also be a great time to discuss problems within the criminal justice system, the challenges to evidence that may occur, and the tragedies of justice that may occur at the expense of both victims and professionals serving the SART program.

Community Partners and Program Component

Essential to any good SART program that wants to be well received is the involvement of the community. The community should be trained on the availability of services, the services provided, and SART concepts. The level of community involvement with the SART should be decided early in the process of setting up the training. In an effort to build the team first and allow a level training field, it is prudent to train SART members separate from community leaders and members of the community. It may be a goal to even have SART members train in the community after learning more about the roles of others who will serve with them. What is essential is that core elements of the community, especially those who may fear talking with police or seeking medical help, be involved. If the coverage area includes a college campus, people at the college who can help disseminate information about the SART program should be identified. If the community is racially or ethnically diverse, cultural leaders who can assist in reaching out to victims of sexual assault should be contacted. The Internet, posters, handbills, pamphlets, confidential phone lines—anything that can be used to advertise SART services to an unaccepting and sometimes intolerant public—should be used. Elected officials should be invited to attend portions of the training, and their assistance should be sought in furthering the goals of both the team and the training.

On a college campus, there are many willing and able departments outside of the SART model that will readily assist with facilitating training and also become active allies for the overall program. In addition to university officers and deans, SART members should consider programs for first-year experience departments, Greek life, athletics, residence life, and judicial affairs, among others. Particular emphasis on programs and training should be placed on those who may have first contact with victims such as faculty, resident assistants, peer leaders, police dispatchers, safety officers, advisors, and counselors. It may not be necessary to get into all of the specifics for team members; however, an overview of the SART mechanism, dissemination of institutional policies and contact information, and even advice recommendation ideas to facilitate both victim utilization of services and evidence preservation and SART activation methods would help these individuals better assist victims at a time when it is needed most.

TRAINING ENVIRONMENT

As with any important training, the training schedule and presenter lineup should be set up well in advance. Training should be arranged to maximize attendance and participation; team members may work varied shifts in the evening, overnight, and on weekends. The location selected should be conducive to support learning as well as in close proximity to team members' locations. For some team members, this will be their first exposure to certain topics, so a fast-paced day with highly stressful topics is out of the question. It might be useful to have a counselor on staff to talk about the stressful topics or a quiet room where people can reflect on difficult topics; A SART must take care of its members in order to effectively help its victims.

The SART coordinator should introduce all speakers and topics as a way to meld all the various components. However long the training sessions are, schedules and work conditions should be respected; professionals are needed at their places of work. There should be no reason a team cannot be trained within a two-day period and perhaps an eight- to ten-hour session depending on the presentation skills of the trainers. Break periods should be utilized, and, if at all possible, refreshments and lunch should be provided. At the end of the day, trainees should evaluate the session and provide a recap of team expectations; on-call lists and any other important materials should be provided while most team members are available and listening. The day should be enjoyable, fun, and meaningful to the SART members—they deserve it.

PUTTING TRAINING INTO ACTION

The most difficult task of the entire SART operation is to put the process into real action. Team members should be able to reflect on the presentations with regard to not only who does what, but, from a victim's point of view, what has been done already and what needs to be done. There can be no greater insult to a person traumatized than having to relive the trauma through bureaucracy and ineptness. Trainees must be given written resources at training and on a continual basis so that they may be able to refer and refresh what they have learned and what they are putting into action. Some SARTs may see activity around the clock; others may see reporting periodically, and this can be troublesome when the team does not retrain, practice, or communicate.

Putting training into action can be a difficult process. SART coordinators will want to closely monitor team members through a variety of methods to ensure that training is meeting the goals of the SART mechanism, and the team should be either retrained or the training methods adjusted if required. The use of postincident reports and case studies can help solidify training assessment and reflect on future training goals and needs.

USING POSTINCIDENT REPORTS AND CASE STUDIES AS CONTINUOUS TRAINING TOOLS

As a way to provide continual training (see Figure 9.1) within the spirit of the SART model, the use of postincident reports and case studies can provide for valuable insight into both the administration of the program as well as identify shortcomings that may occur. A postincident report should originate from either the SART coordinator or the agency that originates the report and services. The report should ask each SART area to summarize its response and point out any inefficiencies as well as accomplishments of services. This will also serve to avoid redundancies in victim services and assist further agencies with their offers of support. At the conclusion of immediate and investigative services, the postincident report should be submitted to the SART coordinator for review. Any issues that may arise from the postincident report should be addressed function by function so that similar problems are avoided; agencies must not look at the postincident report as a reflection of their agency; rather it should be looked at as a chance to improve services further. In a campus setting, postincident reports can include a review of protocol adherence and assurance of compliance with all federal requirements of reporting.

Case studies, as we know, can present challenges for future training sessions. Before the case study can be considered, all privacy laws and protocols must be observed. The case study shows the trainee a step-by-step analysis of just what went right and where

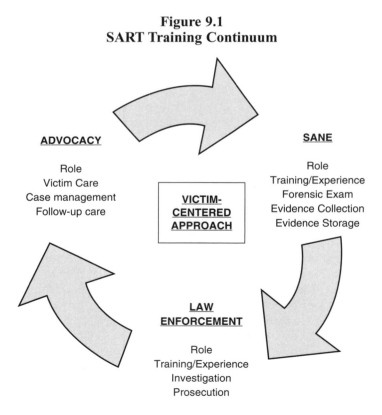

Figure 9.1
SART Training Continuum

ADVOCACY

Role
Victim Care
Case management
Follow-up care

SANE

Role
Training/Experience
Forensic Exam
Evidence Collection
Evidence Storage

VICTIM-CENTERED APPROACH

LAW ENFORCEMENT

Role
Training/Experience
Investigation
Prosecution

a SART response can go wrong. As a precaution, it is also wise to redact any professional's names in the case study. The best thing about SART case studies is that the vast majority will show just what is right about the workmanship of each team member and the victim services provided. Trainers will want to use examples of actual written work and photography to evaluate and improve communication and response.

Another tool that may assist in ongoing training is the use of training evaluation. At the conclusion of training, trainees should be provided with a series of questions related to the training, and they are asked to be specific about goals and achievement of those goals. Input from fellow professionals should be utilized to generate new and exciting ways to present difficult topics. The advice of others should be considered, and the overall message the audience is sending should be heard; changes should be made so long as the core goals remain the same. Evaluations may assist in identifying whether further training is required, whether an individual desires more advanced or specialized training, or whether training facilities or trainers need to be adjusted to meet the needs of the audience.

THE PERFECT SART TRAINING MODEL

Like so many things in life, there is no perfect SART training model. However, the wheel does not have to be reinvented. As training goals are set, all team members should be included in the process; it is key to remember the victim-centered approach, and this will make training second nature. Time frames should be set; the training should be organized and continuous. Refresher training should occur at no longer than one-year intervals. If presenters are forward thinking and utilize modern presentation techniques as well as case studies and a little bit of audience involvement, the team members will be provided with the necessary tools they need to succeed. Food should be served (if affordable), and there should be planned breaks. Constant communication between team members, administrators, and community members will allow for a continuum of training that will serve all goals well. All team members have the ability to teach something about the way every other team member does his/her job—it may just be exactly what a sexual assault victim needs to become a survivor.

References

Ledray, Linda E. (2001). Evidence collection and care of the sexual assault survivor: The SANE –SART response. *Violence against women online resources.* Retrieved May 8, 2007, from http://www.mincava.umn.edu/documents/commissioned/ 2forensicevidence/2forensicevidence.pdf

United States Department of Justice. (2005). *Sexual assault on campus: What colleges and universities are doing about it* (NIJS Publication No. NCJ 205521). Washington, DC: National Institute on Justice.

Chapter 10

Putting It All Together for a Best Practice Approach

by Donna M. Barry, APN, FN-CSA, and Paul M. Cell, Chief of Police

A solid foundation is necessary for any type of best practice model and vital to its success. For sexual assault response teams (SARTs), this foundation will be reflected through an institution's policies, regulations, and actions regarding sexual violence. The Office on Violence Against Women has created Minimum Standards for Creating a Coordinated Community Response to Violence Against Women on Campus as a comprehensive resource. This chapter provides an overview of these standards as well as additional considerations to support a successful response (see Exhibit 10.1).

INSTITUTIONAL COMMITMENT

No matter how many services are offered to victims or the manner in which they are provided, an institution's administrative leadership will need to demonstrate a "visible commitment" to end sexual violence in order to create a successful SART. A visible commitment cannot be solely interpreted to mean active participation in specific campus events by provosts, chancellors, and university presidents. It needs to be evident in policies that reflect intolerance to sexual violence and the severity of these offenses, a response that acknowledges victim dynamics and meets victim needs, and prompt actions that ensure offender accountability in a manner that is fair to both the accused and the victim.

Often this is the most difficult obstacle to overcome in developing an effective response system. As stated in Chapter 1, multiple variables can influence an administrator's perspective on "what is best for the community." So, the question remains: How does one convince the decision makers to take a stand? The answer lies primarily through assessment and strategic actions.

A thorough assessment of the institution's political climate is important in determining which individuals in leadership positions are more apt to "buy in" to a commitment on the issues. These key players can also provide much insight into effective approaches to more resistant leadership that can lead to success. Again, the importance of solid research regarding the need for services will lend credence to a proposal for even the key players that are approached in the initial phases of development.

The introduction to Part 3 lists several "pearls of wisdom" that can be utilized for an effective strategic plan. In some respects, institutional administrators prefer to see a business plan approach when presented with a new concept. Thus, application of these suggestions can be used to create a fact-based introduction to the problem, effective solutions including risks and benefits, the role of all constituencies, and a cost analysis.

Once an institutional commitment is accomplished, current policies, regulations, and departmental procedures can be reviewed and revised to reflect this commitment. A critical evaluation and revision of these areas is often a long and arduous process but well worth the efforts involved. Prospective students, parents, and community resources will gain assurance of the institution's acknowledgment and sense of responsibility toward the issue of sexual violence. Many schools have actually taken a proactive perspective, viewing the changes to policies and procedures as a media opportunity. It is viewed as an opportunity to identify the institution as a campus intolerant of these behaviors as well as one that is not fearful of taking a stand. This alone begins to dispel the "ivory tower" myth and places a college or university in the forefront in addressing sexual violence.

Creation of a Position Statement is an effective way to capture the essence of an institution's commitment. It can summarize acknowledgment of the issues, actions taken to reduce and respond to incidents, as well as compliance with regulations. This statement need only be two or three paragraphs, which will allow posting in brochures, media campaigns, Web sites, and other means of distribution of information to students, staff, and parents.

Once a Position Statement is written and approved, a full evaluation of current policies regarding sexual violence can be done. Most campuses have multiple publications (i.e., faculty and staff handbooks, human resource policies, handbooks for undergraduate and graduate students, conduct codes, and residential life policies). It is vital that each document provides the same policy statement, and the policy statement flows directly from the Position Statement of the institution. These statements also need to reflect how the individual campus meets compliance with federal and state regulations as well as procedures to assist victims of sexual violence.

A review and possible revision of the Code of Conduct and disciplinary process is especially important. The judicial process needs to be considerate of victim response and needs, but it should also protect the rights of the accused and provide due process for both parties. Utilization of the Model Code of Conduct (see Appendix H) as a guide is encouraged with individualization to each campus's organizational structure. The sanctions for incidents of sexual violence should also reflect the seriousness of the violation. It is usually not recommended that a Code of Conduct integrate actual statutory codes, but rather be founded in these laws in regard to rights, violations, process, and levels of sanctions.

The creation of a Position Statement and revision of policies and procedures will require input from several departments on campus. Legal counsel, Title IX compliance officers, Jeanne Clery Disclosure of Campus Security Policy and Campus Crime Statistics Act (Clery Act; 20 U.S.C. § 1092(f); see also Chapter 4 and Appendix D) coordinators, law enforcement, health services, student affairs administrators, judicial affairs officers, community partnerships, and many others may need to be involved in order to address the multiple aspects of these policies. This process will be time consuming and will have delays and obstacles. As with many institutional initiatives, change can be slow and happen with resistance. Perseverance is important since this area is critical to the success of a campus SART.

DEFINING AN EFFECTIVE RESPONSE

A SART structure will vary considerably from campus to campus. Some institutions may be able to provide all services directly from campus resources. Others will need to rely solely on outside community services and partnerships. The majority however, will use a combination of both campus and municipal resources (American College Health Association, 2008).

Despite different structures, certain critical concepts need to be a part of all campus SARTs. These components are identified in Figure 10.1 as an *Effective Response Pyramid* that can be used as a development guide and are explained in detail below.

Victim Driven

The provision of a victim-centered approach to campus SARTs is probably the most important factor in an effective response. Victims of sexual assault often sense a loss of control during and after an incident. This is compounded by other common emotions such as guilt, self-blame, embarrassment, fear of punishment, and many more as stated in Chapter 7. Recognition and understanding of the psychology of victim response should be the primary consideration during the development process.

This perspective can assist in creating mechanisms within policies and procedures that place all decisions of response and action in the hands of the victim. A truly victim-centered approach is utilized when the victim's wishes and needs remain the primary goal of the SART and determine every aspect of response. By doing so, what occurs after an assault and how an institution reacts is completely *driven* by a victim's choices. An example of this approach can be seen in the following example:

> *Example:* Victoria, a nineteen-year-old basketball player, reported she was sexually assaulted at an off-campus house rented by several members of the university's football team. She recalls very few details except that the individual who allegedly assaulted her was not a fellow student, and they both had been drinking heavily at the time of the assault. The victim's teammates brought Victoria to the university Police Department shortly after the incident. The victim was offered multiple options for services and response. Her primary concerns revolved around possible injuries and exposure to infection. However, she also chose to have a forensic examination completed but did not want to file criminal charges at that time. At her request, a rape care advocate was contacted and responded as well.

Figure 10.1
Effective Response Pyramid

Victoria was examined by a Sexual Assault Nurse Examiner (SANE) for injuries, treated for potential infections and pregnancy, and a forensic examination was completed. The Sexual Assault Forensic Examiner (SAFE) Kit was securely stored as evidence by police and recorded as an anonymous report of a Jane Doe assault. Law enforcement did not investigate the incident further at the victim's request but held the evidence in case the victim chose to file charges at a future date. University administrators were notified that an assault had occurred and were given only Clery Act statistical information without personal identification. Since the victim declined further services from the institution and did not wish to be identified, no action was taken by administrators.Under a sexual assault victim amnesty policy developed by the university, the victim was not penalized for a violation of underage drinking. All available resources were provided to the victim in writing. Permission was obtained from the victim for the rape care advocate to also work with her teammates and inform her coach of the incident. The coach agreed to work closely with the entire team in the form of support and future prevention programming and to assist the victim as needed.

The primary questions to ask when determining a victim-driven methodology are:

- What procedures can be implemented that will encourage victims to seek services and feel protected by the institution? Suggestions include:
    1. Blind or anonymous reporting in which a victim can obtain all SART services without identifying herself is available,
    2. Services demonstrate competency in responding to all victims regardless of gender, sexual orientation, or disability. Just as the demographics of campuses vary, so do those of victims. Recognition of the varying needs and

concerns of *all* victims and the ability to respond effectively is essential to maintain a victim-centered service.

3. A sexual assault victim amnesty policy is in place in which a victim will not be punished for behaviors that may violate state statutes or the campus Code of Conduct.

4. The actions taken by law enforcement and campus administrators after an incident are determined by the victim's wishes alone, unless there is a potential safety concern for the victim or the campus community. In this instance, a victim's identity is protected as best as possible by the institution.

5. An emphasis is placed on confidentiality when all training and education campaigns occur. It can safely be stated that victims truly do not want others to know what has happened. Thus, a focus on confidentiality assurance should take place in order to allay this concern. Otherwise, victims fear notifying anyone, especially those who may hold a role of authority.

- Who *must* know about the incident and what information *must* be shared? It is important to determine the necessary dissemination of information regarding a sexual assault incident. Administrators need to stay informed of what is happening on campus and with all students in order to carry out their job responsibilities. Residence life should be informed that an incident has occurred in a residence hall. In the same manner, student affairs leadership, public safety officials, and conduct officers need to be aware of these incidents. However, if a victim has chosen options that do not require action on the part of these or other administrators, it is unnecessary to reveal the identity of a victim. Thus, unless a victim grants permission to be identified to specific individuals on campus, the only information that is necessary to be shared is the statistical data required for reporting regulations:

    1. What is the date of incident?
    2. What is the time of incident?
    3. What is the location of incident?
    4. Is victim male or female?
    5. Is victim a student, staff, or visitor?
    6. What is the age of victim?
    7. Was physical force or a weapon used?
    8. Is the alleged offender a male or female?
    9. Is the alleged offender a stranger, acquaintance, or dating partner?
    10. Is the alleged offender a student, staff, or nonstudent?
    11. Was the safety of the victim and campus community assessed and a timely notification done if appropriate?
    12. If a timely notification was issued, was the victim informed of the necessity of this action?
    13. If a timely notification was issued, was the victim's identity protected to the best extent possible?
    14. Was the victim given a copy of the Campus Sexual Assault Victims' Bill of Rights (20 U.S.C. § 1092(f)(8))?
    15. Was the victim offered all options for assistance?
    16. Which services did the victim choose to utilize?

The concept of granting one individual, especially a student, total control over decisions regarding how an institution responds to a sexual assault is quite unique and may cause resistance from many constituents. The lack of control felt by the victim is transferred to all parties involved with response and contradicts the traditional manner in which most institutions have addressed sexual assault incidents. The importance of this concept cannot be overemphasized. Without a victim-driven system, individuals will be resistant to come forward to obtain services for fear of punishment and lack of confidentiality. As a result, underreporting of incidents will continue, the institution will fail in assisting victims to begin the healing process, and justice will not be served for the victim.

Timely and Accessible

As stated in previous chapters, the dynamics of campus social life, compounded by alcohol use, place college students at high risk for sexual violence. Most social events that increase this risk occur during evening hours and on weekends. Therefore, it can safely be assumed that the majority of sexual assaults involving college students occur during nonbusiness hours. In addition, many institutions now offer opportunities for coursework during semester breaks and summer months. As a result, colleges and universities commonly have students on campus throughout the year, extending the traditional model of the ten-month academic calendar. These factors need to be considered in determining the availability of SART services. If the SART is truly victim centered and driven, it must be available to victims at the time the victim desires services. One can never predict when a victim will seek care. Although many delay reporting, the majority of assaults occur during nonbusiness hours, and it cannot be assumed that a victim will not choose to access services shortly after an incident. Thus, the solution can only be to offer all services twenty-four hours a day, seven days a week throughout the calendar year.

For those campuses that choose to develop services on campus, this can be a complicated issue but should not be a deterrent. It may necessitate the implementation of an on-call system for SART members. Campus responders can also be supplemented by back-up services from available community resources during nonbusiness hours. However a campus chooses to implement 24/7 availability, it is vital that coordination and oversight of the methodology takes place to ensure a team approach and good communication among responders.

Services that are available immediately upon the request of a victim are truly a best practice approach. The key to their use, however, is accessibility. Prior to the inception of a universal 911 system for emergencies, individuals needing acute care were often confused and frustrated attempting to obtain help. This frustration and confusion caused delayed responses by emergency services and often deaths and increased morbidity.

In the same manner, sexual assault victims who attempt to access care may experience these same difficulties due to lack of information on services or poor communication on how to obtain services. The suggestions listed below will assist in improving access to care for college victims:

- *Effective communication of available services.* This is the area in which institutions need to "think out of the brochure box" and implement strategies for communication of services that the current generation of students utilize. The millennial student of today seldom accesses information in written form. Use of the Internet is the more common mode. Information regarding the SART should be obtainable easily and quickly throughout the institution's Web site. Suggested methods might be:
  1. A designated URL specific to the SART;
  2. SART services linked to multiple department homepages; and/or
  3. SART listing in alphabetical and/or "quick links" Web site menu.

- *Multiple points of entry.* When the psychology of victim response is taken into consideration, it can be concluded that victims will only seek care from a location in which they are comfortable—an individual or department where they feel safe and have a sense of trust in sharing their experience. Anecdotal experiences often refer to this as the "back door" approach to care. Many health care providers can share tales in which a student uses emergency contraception or sexually transmitted infection (STI) screening as a reason for a visit, finding this a far more comfortable topic to use than sexual assault in order to enter the system.

Students will often turn to peers, mentors, student leadership, coaches, and others that they feel will provide nonthreatening assistance. In order to ensure that victims will be able to access care regardless of the point of entry, training needs to occur for all individuals to whom victims may report (see Chapter 9). Thus, campus-wide programming about services, options, and how to assist victims will be an important consideration in a successful SART service.

Comprehensive and Coordinated

A system that offers multiple options and meets all victim needs is another component of an effective response. In some respects, institutions of higher education are held to a higher standard than a community SART with regard to the required response to sexual assault incidents. Within a traditional SART, a comprehensive approach would include options for law enforcement involvement, advocacy, medical care, and a forensic examination. Besides the initial response from these members, follow-up and resource referrals are normally offered as well. A campus SART would include all of these services with additional response components that supplement the traditional SART response to meet the unique needs of campus victims and maintain compliance with federal regulations.

Therefore, a comprehensive campus SART would include the following response components:

1. Law enforcement;
2. Medical care;
3. Forensic examination;
4. Advocacy;
5. Academic accommodations;
6. Housing accommodations;
7. Judicial affairs; and
8. Follow-up counseling.

It is important to remember the concept of a victim-driven approach when integrating these components. Each action needs to be a free-standing option and not required on the part of the victim. Mandatory notifications or actions would only be appropriate under the circumstances in which victim safety or the safety of others may be in jeopardy.

That is not to say that some of the choices may be interdependent on each other. For example, a victim who requests that the alleged offender be removed or relocated in a residence hall would most likely be required by the institution to file either criminal charges or a judicial complaint against the accused student. If not, the loss of housing privileges without notification of cause may be viewed as a violation of the rights of the accused student. The victim should, however, have the option to request her own room relocation and not be required to file specific complaints. This same concept would also apply to a request for academic accommodations.

There are no recommended ways in which these additional options are integrated into the SART. The primary consideration when determining the best approach for a campus will be what works best for a victim. *Who* responds should only be determined by the victim.

Another appropriate consideration will be who fulfills the response role for each service. For example, many institutions currently use counseling staff in the advocacy role. The determination of whether counseling staff actually are considered rape care advocates during response needs to be made as well as when the role of the advocate ends and counselor begins. This is an important legal question, especially if a sexual assault case goes forward as a criminal case. Issues of these specific roles, client confidentiality, records subpoena, and other legal questions can be answered by an institution's legal counsel.

Given the multiple options that need to be available to campus victims, the need for coordination and oversight of response is vital to an effective response. Even with the best intentions, a "who's on first" scenario can occur without a designated individual to coordinate efforts. As a case in point, the following example demonstrates the difficulties that may occur.

> ***Example:*** In the fall of 2005, a twenty-year-old resident student reported to campus law enforcement that she had been assaulted by an acquaintance in her room while watching a movie the night prior to the report. The alleged offender was a fellow student who lived across the hall from the young woman.
>
> The victim accessed services through her resident assistant and chose all options for response including relocation of her room and removal of the assailant from the residence hall and shared classes. The victim left campus for the weekend with the understanding that all requests would be completed by her return the following Monday.
>
> When the victim arrived at class for the first time after the incident, the alleged offender was present. She promptly left the class and reported this to the dean of students. She then returned to her residence hall only to discover that the new room had not been prepared for her move and, in fact, the individual accused of the assault had not been removed.
>
> After review, it was determined that miscommunication and lack of follow-up among responders had occurred regarding these aspects of the victim's requests. Each responder believed another individual was handling these requests and did not see the need to check whether all requests had been completed. In addition, the victim was required to interact with numerous individuals and repeatedly explain what was needed.

Lack of coordination of services in the above example caused further trauma to the victim, enraged her parents, and eventually caused the student to transfer to another institution. Both criminal and judicial charges were dropped by the victim, and justice was never served for the victim or the community. Thus, the importance of a designated individual to coordinate, oversee, and evaluate SART response is evident. The institution was fortunate that legal action was not taken by the victim or her parents against the school for failure to adequately address victim needs.

An appropriate question to ask during SART development is who will fulfill the role of coordination and oversight. Again, there are no specific recommendations. Institutions can make different decisions based on what works effectively for their campus. Factors to consider in making this determination include the following:

1. The individual should be at a level of administrative authority capable of making primary decisions for the university and SART members.

2. The individual should have an intimate knowledge of sexual violence issues, victim needs, response roles, and the concept of a SART response.

3. The individual should not have a conflict of interest. Unless there will be shared administrative responsibilities between two persons that provides checks and balances for objectivity, the position will be a difficult one for someone who also holds another role in the SART response. For instance, if a dean of students fills this role and also is the individual responsible for judicial decisions, it may be difficult to be privy to detailed information of an incident and then remain objective during the judicial process.

Specialized Cross-Training of All Responders

The importance of training in providing an effective SART response has been stressed in Chapter 9 and need not be repeated. It would be prudent however to emphasize some of the primary points of the chapter. Recommended areas for training are:

1. Objectives and purpose of the SART;
2. Coordination between campus/community responders, as appropriate;
3. Individual roles and responsibilities;
4. Roles and responsibilities of other members;
5. Institutional procedures for response;
6. Individual departmental procedures for response;
7. Federal, state, and campus regulations;
8. Campus culture and dynamics;
9. Alcohol and drugs and the impact on sexual violence;
10. Nonstranger assault; and
11. Offender profiling.

In a best practice approach, the above training topics are covered prior to initiation of a campus SART for all responders, and they are repeated yearly. Community partners that respond as part of a campus SART will require the same training. Responders from the community may not understand the campus culture or be aware of the specific needs or rights of campus victims. It is critical that a SART system that utilizes a combination of campus and community resources has the same foundation of knowledge and work together so that identical services are provided regardless of where a victim receives care.

Similar but abbreviated campus-wide training is then provided to administrative leadership, faculty, staff, student leadership, and others identified as a potential point of entry for victims to access services. For additional guidelines and considerations in regard to campus training on sexual violence, see The Office on Violence Against Women's Minimum Standards of Training for Campus Security Personnel and Campus Disciplinary and Judicial Boards (Exhibit 10.2).

Addresses the Needs of Victims and the Justice System

A comprehensive response system that meets all of the above criteria will assuredly appear to meet the needs of campus victims from an organizational perspective. Theoretically, it should also assist the justice system in holding individuals accountable for the crime of sexual assault. A true measurement of this component however would be most accurate if this question was asked of victims that have received services through a campus SART as well as the overall campus community. In other words, does the campus response system actually function in the manner it states on paper, or is a campus simply giving "lip service" to its response?

An assessment of this important component can be done in several ways and covers several aspects of the SART system:

- *Awareness of services throughout the campus community.* Surveys by students and faculty/staff are a simple way to determine how successful training and programming has been to spread the word of available services. These should include questions regarding:
  o Identification of additional training needs for judicial boards; and
  o Sanctions delivered, where appropriate, based on type of offense and student status, which did not impact on type of sanction (i.e., leadership or influential position, athlete position).

- *Use of postcall action reports.* The implementation of a formal postresponse tool by all responders will assist in the identification of strengths and weaknesses of a single incident and reveal trends in response services and reporting statistics. These reports are completed individually by all responders involved in a specific incident to identify:
  o Proper use of procedures by all responders;
  o Identification of obstacles within individual response areas;
  o Unique issues that may need to be considered in future SART response; and
  o Ineffective or non–victim-centered interactions on the part of a specific responder.

  The review of all postcall reports can also help to identify trends in location of incidents or specific behavioral risks by students that can be addressed through additional educational programming beyond the scope of the SART.

- *Use of victim surveys.* Conceptually, these tools are the most valuable method to evaluate services since the primary mission of a campus SART is victim driven. Anecdotally however, there appears to be a very low return rate and thus can be unreliable as the only means of assessment. Despite a reduced response rate from victims, it is suggested that integration of this type of instrument always be a required component of the SART. Even a small amount of feedback from victims can offer significant insight into the effectiveness of campus response services.

An assessment of whether a campus SART meets the needs of the justice system can be a more complex process. Effectiveness relies primarily on evaluating how many cases actually move forward to the court system as well as the number of conviction rates. There are multiple variables that may impact on this area, and some will be out of the control of those responsible for the effectiveness of the SART. In particular, campuses can have minimal influence on local prosecutor actions and his/her commitment to bringing sexual assault cases to trial. In the same respect, the response of judges and juries can be highly unpredictable. There are some areas however that can be measured. These would be:

- *The effective use of SANEs.* Yearly competency testing is necessary to be assured that evidence collection is done accurately and according to procedures, and that chain of custody is continually maintained between law enforcement and the examiner. Communication between these two disciplines is critical to the investigative process as well and should be monitored for effectiveness on a continuous basis and revised as necessary.

- *The investigative skills and techniques of law enforcement.* Specialized training in those areas specific to sexual assault criminal investigations is especially important. Prosecutors can only be effective if they have strong evidence to prove their case, and they rely on law enforcement to provide this information. Thus, officers will be at a disadvantage in gathering critical information for a case without this type of training.

- *Determination of effectiveness of responder interactions with a victim.* This is a difficult area to measure and will require a great deal of self-reflection on the part of responders. Ideally, all individuals involved in a campus SART response, including community partners, will have an opportunity prior to start up to evaluate his/her own personal feelings and potential biases regarding sexual assault victims in general and campus victims in particular. For instance, outside providers may have a shaded perspective on the social behaviors of college students and specifically those of college women. As a result, myths and beliefs about sexual assault are perpetuated due to lack of knowledge and understanding of a campus environment. This perspective can have a negative influence on the efforts placed on the investigative aspect of an incident if those individuals feel it "wasn't really sexual assault." In the same respect, campus administrators may also hold personal beliefs regarding assault that prevent them from interacting with victims in a compassionate and nonjudgmental manner.

Failure to identify and implement actions for improvement and change in the above areas will result in services that do not meet the needs of victims, whether through the campus system or outside partnerships, and the system will be unsuccessful in the provision of effective services. As a result, those responsible for meeting the needs of the justice system will be unable to move forward and seek justice for victims.

Compliance With Federal and State Regulations

Interpretation of federal and state regulations can be confusing and overwhelming to many involved in creating a campus SART. It is best, after review of Chapter 4, to seek guidance from campus compliance officers, institutional legal counsel, and outside resources with expertise in these areas. For federal regulations, Security on Campus, Inc. (http://www.securityoncampus.org) serves as the primary national resource for interpretation, training, and monitoring of these regulations. The organization can provide invaluable insight into the methodology used by a campus to meet compliance in all aspects of sexual assault mandates.

Many states also have statutes specific to sexual assault response that will influence SART development. It is strongly recommended that institutions become familiar with those laws unique to their state in order to assure any necessary state requirements. These regulations may also provide guidance in determining the specific training, roles, responsibilities, and limitations of each response discipline involved in the SART.

RESPONSE STRUCTURE

The traditional SART model involves the triad of law enforcement, advocacy, and the medical/forensic examiner as the primary responders when the SART system is activated. The additional components required for a campus response, when added as primary responders, may be overwhelming to a victim. Thus, it is recommended that a campus team be divided into a layered response system. This would divide response members as follows (assuming the victim has chosen all options for services):

- *Primary response.* Law enforcement, advocacy, and the medical/forensic examiner are the initial team activated at the time of an incident and meet the critical needs early in the response effort. After all services are provided, the secondary response occurs.

- *Secondary response.* Housing and academic response, judicial affairs, and follow-up counseling occur after the primary response. The timing of each of these options may vary based on the time of care and the victim's wishes. As an example, housing and academic arrangements would most likely be the most immediate need. Filing a disciplinary complaint may occur in the next few days as along with counseling services.

Formatting the SART response into a layered approach protects the victim against interacting with multiple individuals in the first hours after an assault. It also provides the critical services necessary to address the most immediate victim needs and preserves valuable evidence in a timely manner, thus assisting the justice system (a sample SART structure appears in Figure 10.2).

PROCEDURES AND PROTOCOLS FOR RESPONSE

In order for a timely, efficient, and coordinated system to be developed, campus-wide activation protocols will need to be created. This can be broken down into two areas for procedural development:

- The campus-wide process of response based on "where" a victim enters the SART system; and

- The internal procedures for responder's area or department.

Campus-Wide Procedure

A campus-wide SART activation procedure will define the specific actions individuals are expected to take in assisting victims of sexual assault. This will include safety

Figure 10.2
Montclair State University SART

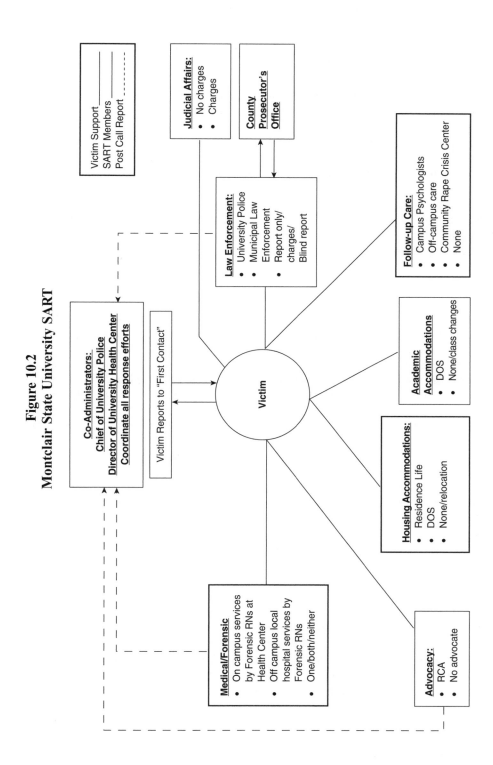

assessment, available options, victim rights, contact information to activate the SART, and reporting obligations. In addition, campuses that utilize community partnerships will need to develop written Memorandums of Understanding that define all roles, responsibilities, and communication methodology with campus responders. This may include municipal law enforcement, local emergency rooms, rape crisis centers, sheriff's office, prosecutor's office, and others specific to the institution's location and jurisdictional structure.

The formation of a campus-wide response system can be a difficult task since victims typically enter the system for assistance from multiple points of entry. Seldom does a college victim call 911 for help or contact law enforcement as the first action. With this in mind, the overall procedure will need to account for the most common ways that victims are known to access care on campus. Once this is determined, protocols can be developed on how these areas will assist victims in accessing care.

The importance of training is again emphasized here so that all individuals who may be likely to be a victim's first contact have a full and accurate knowledge of SART activation and have been trained to respond in a compassionate and nonjudgmental manner including training of community responders.

Internal Procedures

The primary response disciplines of law enforcement, advocacy, and the medical/forensic examiner have been discussed at length in previous chapters (see Chapters 6, 7, and 8) in regard to best practice recommendations for protocols. Many of the details specific to the internal departmental operating procedures will be defined by federal requirements, the capabilities of resources, and should be reviewed carefully prior to protocol development. For example, student health centers will vary greatly from small, two-person offices that function simply as a first aid/infirmary type service to large, university hospitals with multiple capabilities. As a result, the medical/forensic care needed by a victim may occur either on or off campus and sometimes may be offered at both locations. Again, the key component is that the procedures and response be coordinated regardless of where services take place or who provides the response.

Secondary responder departments will then need to develop individual response procedures based on the initial SART activation procedures. Many campuses may already have departmental protocols for addressing sexual assault incidents. In order for the complete SART response to be effective, changes in current response actions may need to take place so that all responders work together to meet victim needs. Making these changes can be a difficult process for some individuals and areas, but they will be required if a campus SART is to achieve its goal.

Departments that will require response protocols will be residence life, counseling services, health services, dean of students, women's center, and others that have traditionally been identified on campus as responders. It is also recommended that specific groups, such as health promotion, athletics, student organizations, and Greek advisors, have specific training and written procedures on how to assist sexual assault victims even though they are not routinely part of an actual response system. These groups are the "voice" of college students and commonly provide the bridge between victims and resources as first contacts.

Coordination and Oversight

The individual identified on campus to be the administrator of a campus SART has the primary mission of assuring that all individuals responsible for response to each incident of sexual assault provide effective, victim-driven services. This will require active involvement from an administrative perspective in determining training needs, coordination of services, oversight of each response, evaluation of response efforts, and maintenance of statistics and regulatory compliance. Some of these responsibilities may be assigned to other individuals, but the SART administrator will have ultimate responsibility for the effectiveness of the SART response.

CONCLUSION

The creation of a best practice approach to sexual assault response in the form of a campus SART is not an easy task, but it is one worth the effort. In conclusion, regardless of the structure of the SART on campus, an institution can offer the best services possible to victims by ensuring that the following objectives or actions have been met:

- Demonstrate institutional commitment through a position statement that reflects an intolerance for sexual violence;

- Create policies and regulations that support the institution's position statement and take actions appropriate to the seriousness of the crime of sexual assault;

- Provide services that are victim driven with options that are independent of each other and determined only by the victim;

- Offer all services 24/7 and create simple methods for access to care;

- Identify a specific individual(s) for coordination and oversight of all services and response;

- Utilize specialized training for all responders and point of entry contacts on and off campus;

- Address the needs of both victims and the justice system through continual evaluation of services and responder actions through the use of multiple assessment tools; and

- Maintain compliance with state and federal statutory regulations.

Consideration of the above factors will assist institutions to develop a victim-centered and effective multidisciplinary response to sexual assault incidents and create a best practice approach for campus victims.

References

American College Health Association. (2008). *SART survey.* Baltimore, MD: Author.

Lancaster, J. M., & Waryold, D. M. (Eds.). (2008). *Student conduct practice: The complete guide for student affairs professionals.* Sterling, VA: Stylus Publishing.

Exhibit 10.1
Minimum Standards for Creating a Coordinated
Community Response to Violence Against Women on Campus

BACKGROUND

Violence against women—including domestic violence, dating violence, sexual assault, and stalking—is a serious problem on campuses, as it is across the nation. On campuses, however, unique issues arise. To address these particular circumstances, Congress created the Grants to Reduce Violent Crimes Against Women on Campus Program (hereinafter referred to as the Campus Program). The Campus Program implements certain provisions of the Higher Education Amendments of 1998, as reauthorized by Congress in the Violence Against Women Act of 2000 and the Violence Against Women Act of 2005. The primary purposes of the Campus Program are to develop and strengthen effective security and investigation strategies to prevent and prosecute domestic violence, dating violence, sexual assault, and stalking on campuses and to develop and strengthen victim services in cases involving such crimes against women on campuses.

The Violence Against Women Act of 2005 included a provision stating that grant funds could be used to "support improved coordination among campus administrators, campus security personnel, and local law enforcement to reduce domestic violence, dating violence, sexual assault, and stalking on campus." In addition, OVW policy requires campus grantees to create a coordinated community response relating to domestic violence, dating violence, sexual assault and stalking on campus. The multidisciplinary response to violence against women on campus involves the entire campus as well as the larger community in which the campus is located.

The Office on Violence Against Women (OVW), working with the California Coalition Against Sexual Assault (CALCASA) (the Technical Assistance provider for grantees under the Campus Program) as well as CALCASA's National Campus Advisory Board, has developed guidelines and standards. The following adaptation of these guidelines and standards is not intended to limit a campus' ability to develop programming appropriate for their school. Rather, OVW strongly recommends that the proposed activities outlined in this document be expanded upon as an individual campus deems appropriate or tailored specifically to meet the needs of an individual campus.

CREATING A COORDINATED COMMUNITY RESPONSE TEAM

The FY 2007 Campus Program Solicitation requires that all campuses "create a coordinated community response to violence against women on campuses" and that "multi-disciplinary response should involve the entire campus as well as the larger community in which the campus is located." It also requires that all campuses "must develop partnerships with at least one local nonprofit, nongovernmental victim services organization within the community which the institution is located *and* one or more of the following criminal justice or civil legal agencies: external law enforcement, prosecution, civil legal assistance providers, systems-based victim services units, or judiciary and court personnel. An applicant who is partnering with campus law enforcement or campus security *must* still partner with a criminal justice or civil legal agency."

Coordinated community response teams and task forces should reflect the wide variety of organizations that are involved in campus life in order to involve all the different entities who have a role in meeting the needs of victims of violence against women on campus and holding offenders accountable. Consider including the following campus-based representatives and entities:

- students, especially victims;
- campus-based victim services providers and violence prevention programs;
- campus law enforcement or department of public safety;
- faculty and staff;
- administrators, including the institution's president and student affairs administrator;
- women's centers;
- women's studies and other relevant academic departments;
- student groups, including those representing diverse or underserved student populations;
- the athletic department;
- sororities and fraternities;
- student health care providers and campus health centers and hospitals;
- campus counseling centers;
- faith-based and community organizations;
- campus clergy;
- campus housing authorities, and residence hall assistants;
- library administrators;
- campus disciplinary boards and judicial boards; and
- representatives from student government.

Coordinated campus and community response teams or tasks forces should review protocols, policies and procedures of member organizations and provide cross-training on their individual missions and roles. In addition, coordinated response teams should work together on a consistent basis with scheduled meetings to develop formal policies and protocols for responding to violent crimes against women when they occur. The goal of ongoing meetings should be to develop and enhance a response to violence against women on campus that is timely, appropriate, sensitive, and respectful to victims needs and that holds offenders accountable.

1. Ongoing communication with community partners when implementing a response for campus communities is essential. Involving partners in program planning, training and curriculum development and event sponsorship is critical to a successful coordinated community response. Programs should consider the following:

   - Maintain ongoing communication by following through with meetings, events, and activities that further strengthen the partnerships after the partnership is initiated, the Memorandum of Understanding is signed, and the grant is awarded. Sometimes schools will have several different organizations initially sign on to the memorandum and then never have any contact or interaction with them again.

- Continue to support the partnership by scheduling regular meeting dates and maintaining that schedule.
- Not allowing staff turnover (either within the program or within the program partners) to sabotage the partnership.Not allowing staff turnover (either within the program or within the program partners) to sabotage the partnership.
- Utilize community partners fully in the development of trainings given the agency's funding and/or staffing situations.

GENERAL CONSIDERATIONS

First and foremost, campuses should work in close collaboration with experts on addressing violence against women issues. OVW recommends that campuses incorporate as many of the following general guidelines when forming and building coordinated community response teams or taskforces:

- Identify and contact each partnering campus office and community agency and provide notification of developments, programming, and implementation of taskforce activities addressing violence against women issues on campus.

- Create a written policy with each campus and community partner to reinforce partnerships (building upon the original Memorandum of Agreement) and outline responsibilities assigned to individuals by specific job title instead of individual names. This will assist in having the partner responsibility remain with the partner organization rather than to a specific person, and will help minimize the impact of staff turnover on the partnerships with campus and community organizations.

- Schedule meetings on a consistent basis and at a regularly set date and time that is convenient for all partners. Monthly meetings are recommended. For example, schedule the meeting of the community coordinated response team for the third Thursday each month at 4:00 pm. Take notes during each meeting memorializing tasks and for distribution to all partners.

- Utilize fully the experience, expertise, input, and resources of all partners. Make consistent efforts to have the partnership be real, meaningful and useful-not just a partnership on paper.

- Keep partners apprised of program developments throughout program implementation.

- Maintain a current list of all staff from partner organizations.

Prepare in advance for staff turnover so that transition for staff replacement on the community partnerships cover the coordination of the response team, its members, meetings, activities, roles and responsibilities.

Exhibit 10.2
Minimum Standards of Training for Campus Security Personnel
and Campus Disciplinary and Judicial Boards

BACKGROUND

Violence against women—including domestic violence, dating violence, sexual assault, and stalking—is a serious problem on campuses, as it is across the nation. On campuses, however, unique issues arise. To address these particular circumstances, Congress created the Grants to Reduce Violent Crimes Against Women on Campus Program (Campus Program). The Campus Program implements certain provisions of the Higher Education Amendments of 1998, as reauthorized by Congress in the Violence Against Women Act of 2000 and the Violence Against Women Act of 2005. The primary purposes of the Campus Program are to develop and strengthen effective security and investigation strategies to prevent and prosecute domestic violence, dating violence, sexual assault, and stalking on campuses and to develop and strengthen victim services in cases involving such crimes against women on campuses.

The Violence Against Women Act of 2005 included a provision stating that grant funds could be used to "train campus administrators, campus security personnel, and personnel serving on campus disciplinary or judicial boards to develop and implement campus policies, protocols, and services that more effectively identify and respond to the crimes of domestic violence, dating violence, sexual assault and stalking." In addition, the provision required the Attorney General to issue and make available minimum standards of training relating to domestic violence, dating violence, sexual assault and stalking on campus for all campus security personnel and personnel serving on campus disciplinary or judicial boards.

The Office on Violence Against Women (OVW), working with the California Coalition Against Sexual Assault (CALCASA) (the Technical Assistance provider for grantees under the Campus Program) as well as CALCASA's National Campus Advisory Board, has developed guidelines and standards. The following adaptation of these guidelines and standards is not intended to limit a campus' ability to develop programming appropriate for their school. Rather, OVW strongly recommends the proposed activities outlined in this document be expanded upon as an individual campus deems appropriate or tailored specifically to meet the needs of an individual campus.

TRAINING FOR CAMPUS SECURITY PERSONNEL

The FY 2007 Campus Program Solicitation requires that all applicants must train campus police to respond effectively in domestic violence, dating violence, sexual assault, and stalking cases." It states that training programs should be developed in collaboration with campus or community-based victim advocacy programs and should include information about relevant federal and state laws and arrest protocols; information on enforcement of orders of protection; and instruction on making primary aggressor determinations.

Campuses should carefully coordinate and plan training sessions for campus security personnel, and should design all trainings in close collaboration with experts on violence against women issues. The emphasis of the trainings should be that the response to victims needs to be timely, appropriate, sensitive, and respectful.

Programs should work closely with campus security personnel to schedule convenient events to ensure attendance by the maximum number of officers. In designing training programs for campus security personnel, campuses should be flexible and earnestly consider the following possible challenges:

- Recognize that some campuses must work with public safety units, not campus "police," and that some public safety officers are "non-sworn." As first responders on a case, public safety officers have the ability to request mutual aid from the jurisdiction of record and the appropriate investigative law enforcement agency.

- Provide training that is Police Officer Standard Training (POST) certified or training that is required in the jurisdiction in order for officers to receive credit towards meeting their continued education requirements.

- Determine whether a longer training on four broad topics such as domestic violence, dating violence, sexual assault, and stalking is preferable to a series of shorter, "rollcall" trainings on specific topics such as drug- facilitated rape cases or cyberstalking.

- Coordinate training, easing competition for time, by working with other campus police "trainers" to infuse violence against women issues in other areas of ongoing and pre-scheduled routine training.

- Include, if possible, in every training, a cross section of supervisors, patrols, and detectives. This will help ensure that the information is given to all levels of rank and will facilitate the institutionalization of training protocols and procedures.

- Promote effective collaboration and community-wide participation in all training events addressing violence against women on campus.

General Considerations

OVW recommends that campus security personnel trainings incorporate as many of the following general topics addressing violence against women as possible:

- Relevant federal and state laws.
- Working with law enforcement officials from neighboring jurisdictions.
- Jurisdictional issues.
- Confidentially issues.
- Risk assessment for victims.
- Crime scene preservation and evidence collection.
- Interviewing techniques for working with victims and avoiding "victim blaming."
- Probable cause as it relates to violence against women cases.
- Review of the student code of conduct and judicial/disciplinary process on campus.
- Information on enforcement of orders of protection including full faith and credit issues.

- Arrest protocols.
- Working with advocates and advocacy groups, including clarification of roles and responsibilities.
- Availability of local services for victims and local training resources.

Domestic Violence and Dating Violence Considerations

OVW recommends that campus security personnel training on domestic violence and dating violence include the following specific topics:

- Officer safety when responding to domestic violence calls.
- Review of basic domestic violence dynamics, including issues of power and control.
- Laws of search and seizure.
- Avoiding mutual arrests.
- Relevant federal and state statutory firearms prohibitions and seizure policies including protection order provisions.
- Definitions of dating violence and its effects.
- Making predominant aggressor determinations including, interfacing with and interviewing primary/predominant aggressors.

Sexual Assault Considerations

Where appropriate, the information provided in "A National Protocol for Sexual Assault Medical Forensic Examinations" should be available to all instructors. OVW recommends that campus security personnel training on sexual assault include the following specific topics:

- Specific procedures for sexual assault exams and for evidence collection at the crime scene.
- "Known" perpetrator investigations.
- Communicating with victims about the course of the investigation.
- Appropriate interviewing techniques when questioning sexual assault victims.
- Appropriate discussion with the victim regarding prosecution decisions.
- Specifics of rape trauma syndrome and its effects on victims.
- Relevant rape shield laws.
- Departmental decisions on how appropriately to handle victims who are facing issues of other violations in connection with their assault – such, as underage consumption or marijuana and other illegal substance possession.
- Coordination between campus security personnel and campus health units or local hospitals working with Sexual Assault Forensic Examiner or Sexual Assault Nurse Examiner protocols.

Stalking Considerations

OVW recommends that campus security personnel training on stalking include the following specific topics:

- Understanding stalking properly as a crime.

- Methods to help officers/detectives to identify stalking cases more effectively.

- Orders of protection and their effectiveness or lack of effectiveness in a campus environment.

- Issues surrounding cyberstalking as the misuse of campus computers/property. Officers should be encouraged to be familiar with campus policies on computer use and what constitutes violations of the student conduct code.

- Insight on intervention training.

- How to document stalking violations by keeping notes, tracking phone calls, and collecting evidence to support the victim's account of the incidences.

TRAINING FOR CAMPUS DISCIPLINARY OR JUDICIAL BOARDS

Review of Campus Code

Prior to conducting training for campus disciplinary or judicial boards, a campus should review the current code of student conduct and ensure that the code addresses the following issues:

- The code is victim-centered over offender-focused.

- The code considers offender accountability.

- The code defines a clear and concise disciplinary process.

- The code defines uniform and consistent penalties.

- The code identifies and clearly defines domestic violence, dating violence, sexual assault, and stalking.

- The code addresses confidentiality issues.

The FY 2007 Campus Program Solicitation requires that all applicants "establish or strengthen programs to train members of campus disciplinary boards to respond effectively to charges of domestic violence, dating violence, sexual assault, and stalking." It states that "[A]ll members of campus disciplinary boards, including faculty, staff, students, and administrators should receive expert training on these crimes. Training topics could include information about the causes and effects of violence against women; a review of the student conduct code; definitions of domestic violence, dating violence, sexual assault, and stalking; information on the issue of consent in sexual assault cases; how to judge credibility; drug facilitated sexual assault; and the available range of sanctions should the charged student be found responsible by the disciplinary board."

General Considerations

The structure of campus disciplinary boards or judicial boards varies widely. Some boards are made up of faculty and administration officials while others are comprised of student representatives. Campuses should design all trainings in close collaboration with experts on violence against women issues. When designing and implementing training programs, campuses should consider the following issues:

- The differences between the processes of the criminal justice system and those involved in the academic judicial/disciplinary system.

- Ensuring that the training is continuous and on-going so that all new members of the judicial/disciplinary boards receive information, especially if the board is appointed on a rotation.

- Maintaining retention of "trained" board members given the complexities and difficulties of such cases.

- Creating training that is effective and does not "promote bias" for either victims or offenders.

- Ensuring that all judicial/disciplinary cases are pursued in the same manner, regardless of "who" the victim and/or offender may be.

- Confidentiality issues: open or closed hearings.

- Relevant state and federal laws.

- Working with law enforcement officials from the local jurisdiction.

Specific Considerations

When developing trainings for disciplinary or judicial boards, campuses should also address the following specific topics:

- Reasons why victims may or may not choose (and/or wait) to report.

- Ways that the disciplinary system can "re-traumatize" victims.

- The importance of avoiding victim blaming.

- Viewing all information without bias.

- Review of general domestic violence information including issues of power and control.

- Dating violence as a form of domestic violence, including relevant laws.

- "Known" perpetrator sexual assault.

- Stalking in a "closed" campus environment.

Appendix A

State Rape Statutes

[Editors' note: Appendix A is provided as an overview and comparison for the reader of state rape statutes and for informational purposes only. This chart was compiled in 2006, and readers should double check for any more recent changes to the law that may have been made in their state after the chart was created. The authors strongly recommend the reader seek legal counsel guidance for detailed interpretation of individual state statutes.]

State	Statute	Classification	Penalty	No Means No
Alabama {Ala. Code § 13A-6-60 (2005)}	Rape—1st degree	Class A felony	Life or 10-99 years; not less than 20 year sentence if deadly weapon used	NO
*See 13A-5-9 for classification of repeat offenses:	Rape—2nd degree	Class B felony	2-20 year sentence; not less than 10 years if deadly weapon used	NO
Second felony offense: Class C reclassified as B; Class B reclassified as A; Class A: 15-99 years	Sodomy—1st degree	Class A felony	Life or 10-99 years; not less than 20 year sentence if deadly weapon used	NO
Third felony offense: Class C reclassified as A; Class B: 15-99; Class A: life/99 year minimum	Sodomy—2nd degree	Class B felony	2-20 year sentence; not less than 10 years if deadly weapon used	NO
*See 13A-5-6 & 7 for felony sentences to include hard labor for state or county	Sexual Misconduct	Class A misdemeanor	not more than one year	NO
13A-6-70 specifically addresses consent	Sexual Torture	Class A felony	Life or 10-99 years; not less than 20 year sentence if deadly weapon used	YES
	Sexual Abuse—1st degree	Class C felony	Not more than 10 years or less than 1 year and one day; not less than 10 if firearm/ deadly weapon used	
	Sexual Abuse—2nd degree	Class A misdemeanor; if subsequent offense is committed within one year, Class C felony	not more than one year	YES
Alaska {Alaska Stat. § 11.41.470 (2005)}	Sexual Assault—1st degree	Unclassified felony	Not more than 40 years. See AS 12.55.125(i)(1)	NO
*See 12.55.155 (2005) for aggravating and mitigating factors which may affect sentencing	Sexual Assault—2nd degree	Class B felony	Not more than 20 years with a presumptive term of 2 - 4 years for a first felony offense; presumptive term of 5-8 yrs for 2nd felony or 10-14 yrs for 2nd sexual felony conviction; 10-14 years for third or 15-20 yrs for 3rd sexual felony conviction. See 12.55.125(i)(3).	NO

Reprinted with permission from the American Prosecutors Reseach Institute. This project was supported by Grant No. 2004-WT-AX-K047 awarded by the Office on Violence Against Women, U.S. Department of Justice. The contents of this publication do not necessarily reflect the views of the DOJ on Violence Against Women.

State	Statute	Classification	Penalty	No Means No
	Sexual Assault—3rd degree	Class C felony	Not more than 10 years with a presumptive term of 1 - 2 years for a first felony offense; presumptive term of 2 - 5 years for 2nd felony or 3 - 6 years for a 2nd sexual felony conviction; 3-6 years for third or 6-10 years for 3rd sexual felony conviction. See 12.55.125(i)(4).	NO
	Sexual Abuse of a minor—1st degree	Unclassified felony	Not more than 40 years. See, 12.55.125(i)(1)	NO
	Sexual Abuse of a minor—2nd degree	Class B felony	Not more than 10 years; presumptive term of 1-3 yrs for 1st felony conviction; presumptive term of 4-7 yrs for 2nd; presumptive term of 6-10 yrs for 3rd.	NO
	Sexual Abuse of a minor—3rd degree	Class C felony	Not more than 5 years; presumptive term of 0-2 yrs for 1st felony conviction; presumptive term of 2-4 yrs for 2nd; 3-5 yrs for 3rd.	NO
	Sexual Abuse of a minor—4th degree	Class A misdemeanor	Not more than 1 year	
Arizona {**Ariz. Rev. Stat. Ann. § 13-1401 (2002)**} *See *13-604* for repeat offenders Force or threat of force against person or property = without consent * See *13-702(B), (C), & (D)* for aggravating and mitigating factors.	Sexual Assault	Class 2 felony	First offense-5.25 to 14 years with a presumptive term of 7 yrs. Prior felony - 7-21 years with a presumptive term of 10 yrs. Two prior felonies - 14-28 years with a presumptive term of 15.75 yrs. (*A.R.S. 13-1406*) If victim under 12, life in prison (*13-604.1*)	NO
	Violent Sexual Assault	Class 2 felony	Natural life sentence (*A.R.S. 13-1423*)	NO
	Sexual Abuse	Class 5 felony; Class 3 felony if victim under 15	1.5 years; (*13-604* for repeat offender sentencing). If victim is 12 or younger, see 13-604.01.	NO
	Sexual conduct w/ a minor	Class 2 felony if victim under 15 or offender is guardian; Class 6 felony if victim 15+	If victim under 12, life in prison w/o probation until 35 years served. 13-604.01. If victim is 12-14, presumptive term of 20 yrs. 13-604.01. If victim is over 15, 1 yr. 13-701.	NO

State	Statute	Classification	Penalty	No Means No
Arkansas {Ark. Stat. Ann. § 5-14-101 (2005)}	Rape	Class Y felony	10-40 yrs.	
*See *A.C.A. 5-3-203* (2002) for attempted crimes being prosecuted:	Sexual Assault—1st degree	Class A felony	6-30 years.	NO
Class A if Class Y attempted; Class B if Class A attempted, Class C if Class B attempted; Class D if Class C attempted; Class A misdemeanor if Class D felony attempted; Class B misdemeanor if Class A misdemeanor	Sexual Assault—2nd degree	Class B felony	5-20 years.	NO
	Sexual Assault—3rd degree	Class C felony	3-10 years.	NO
attempted	Sexual Assault—4th degree	Class D felony if, being 20 yrs or older, a person engages in sexual intercourse or deviate sexual activity with a person who is less than 16 years of age and not the person's spouse. Class A misdemeanor if the person being less than 20 yrs older, engages in sexual contact with another person who is less than 16 years of age and not the person's spouse.	Class D Felony: maximum 6 yrs. Class A Misdemeanor: maximum 1 yr.	NO
	Sexual Indecency with a Child	Class D felony	Maximum 6 yrs.	NO
California {Cal. Penal Code § 261 (2005)}	Rape	Felony	Rape punishable by state prison sentence of 3, 6, or 8 years (CA Penal Code 264)	NO

State	Statute	Classification	Penalty	No Means No
* See *CA Penal Code 264* for AIDS education fine information	Unlawful Sexual Intercourse w/ a minor	Misdemeanor if actor is less than 3 yrs older than the victim. Misdemeanor or felony if actor is three+ years older than victim. Misdemeanor or felony if agent is over 21 and victim is under 16	Less than 3 years older than the victim, unspecified punishment. 3 years older, state prison or county jail for maximum of 1 year. If over 21 and victim under 16, imprisonment in state jail for 2-4 years.	NO
"Consent - positive cooperation in act or attitude, act and free will	Oral copulation	Anyone who performs lewd or lacivious acts on a child under 14 is guilty of a felony.	If oral copulation occurs between a person and someone under 18, then then that person can be sentenced to state or county jail for a maximum of one year. 288a(b)(1). If performed by force, then life imprisonment with parole no earlier than 15 years into the sentence. 667.61(b).	YES
	Penetration by foreign object	Felony	State prison for 3, 6, or 8 yrs if by force or violence.	YES
	Aggravated Sexual Assault of a child	If actor is 10 or more years older than the child, who is under 14, then felony. *Cal. Pen. Code § 269.*	15 years to life.	NO
Colorado {Colo. Rev. Stat. § 18-3-401 (2005)} *See *C.R.S. 18-1.3-801* for habitual offenders	Sexual Assault	Class 4 felony unless otherwise provided (see below) Class 1 misdemeanor and an extraordinary risk crime (see 18-1.3-501(3)) if victim is 15-16 and actor is at least 10	2 - 6 years and/or $2,000 - $500,000 fine. 6 months - 24 months and/or $500-$5,000.	NO
*See *C.R.S. 18-1.3-406* for violent offenders Consent = cooperation in act or attitude -See C.R.S. 18-1.3-501 for misdemeanors sentencing See C.R.S. 18-1.3-401 for felony sentencing		Class 2 felony if actor is aided by one or more persons; victim suffers serious bodily injury; actor has or claims to have a deadly weapon.	16-48 years (see 18-1.3-401(8)). Fine of $5,000 - $1,000,000.	

State	Statute	Classification	Penalty	No Means No
		Class 3 felony if the actor: knew the victim was physically helpless and victim did not consent; used physical force or violence; threatened imminent death, serious bodily injury, extreme pain, or kidnapping against anyone and victim believed actor could presently execute the threats; threatened to retaliate in the future against anyone and victim reasonably believed the actor...	4-12 years and/or $3,000-$750,000 fine.	
	Unlawful sexual contact	Class 4 felony; Class 3 felony if force or believeable threat	Class 3 felony: 4-12 years and/or $3,000-$750,000 fine. Class 4 felony: 2-6 years.and/or $2,000-$500,000 fine.	YES
	Sexual Assault on a child	Class 3 felony if victim under 15 or pattern of abuse exists; Class 4 if victim 15-18 and no pattern exists	Class 3 felony: 4-12 years and/or $3,000-$750,000 fine. Class 4 felony: 2-6 years.and/or $2,000-$500,000 fine.	NO
	Sexual Assault on a child; in position of trust	Class 4 felony if is child is 15-17. Class 3 felony if child is under 15.	Class 3 felony: 4-12 years and/or $3,000-$750,000 fine. Class 4 felony: 2-6 years.and/or $2,000-$500,000 fine.	NO
Connecticut {Conn. Gen. Stat. Ann. § 53a-65 (West 2005)} * See Conn. Gen. Stat. § 53a-40d; Conn. Gen. Stat. § 53a-40 for persistent offenders	Sexual Assault—1st degree	Class A felony if victim is under 16. Otherwise, Class B felony.	Class A felony: 10-25 years. Class B felony: 5-20 years.	NO
	Sexual Assault—2nd degree	Class B felony if victim is under 16. Otherwise, Class C felony.	Class C felony: 1-10 years.	NO
	Sexual Assault—3rd degree	Class C felony if victim is under 16. Otherwise, Class D felony.	Class D felony: 1-5 years.	NO

State	Statute	Classification	Penalty	No Means No
	Sexual Assault in the 3rd degree with a firearm	Class C felony. It is a Class B felony if the victim was under 16.	Class C felony: 1-10 years. Class B felony: 5-20 years.	
	Sexual Assault—4th degree	Class D felony if the victim is under 16. Otherwise, Class A misdemeanor.	Class A misdemeanor: maximum 1 year.	NO
	Aggravated Sexual Assault 1st degree	Class A felony if the victim is under 16. Otherwise, Class B felony.	Class A felony: 10-25 years. Class B felony: 5-20 years.	NO
Delaware {Del. Code Ann. tit. 11, § 761 (2005)} Without consent no force required. Only need *See 11 Del. C. § 4214 for life imprisonment sentencing of habitual offenders	Rape—1st degree	Class A felony	Life imprisonment without parole if the victim was less than 16, actor intentionally causes disfigurement or amputation or permanent organ disability, the actor is	YES
	Rape—2nd degree	Class B felony	10 years minimum sentence	YES
	Rape—3rd degree	Class B felony	2-25 years	YES
	Rape—4th degree	Class C felony	Maximum 15 years	YES
	Unlawful Sexual Contact—1st degree	Class F felony	Maximum 3 years	NO
	Unlawful Sexual Contact—2nd degree	Class G felony	Maximum 2 years	NO
	Unlawful Sexual Contact—3rd degree	Class A misdemeanor	Maximum one year; up to $2,300 fine	YES
District of Columbia {D.C. Code Ann. § 22-3001 (2005)} * For aggravating circumstances in sentencing, see D.C. Code 22-3020. Consent - words or overt actions indicating freely given agreement	Sexual Abuse—1st degree		Any term of years up to life; fine of up to $250,000.	NO
	Sexual Abuse—2nd degree		Up to 20 years in prison; fine of up to $200,000	NO
	Sexual Abuse—3rd degree		Up to 10 years in prison; fine of up to $100,000	NO

State	Statute	Classification	Penalty	No Means No
	Sexual Abuse—4th degree		Up to 5 years in prison; fine of up to $50,000	NO
	Misdemeanor Sexual Abuse		Up to 180 days; fine of up to $1,000	YES
	Child Sexual Abuse—1st degree		Any term of years or life; fine of up to $250,000. Punishment in excess of 30 years must be pursuant to § 22-3020 or § 24-403.01(b-2).	NO
	Child Sexual Abuse—2nd degree		Up to 10 years in prison; fine of up to $100,000	NO
	Assault w/ intent to…commit 1st or 2nd degree Sexual Abuse or Child Sexual Abuse		2-15 years	NO
	Attempt to commit Sex Offenses		Up to 15 years for a crime that can be punished by life imprisonment; not more than half the maximum sentence for offense or half the maximum fine.	NO
Florida {Fla. Stat. § 794.011 (2005)}	Sexual Battery	Capital felony if person over 18 sexually batters person under 12 or if a person in familial or custodial authority engages in anal, oral, or vaginal penetration with a sex organ or an object regardless of consent (but this may be a life felony in some cases).	Death or life imprisonment without the possibility of parole. *See* Fla. Stat. 775.082.	NO

State	Statute	Classification	Penalty	No Means No
* For reclassification of offenses committed by multiple perpetrators, see *Fla Stat. 794.023* .		Life Felony if under 18 offender sexually batters victim under 12 or if a person in familial or custodial authority engages in anal, oral, or vaginal penetration with a sex organ or an object regardless of consent (but this may be a capital felony in some cases).	Sentence not to exceed life	NO
* For mandatory minimum sentences for certain reoffenders, see *Fla Stat. 775.082.*		Life felony if batterer uses deadly weapon on person over 12	Sentence not to exceed life	YES
* For felony reclassification for possession or use of a weapon, see *Fla. Stat. 775.087.*		1st degree felony when the victim is over 12 and is helpless to resist; the actor threatens violence that will cause serious injury and the victim reasonably believed it was presently possible; the actor threatens future retaliation; actor administers intoxicating substance without victim's knowledge or consent; victim is mentally defective or physically incapacitated; offender is officer of law or an elected official; or victim is between 12 - 17 and actor is in a position of familial or custodial authority and engages in anal, oral, or vaginal penetration with a sex organ or an object.	Maximum 30 years	YES

State	Statute	Classification	Penalty	No Means No
* For enhanced prison terms for habitual felony offenders, see *Fla. Stat. 775.084* .		2nd degree felony: victim is over 12 and force unlikely to cause serious injury; 1st degree felony for multiple perpetrators	Maximum 15 years	YES
		3rd degree felony when persons of authority (familial or custodial) solicits victim to engage in anal, oral, or vaginal penetration with a sex organ or object	Maximum 5 years	NO
	Sexual Battery by Multiple Perpetrators; Reclassification of Offenses	A 1st degree felony is reclassified as a life felony. A 2nd degree felony is reclassified as a 1st degree felony.		
	Unlawful Sexual Activity With Certain Minors	2nd degree felony is actor is at least 24 and victim is 16 or 17.		
Georgia {Ga. Code Ann. § 16-6-1 (2005)} * See *O.C.G.A. § 17-10-6.1* for serious violent offenders	Rape		Death, life in prison w/ or w/o parole, or 10-20 years in prison; *(17-10-6.1, 17-10-7)*	NO
	Statutory Rape	If victim is 14 or 15 and actor is no more than 3 years older, then the offense is a misdemeanor.	If the offender is 21 or older, 10-20 years in prison. Otherwise, 1-20 years in prison. If a misdemeanor offense, then punishable by up to $1,000 fine and/or maximum of 12 months imprisonment.	NO

State	Statute	Classification	Penalty	No Means No
* See *O.C.G.A. § 17-10-7* for repeat offenders	Sexual battery	Misdemeanor of high and aggravated nature, except that if victim is under 16 then it is a felony.	Maximum 12 months; $5,000 fine. However, if victim is under 16 then punishable by 1-5 years imprisonment.	
	Aggravated sexual battery		10-20 years in prison	NO
	Sodomy and Aggravated Sodomy	Felony	1-20 years; 10-30 if aggravated.	NO
Hawaii {**Haw. Rev. Stat. § 707-700 (2005)**} Compulsion language that states lack of consent, but doesn't define consent	Sexual assault—1st degree	Class A felony	Up to 20 years, with minimum determined pursuant to HRS § 706-669.	NO
* See *HRS § 706-662, HRS § 706-661* for sentence extensions	Sexual assault—2nd degree	Class B felony	Up to 10 years, with minimum determined pursuant to HRS § 706-669.	NO
* See *HRS § 706-660.1* for felonies committed w/ a firearm	Sexual assault—3rd degree	Class C felony	Up to 5 years, with minimum determined pursuant to HRS § 706-669.	NO
* See *HRS § 706-606.5* for repeat offender sentencing	Sexual assault—4th degree	Misdemeanor	Up to 1 year.	NO
Idaho {**Idaho Code § 18-6101 (2005)**} Resistance language, but unclear if physical, verbal, or both	Rape	Felony	1 year to life based on judicial discretion. Idaho Code § 1801-6104.	NO
	Lewd conduct w/ a minor child under	Felony	Up to life in prison	NO
	Sexual Battery of a minor child 16-17	Felony	If actor is at least 5 years older than the victim and commits a lewd or lacivious act with victim, then punishment up to life. If solicits, causes contact, or photographs minor, thenup to 15 years.	
	Male Rape	Felony	1 year to life	NO
	Forcible sexual penetration by use of foreign object	Felony	Not more than life	NO

State	Statute	Classification	Penalty	No Means No
Illinois {Ill. Crim. Code 720 ILCS 5/12-13 (2005)}	Criminal Sexual Assault	Class 1 felony	4-15 years. Subsequent offense: Class X felony of 30-60 years in prison if person is convicted of 720 ILCS 5/12-13(a)(1) or (a)(2) after having previously been convicted of criminal sexual assault or its substantial equivalent or if convicted after having been convicted of aggravated criminal sexual assault, then life imprisonment.	NO
	Aggravated Criminal Sexual Assault	Class X felony	Class X felony punishable by 6 - 30 years, except as specified by a particular statute. A violation of subsection Ill. Crim. Code 720 ILCS 5/12-14(a)(1) is a Class X felony for which 10 years shall be added to the term of imprisonment imposed by the court. A violation of subsection (a)(8) is a Class X felony for which 15 years shall be added to the term of imprisonment imposed by the court. A violation of subsection (a)(9) is a Class X felony for which 20 years shall be added to the term of imprisonment imposed by the court. A violation of subsection (a)(10) is a Class X felony for which 25 years or up to a term of natural life imprisonment shall be added to the term of imprisonment imposed by the court. Subsequent offense gets life	NO
	Criminal Sexual Abuse	Class A misdemeanor if accused was under 17 and engages in sexual penetration or conduct with victim who is 9-16 yrs old, or if accused engages in sexual penetration or conduct with 13-16 yr old and actor is at least 5 yrs older than the victim.	Less than one year	NO
		Class 4 felony if sexual	1-3 years	
		Subsequent offense is a Class 2 felony.	3-7 years	

State	Statute	Classification	Penalty	No Means No
Indiana {Ind. Code Ann. § 35-42-4-1 (2005)} * See § 35-50-2-14 and § 35-50-2-8 for repeat and violent offenders	Aggravated Criminal Sexual Abuse	Class 2 felony	3-7 years	NO
	Rape	Class A felony if committed by using or threatening deadly force; committed while armed with deadly weapon; results in serious bodily injury; or victim is incapacitated w/o consent. Class B felony if threat of force used; victim is unaware that intercourse is occurring; or victim is mentally disabled or deficient.	20-50 year sentence, with advisory sentence being 30 yrs. § 35-30-2-4 (2005); up to $10,000 fine 6-20 year sentence, with advisory sentence being 10 yrs.; up to $10,000 fine	NO
	Criminal Deviate Conduct	Class A or B felony; see requirements for Rape class distinctions		NO
	Sexual Battery	Class D felony if compelled to submit by force or imminent threat of force; or victim is too mentally disabled to consent. Class C felony if committed by use or threat of deadly force or w/ deadly weapon; or victim is incapacitated without consent.	0.5-3 year sentence with advisory sentence being 1.5 yrs.; up to $10,000 fine. 2-4 year sentence; up to $10,000 fine	NO

State	Statute	Classification	Penalty	No Means No
	Vicarious Sexual Gratification	Class C felony if committed by use or threat of deadly force or w/ deadly weapon; or victim is incapacitated without consent	2-8 year sentence with advisory sentence being 4 yrs.; up to $10,000 fine	NO
		Class A if actor is 18 or older and knowingly causes a child under 16 to engage in sexual intercourse with a child under 16, engage in sexual conduct with an animal or another	Class A: 20-30 year sentence	
		Class B if deadly force used or threatened or if deadly	Class B: 6-10 year sentence	
		Class C if victim under 14	Class C: 2-4 year sentence	
		Class D felony if a person 18	Class D: 0.5-1.5 year sentence	
	Sexual Misconduct	Class C felony if actor 18-20	Class C: 2-4 year sentence	
Iowa {**Iowa Code § 702.17 (2005)**} * See *Iowa Code § 902.8* for habitual offenders * See *Iowa Code § 902.12* for mandatory sentencing guidelines	Sexual Abuse—1st degree	Class A felony	Life in prison without parole.	NO
	Sexual Abuse—2nd degree	Class B felony	Maximum of 25 years	NO
	Sexual Abuse—3rd degree	Class C felony	Maximum of 10 years and $1,000 - $10,000 fine.	NO

State	Statute	Classification	Penalty	No Means No
* See *Iowa Code § 901A.2* for enhanced sentencing factors	Lascivious acts with a child	Class C felony if a person 16 or older fondles the pubes or genitals of a child or permits or causes a child to fondle or the person's genitals or pubes in order to arouse or satisfy th esexual desires of either. Class D felony if a person 16 or older solicits a child to engage in a sex act, solicits a person to arrange a sex act with a child, or inflicts pain or discomfort on a child or permits or causes a child to inflict pain or discomfort on the person.	Class C: maximum of 10 years and $1,000-$10,000 fine. Class D: maximum of 5 years and $750-$7,500 fine.	
"Against the will" language	Assault w/ intent-Sexual Abuse	Class C felony if "serious injury" is caused Class D felony if "bodily injury" results Aggravated misdemeanor if no injury results	Maximum of 10 years and $1,000 - $10,000 fine. Maximum of 5 years and $750 - $7,500 fine. Aggravated Misdemeanor punishable by a maximum of 2 years imprisonment and a mandatory fine of $500 - $5,000.	NO
Kansas {**Kan. Stat. Ann. § 21-3501 (2005)**}	Rape	Severity Level 1, "person felony" if victim overcome by force or fear, or is unconscious or physically powerless, or is incapable of consenting b/c of mental deficiency, incapacitation was known to offender, or victim was under 14	Kan. Stat. Ann. 21-4704 has sentencing grid, but it is not available online.	NO

State	Statute	Classification	Penalty	No Means No
		Severity Level 2 "person felony" if consent obtained through knowing misrepresentation of necessity (medical, therapeutical, or legal)		NO
	Criminal Sodomy	Class B nonperson misdemeanor if w/ same sex persons over 16 or with an animal		
		Severity Level 3 person felony if victim is child between 14-16		NO
	Aggravated Criminal Sodomy	Severity 2, person felony		
	Sexual Battery	Class A person misdemeanor		NO
	Aggravated Sexual Battery	Severity 5, person felony		NO
	Indecent Liberties with a Child	Severity 5, person felony		

State	Statute	Classification	Penalty	No Means No
	Aggravated Indecent Liberties with a Child	Severity 3, person felony when actor has sexual intercourse with a child who is 14-15; engages in lewd fondling or touching with a child under 14; or solicits a child under 14 to engage in lewd fondling or touching. Severity 4, person felony when actor engages in lewd fondling or touching with a child 14-15 or causes a child 14-15 to engage in lewd fondling or touching with another.		
Kentucky {Ky. Rev. Stat. Ann. § 510-010 (Michie-Bobbs-Merrill 2005)} * See *KRS § 506.010* for attempted crime reclassification: B felony when A is attempted	Rape—1st degree *510.040*	Class A victim under 12 or seriously injured / Class B felony	Class A: 20-50 years / Class B: 10-20 years	NO
C felony when B is attempted	Rape—2nd degree	Class C felony	5-10 years	NO
A misdemeanor when C or D felony is attempted	Rape—3rd degree	Class D felony	1-5 years	NO
* See KRS § 532.080 for persistent felony offenders	Sodomy—1st degree	Class A felony when victim is under 12 or serious injured / Class B felony	Class A: 20-50 years or life imprisonment / Class B: 10-20 years	

State	Statute	Classification	Penalty	No Means No
	Sodomy—2nd degree	Class C felony	5-10 years	
	Sodomy - 3rd degree	Class D felony	1-5 years	
	Sexual Abuse—1st degree	Class D felony	1-5 years	
	Sexual Abuse—2nd degree	Class A misdemeanor	Up to 12 months	
	Sexual Abuse—3rd degree	Class B misdemeanor	Up to 90 days	NO
	Sexual Misconduct	Class A misdemeanor	Up to 12 months	NO
Louisiana {**La. Rev. Stat. Ann. § 14:41 (2005)**} * See *L.A. R.S. 15: 529.1* for second and subsequent offenses "Without person's lawful consent" doesn't clarify	Aggravated Rape		Life in prison w/o parole; if victim under 12, death or life imprisonment.	NO
	Forcible Rape		5-40 years in prison with hard labor; 2 year minimum without probation/parole/suspension.	NO
	Simple Rape		Up to 25 years in prison (w/o hard labor) w/o probation/parole/ suspension.	NO
	Sexual Battery		Up to 10 years in prison (w/ or w/o hard labor) w/o probation/parole/ suspension	NO
	Second Degree Sexual Battery		Up to 15 years in prison (w/ or w/o hard labor) w/o probation/parole/ suspension	NO
	Oral Sexual Battery		Up to 10 years in prison (w/ or w/o hard labor) w/o probation/parole/ suspension	NO
Maine {**Me. Rev. Stat. Ann. Tit. 17-A, § 251 (2005)**} * See Section 4 of *17-A M.R.S. § 253* for	Gross Sexual Assault	Class A, B or C (See *Me. Rev. Stat. Ann. Tit. 17-A, § 253.*)	Class A: up to 30 years imprisonment. Class B: up to 10 years imprisonment. Class C: up to 5 years imprisonment. *A.M.R.S. 1252 (2005)* Class 17-	NO
	Sexual Abuse of minors	Class C if the victim is 14-15 and the actor is 5 or more years older and knows victim is within second degree family relationship; or if victim is 14-15 and the actor is at least 10 yrs older.		NO

State	Statute	Classification	Penalty	No Means No
factors involved in the commission of certain sexual offenses for which defendants may be sentenced to any term of years		Class D if sexual act with 14-15 year old and actor is at least 5 years older; or if victim is 16-17 and actor is 21 or older and an employee at victim's school and knows that victim is within 2nd degree of familial relationship; or if victim is 16-17 and actor is at least 10 years older; or if victim is 14-15 and actor is at least 10 years older.	D: up to 1 year.	NO
* See Section 4 of *17-A M.R.S. § 253 for* factors involved in the commission of certain		Class E if victim is 16-17 and actor is at least 21 and is an	E: up to 6 months.	NO
* See *17-A M.R.S. § 257* for factors aiding in predicting high-risk sex offenders for * See *17-A M.R.S. § 1231* for supervised period of release information	Unlawful sexual contact	Class E crime if the victim is under 18 and the actor is at Class D crime if the victim hasn't expressly or impliedly consented; is unconscious or incapable of resisting and has not consented; has a mental disability that is known to Class C crime if the victim has not expressly or impliedly consented and there is penetration; is unconscious or physically cannot resist and Class B crime if the victim is under 12 and the other person is at least 3 years older; under 14 and actor at least 3 years older and penetration; under 18 and actor is parent or		YES NO

State	Statute	Classification	Penalty	No Means No
		Class A crime+C137 if the victim is under 12 and the actor is at least 3 years older and there is penetration.		NO
				NO
				NO
				NO
	Sexual Misconduct w/ child	Class C or D crime. Class D crime if a person 18 or older shows a person under 14 sexually explicit material		NO
Maryland {Md. Crim. Law Code Ann. § 3-301 (2005)}	Rape—1st degree	Felony	Sentence not to exceed life; if victim is under 16 or defendant has prior offenses, then sentence not to exceed life w/o parole	NO
* If defendant found guilty of 2nd degree	Rape—2nd degree	Felony	20 years maximum sentence	NO

State	Statute	Classification	Penalty	No Means No
rape, 2nd degree sexual offense, 3rd degree sexual offense, 2nd degree attempted rape, or 2nd degree attempted sexual offense after being found guilty on a separate occasion of 1st degree rape, 2nd degree rape, 1st degree sexual offense, or 2nd degree sexual offense, then defendant is sentenced to imprisonment not exceeding life	Sexual Offense—1st degree	Felony	Sentence not to exceed life; if victim under 16 or prior offenses, life/ w/o parole	
	Sexual Offense—2nd degree	Felony	20 years maximum sentence	NO
	Sexual Offense—3rd degree	Felony	10 years maximum sentence	NO
	Sexual Offense—4th degree	Misdemeanor	1 year maximum prison sentence, fine up to $1,000, or both. If D has previously been convicted of an offense under §§ 3-303 through 3-312 or § 3-315, then maximum sentence of 3 yrs and/or a fine not exceeding $1,000	NO
	Attempted rape—1st degree	Felony	Sentence not to exceed life	NO
	Attempted rape—2nd degree	Felony	20 years maximum sentence	NO
	Attempted Sexual offense - 1st degree	Felony	1st degree: up to life. 2nd degree: maximum 20 yrs.	NO
	Attempted Sexual Offense - 2nd degree			NO
Massachusetts {**Mass. Ann. Laws ch. 265, § 22 (2005)**} Any resistance is enough	Rape		State prison sentence of life or any term of years if committed by force or threat and results in serious injury,... State prison sentence no to exceed 20 years when committed by force or threat (lesser included offense);... If committed with firearm, 10 year minimum sentence; second offense: 15 years to life	NO
	Rape of child under 16		Up to life in prison when force or threat used; 5 years to life if offender is over 18 and commits subsequent offense.	YES

State	Statute	Classification	Penalty	No Means No
	Rape of a child		Imprisonment for life or any term of years. For subsequent conviction, same but minimum imprisonment of 5 years.	
	Assault w/ intent to rape		State prison for not more than 20 years or jail or corrections house for not more than 2.5 years; second offense punished by state prison sentence of up to life; if committed w/ firearm, 5 year minimum state prison	
Michigan {Mich. Comp. Laws § 750.520a (2005)}	Criminal sexual conduct—1st degree	Felony	Up to life in state prison. For subsequent offense, minimum of 5 yrs. *See* 750.520f.	YES
*If convicted of subsequent 1st, 2nd, or 3rd degree criminal sexual conduct, mandatory minimum sentence of 5 years	Criminal sexual conduct—2nd degree	Felony	Sentence not to exceed 15 years. For subsequent offense, minimum of 5 yrs. See 750.520f.	NO
	Criminal sexual conduct—3rd degree	Felony	Sentence not to exceed 15 years. For subsequent offense, minimum of 5 yrs. See 750.520f.	NO
	Criminal sexual conduct—4th degree	Misdemeanor	Maximum of 2 yrs in prison and/or maximum fine of $500	NO
	Assault with intent to commit sexual conduct.	Felony	For intent to commit sexual conduct involving penetration, maximum sentence of 10 yrs. Assault with intent to commit sexual conduct in the 2nd degree, maximum sentence of 5 yrs.	NO
Minnesota {Minn. Stat. § 609.341 (2005)}	Criminal Sexual Conduct—1st degree		Sentence of 144 months to 30 years, or fine up to $40,000, or both	NO

State	Statute	Classification	Penalty	No Means No
* See *Minn. Stat. 609-342* (2002) for criminal sexual conduct in the 1st –4th degrees, the court may stay the imposition or	Criminal Sexual Contact—2nd degree		Sentence of 90 months to 25 years, or fine up to $35,000, or both	NO
execution of a sentence if such action is in the "best interest of the complainant or the family unit; and a professional assessment	Criminal Sexual Contact— 3rd degree		Sentence of not more than 15 years or fine up to $30,000, or both	NO
indicates that the offender has been accepted to and can respond to a treatment program."	Criminal Sexual Contact— 4th degree		Sentence of not more than 10 years or fine up to $20,000 or both	NO
Consent - words or overt actions	Criminal Sexual Contact— 5th degree		Sentence of not more than 1 year, fine up to $3,000, or both; subsequent offense (under 609.3451, 617.23 subdivision 2, or a statute from another state similar to either) sentencing: five year maximum sentence, or up to $10,000 fine, or both. See, § 609.3451.	NO
Mississippi {Miss. Code Ann. § 97-3-71 (2005)}	Rape; Assault w/ intent to ravish		Up to life sentence. See, § 97-3-71	NO
Only get life if victim was "chaste" prior to rape! 97-3-71	Sexual Battery		Up to 30 years when committed w/o consent, victim is mentally defective/ incapacitated or physically helpless, or victim is under 18 w/ actor who is in a position of authority (e.g., teacher or guardian); subsequent offense is up to 40 years	NO
			If victim is 14-16, and actor is 18-20, sentence of not more than 5 years, fine up to $5,000, or both; if actor is 21 or more, sentence not more than 30 years, fined up to $10,000, or both; up to 40 years for subsequent offense	NO
			If victim is under 14 and actor is 18 or more, then sentence of 20 years-life; if actor is 13-17, court determines sentence	NO
	Statutory Rape		If actor is 18-20 and convicted of sexual intercourse with a child 14-15 who is 36 months or more younger than D and not D's spouse, then maximum sentence of 5 yrs and/or maximum $5,000 fine. If actor is 21 or more and convicted of above, then maximum	NO

State	Statute	Classification	Penalty	No Means No
Missouri {Mo. Rev. Stat. § 566.010 (2005)}	Forcible Rape and Attempted Forcible Rape	Felony	5 years-life; if serious physical injury results or a deadly weapon is used or multiple persons take part, then 10 years life. If D is a "persistent sexual offender" (has pled guilty or been found guilty of a prior sexual felony or an attempt to commit one, *see* Mo. Rev. Stat. 558.018), minimum	
* See *§ 558.018 R.S. Mo.* for repeat offender sentencing guidelines	Statutory Rape—1st degree	Felony	5 years-life; if injury, weapon used, multiple actors, or victim younger than 12, 10 years to life. If a "persistent sexual offender" then minimum 30 yrs w/o probation or parole	NO
	Statutory Rape—2nd degree	Class C felony	Maximum 7 yrs.	NO
	Sexual Assault	Class C felony	Maximum 7 yrs.	NO
	Forcible Sodomy	Felony	5 years-life; if injury, weapon, or multiple actors are involved, 10 years-life. If a "persistent sexual offender" then minimum 30 yrs w/o probation or parole.	NO
	Statutory Sodomy—1st degree	Felony	5 years-life; if injury, weapon, multiple actors, or victim is under 12, then 10 years-life. If a "persistent sexual offender" then minimum 30 yrs w/o probation or parole.	"without consent"
	Statutory Sodomy—2nd degree	Class C felony	Maximum 7 yrs.	NO
	Deviate Sexual Assault	Class C felony	Maximum 7 yrs.	NO
	Sexual Misconduct - 1st degree	Class A misdemeanor. If subsequent offense or committed w/ deadly weapon	Maximum 1 year for a Class A misdemeanor. For a Class D felony, maximum term of 4 yrs.	NO
	Sexual Abuse	Class C felony	Maximum 7 yrs	NO
		Class B felony if injury, weapon, multiple actors, or victim under 14	5-15 years	NO

State	Statute	Classification	Penalty	No Means No
Montana **{Mont. Code Ann. § 45-2-101 (2005)}** * In addition to penalties imposed for sexual intercourse w/o consent, the offender, if able, is required to pay victim's "reasonable medical and counseling costs" that result from victimization	Sexual Assault		County jail sentence not to exceed 6 months, fine up to $500, or both If victim is less than 16 and actor is 3+ years older or bodily injury results, then 4-100 years and fine of up to $50,000	NO
* See *Mont. Code 45-5-512* for offenders who may be required to undergo "medically safe medroxyprogesterone acetate treatment" to reduce sexual fantasies, drive, etc. * See *46-18-303, 46-18-501, 46-18-502* for multiple convictions of sexual assault listed as an aggravating circumstance for death penalty considerations	Sexual intercourse w/o consent		2-100 years and fine of up to $50,000; if victim is under 16 and actor is 3+ yrs older or bodily injury results, then sentence is 4-100 years and fine of up to $50,000* When multiple perpetrators involved, sentence is 5-100 years and fine up to $50,000* For subsequent offenses where serious bodily injury results, sentence is death if actor was 18+ at time of offense or as provided by *46-18-219* or life w/o parole If victim was incarcerated at time of offense, offender is sentenced to no more than 5 years, or fined up to $50,000, or both	"without consent"
Nebraska **{Neb. Rev. Stat. § 28-318 (2005)}** * See *R.R.S. Neb. § 29-2221* for habitual offenders Without consent: Victim expressed a lack of consent through words	Sexual Assault—1st degree	Class 2 Felony	3-50 years. Second offense: minimum sentence of 25 years w/o parole. See NE ST 28-319.	"without consent"
	Sexual Assault—2nd degree	Class 3 Felony if actor caused physical injury	1-20 years and/or $25,000 fine	
	Sexual Assault—3rd degree	Class 1 Misdemeanor if actor did not cause personal injury	Up to one year and/or $1,000 fine	
	Sexual Assault of a child	Class 3A felony for first offense	1-5 years and/or $10,000 fine	YES

State	Statute	Classification	Penalty	No Means No
		Class 1C felony for subsequent offenses	20-50 years	YES
Nevada {Nev. Rev. Stat. Ann. § 200.364 (Michie 2005)}	Sexual Assault	Category A felony	If substantial bodily injury results: life w/ parole or life w/ chance for parole after 15 years. If no substantial bodily injury results: life w/ chance for parole after 10 years. If victim is under 16 and actor has previously been convicted under this section or of any other sexual crime against a child, punishment is life without the possibility of parole.	
			If victim is under 16 serious bodily injury results: sentence is life w/o parole. If no serious bodily injury results, sentence is life w/ chance for parole after serving 20 years	YES
			If victim is under 14 an 8 no serious bodily harm results, sentence is life w/ chance for parole after 20 years	NO
New Hampshire {N.H. Rev. Stat. Ann. § 632-A:1 (2005)}	Aggravated Felonious Sexual Assault	Felony	First time offense: 10-20 years Second offense: 20-40 years Two or more convictions: life w/o parole May be sentenced to lifetime supervision to be lifted only on petition	
	Felonious Sexual Assault	Class B felony	Up to 7 years	
	Sexual Assault	Class A Misdemeanor	Up to 1 year	
New Jersey {N.J. Rev. Stat. § 2C:14-1 (2005)} * See *N.J. Stat 2C: 14-7* unless sentenced according to 2C: 43-7, subsequent offenses receive fixed minimum sentences of not less than 5 years w/o parole.	Sexual Assault	Crime of 1st degree: aggravated Crime of 2nd degree: no sustained injury	1st degree: 10-20 years 2nd degree: 5-10 years	
	Criminal Sexual Contact	Crime of 3rd degree: aggravated	3-5 years	NO
		Crime of 4th degree: no sustained injury	Up to 18 months	

State	Statute	Classification	Penalty	No Means No
New Mexico {**N.M. Stat. Ann. § 30-9-10 (2005)**}	Criminal Sexual Penetration—1st degree	1st degree felony	18 years. See NMSA 31-18-15	
* See *N.M. Stat 31-18-25* for cases where defendants have committed two violent sexual crimes (the second in New Mexico),	Criminal Sexual Penetration—2nd degree	2nd degree felony	9 years	NO
the defendant is sentenced to life in prison w/ parole (but w/o parole if victim under 13), in addition to sentence imposed for a second violent sexual crime	Criminal Sexual Penetration—3rd degree	3rd degree felony	3 years	
	Criminal Sexual Penetration—4th degree	4th degree felony	18 months	NO
	Aggravated Criminal Sexual Contact; Criminal Sexual Contact	3rd degree felony; 4th degree felony	18 yrs; 9 yrs	NO
	Criminal Sexual Contact of a Minor—2nd, 3rd, or 4th degree	2nd, 3rd, or 4th degree felony	9 yrs; 3 yrs; 18 months	NO
New York {**N.Y. Penal Law § 130.00 (McKinney 2005)**}	Rape—1st degree	Class B felony	5-25 yrs.	NO
* See *NY CLS Penal § 70.02* for rape in the	Rape—2nd degree	Class D felony	2-7 yrs.	NO
1st degree and course of conduct against a child being sentenced separately	Rape—3rd degree	Class E felony	1.5-4 yrs.	NO
	Sexual Abuse—1st degree	Class D felony	2-7 yrs.	NO
* See *NY CLS Penal § 70.06* for second and persistent offenders	Sexual Abuse—2nd degree	Class A misdemeanor	Maximum 1 year	NO
* *NY CLS Penal § 70.10*	Sexual Abuse—3rd degree	Class B misdemeanor	Maximum 3 months	YES

State	Statute	Classification	Penalty	No Means No
	Aggravated Sexual Abuse—1st, 2nd, 3rd, and 4th degree	Class B felony; Class C felony; Class D felony; Class E felony	5-25 yrs; 3.5-15 yrs; 2-7 yrs; 1.5-4 yrs.	NO
	Criminal Sexual Act-1st, 2nd, and 3rd degree.	Class B felony; Class D felony; Class E felony	5-25 yrs; 2-7 yrs; 1.5-4 yrs.	NO
	Sexual Misconduct	Class A misdemeanor	Up to 1 year	NO
	Course of sexual conduct against a	1st degree: Class B felony; 2nd degree: Class D felony	5-25 years; 2-7 years	NO
	Forcible Touching	Class A misdemeanor	Up to 1 year	
North Carolina {N.C. Gen. Stat. § 14-27.1 (2005)} See N.C. Stat. § 15A=1340.17 (2006) for the sentencing chart: *All felonies are sentenced based on mitigating circumstances, prior record of the defendant, and class of felony.* *Case law - against the will = without consent State v. Thomas 329 N.C. 423	Rape—1st degree	Class B1 felony	For first offense without mitigating or aggravating circumstances, presumptive range of 16-20 yrs. If victim is under 12 or D has a prior B1 conviction, defendant is give life w/o parole. N.C. Gen. Stat. § 15A-1340.16B.	YES
	Rape—2nd degree	Class C felony	Presumptive range of 58-73 months	NO
	Sexual Offense—1st degree	Class B1 felony		
	Sexual Offense—2nd degree	Class C felony.		"Against the will" language
	Statutory rape/sexual offense of 13-15 year old	Class B1 felony if actor is 6 years older than victim		
		Class C felony if actor is more than 4 but less than 6 years older than victim		
North Dakota {N.D. Cent. Code § 12.1-20-02 (2005)} * See N.D. Cent. Code, § 12.1-32-09 for habitual offenders	Gross sexual imposition	Class AA felony if actor inflicts serious bodily injury; uses force or threatened imminent death, serious bodily injury, or kidnapping against anyone; or if the	*All sentences as follows (N.D. Cent. Code, 12.1-32-01):* AA: Max. is life w/o parole, can be life with parole but not to be considered for parole until after 30 years, unless reduction due to "good conduct" Class A: up to 20 years and/or $10,000 fine	NO

State	Statute	Classification	Penalty	No Means No
		victim is under 15 and the actor is more than 5 yrs older. Class C felony if the victim is under 15 and the actor 4-5 yrs older. Otherwise Class A	Class B: up to 10 years and/or $10,000 fine Class C: up to 5 years and/or $5,000 fine	NO
	Sexual imposition	Class B felony	Class A misdemeanor:1 year and/or $2,000 fine Class B misdemeanor:30 days and/or $1,000 fine	
	Corruption or solicitation of minors	Class A misdemeanor if victim is over 15; Class C felony if under 15 and actor is at least 22.		
	Sexual Assault	Class A misdemeanor if actor is at least 22 and victim is minor of 15 or more. Class B misdemeanor if actor knows or has reasonable cause to believe that the contact is offensive to the other person. Otherwise Class C felony.		NO
Ohio {**Ohio Rev. Code Ann. § 2907.01** (Anderson 2005)}	Rape	1st degree felony	5-10 yrs. If victim was under 10, then D shall be imprisoned for life. If it is a subsequent offense against a person under 13, then D shall be imprisoned for life with or without parole.	NO
	Sexual Battery	3rd degree felony	1-5 years	
	Unlawful sexual conduct with a minor	1st degree misdemeanor if actor is under 4 years older	Not more than 6 months	need not prove physical resist to prosecute

A-30 CAMPUS SEXUAL ASSAULT RESPONSE TEAMS

State	Statute	Classification	Penalty	No Means No
		2nd degree felony if previous conviction for rape, sexual battery, or unlawful sexual conduct with a minor	2-8 years	
		3rd degree felony if actor is 10+ years older	1-5 years	NO
		4th degree felony	6-18 months	NO
	Gross Sexual Imposition	3rd degree felony if actor surreptitiously or by force gives the victim a controlled substances that substant-ially impairs victim's judg-ment or victim is under 13	1-5 years	
		4th degree felony	6-18 months	
	Sexual Imposition	1st degree misdemeanor for subsequent offenses	Up to 6 months	NO, but victim need not prove physical resist to prosecute
		3rd degree misdemeanor	Up to 60 days	
Oklahoma {Okla. Stat. tit. 21, § 1111 (2005)} *See Okla. St. 51.1a (2003) for defendants already convicted of 1st degree rape, forcible sodomy, lewd molestation or sexual abuse of a child who are again convicted of any of these listed crimes, are sentenced to life without parole	Rape—1st degree	Felony	Punishable by death or state prison sentence of not less than five years	
	Rape—2nd degree	Felony	Sentence of 1-15 years	NO
	Lewd or Indecent Proposals or Acts as to child under 16	Felony	Provided that actor is 3+ years older than victim, sentence of 1-20 years	
	Sexual Battery	Felony	Prison for not more than 5 years	NO
Oregon	Rape—1st degree	Class A felony	Up to 20 years; $375,000 fine	NO

State	Statute	Classification	Penalty	No Means No
{Or. Rev. Stat. § 163.305 (2005)} *Force needed for No Means No	Rape—2nd degree	Class B felony	Up to 10 years; $250,000 fine	NO
	Rape—3rd degree	Class C felony	Up to 5 years; $125,000 fine	YES, without consent
	Unlawful sexual penetration—1st	Class A felony	Up to 20 years; $300,000 fine	NO
	Unlawful sexual penetration—2nd degree	Class B felony	Up to 10 years; $200,000 fine	
	Sodomy - 1st degree	Class A felony		NO
	Sodomy - 2nd degree	Class B felony		NO
	Sodomy - 3rd degree	Class C felony		NO
	Sexual Abuse—1st degree	Class B felony		
	Sexual Abuse—2nd degree	Class C felony		
	Sexual Abuse—3rd degree	Class A misdemeanor	Up to 1 year; $6,250 fine	
	Contributing to sexual delinquency of a minor	Class A misdemeanor		
	Sexual misconduct	Class C misdemeanor	Up to 30 days; $1,250 fine	NO
Pennsylvania **{Pa. Cons. Stat. § 3101 (2005)}**	Rape	1st degree felony	Up to 20 years; additional sentencing option of 10 years and a fine up to $100,000 for administering controlled substances to victim w/o consent. Notwithstanding Sec. 1103, the maximum sentence for the rape of a child under	"Victim does not consent thereto"
	Statutory Sexual Assault	2nd degree felony	Up to 10 years	NO

State	Statute	Classification	Penalty	No Means No
* See *42 Pa. C.S. § 9714 (2005)* for second and subsequent offenders	Involuntary deviate sexual intercourse	1st degree felony	Up to 20 years. Notwithstanding Sec. 1103, if the victim was a child under 13 the maximum sentence is 40 yrs; if serious bodily injury resulted, the maximum term is life imprisonment.	
	Sexual Assault	2nd degree felony		NO
	Aggravated indecent assault	2nd degree felony unless the victim is a child under 13, then 1st degree felony		NO
	Indecent assault	1st degree misdemeanor 3rd degree felony if child is under 13 and it is a subsequent offense; there has been a course of conduct of indecent assault by the person; victim's sexual or intimate parts touched by the actor's sexual or intimate parts; or actor's sexual or intimate parts are touched by the victim's sexual or intimate parts.	Up to 5 yrs Up to 7 yrs	NO
Rhode Island {**R.I. Gen. Laws § 11037-1 (2005)**}	Sexual assault—1st degree		Sentence of 10 years-life. For assault w/ intent to commit, sentence of 3-20 year	without consent
* See R.I. Gen. Laws 11-37-10 (2005) for persons convicted of subsequent offenses are	Sexual assault—2nd degree		Sentence of 3-15 years	without consent
given no less than the number of years involved in the minimum sentence for the most recent crime.	Sexual assault—3rd degree		Sentence no more than 5 years	without consent
South Carolina {**S.C. Code Ann. § 16-3-651(Law. Co-op, 2005)**}	Criminal Sexual Conduct—1st degree	Felony	Maximum sentence of 30 years	NO

State	Statute	Classification	Penalty	No Means No
	Criminal Sexual Conduct—2nd degree	Felony	Maximum sentence of 20 years	NO
	Criminal Sexual Conduct—3rd degree	Felony	Maximum sentence of 10 years	NO
	Criminal Sexual Conduct w/ Minors - 1st degree		10-30 yrs	NO
				NO
	Assault w/ intent to commit criminal sexual conduct		Punishable as though crime were completed	
	Spousal Sexual Battery	Felony	Maximum sentence of 10 years	NO
South Dakota {**S.D. Codified Laws Ann. § 22-22-30 (2005)**} * See *S.D. Codified Laws § 22-7-7 (2005)* for enhanced sentences for prior felony convictions	Rape—1st degree: If victim is under 13	Class C felony	Life imprisonment, and a $50,000 fine may be imposed.	
	Rape—2nd degree: If accomplished through force, coercion, or threats	Class 1 felony	50 yrs and a $50,000 fine may be imposed.	NO
	Rape in the 3rd: If victim cannot consent because of physical or mental incapacity; or victim cannot give consent because of intoxicating agent or hypnosis.	Class 2 felony	25 yrs and a $25,000 fine may be imposed.	NO
				NO

State	Statute	Classification	Penalty	No Means No
	Rape in the 4th if victim is 13-15 and actor is at least 3 older.	Class 3 felony: if victim is between 13-16 and actor is 3+ years older; if incest occurs; if victim is 13-18 and stepchild of actor	15 yrs and a $15,000 fine may be imposed.	NO
	Sexual contact w/ child under 16	Class 3 felony; Class 1 misdemeanor if actor is less than 3 years older than victim	Class 3 felony: 15 yrs and a $15,000 fine may be imposed. Class 1 misdemeanor: maximum 1 year and/or $2,000 fine	NO
Tennessee {Tenn. Code Ann. § 39-13-502 (2005)}	Aggravated Rape	Class A felony	15-60 years and, in addition, may impose maximum of $50,000 fine. See TCA 40-35-111	
* See Tenn. Code Ann. § 40-35-114 for	Rape	Class B felony	8-30 years and, in addition, may impose maximum of $25,000 fine.	NO
Rape (of a child)/Sexual Battery, using a substance to cause the victim mental/ physical helplessness is factor in sentence	Aggravated Sexual Battery	Class B felony	8-30 years and, in addition, may impose maximum of $25,000 fine.	NO
	Sexual Battery	Class E felony	1-6 years and, in addition, may impose maximum of $3,000 fine.	NO
*Defendants w/ more than one conviction are required to serve entire sentence	Statutory Rape	Class E felony	1-6 years and, in addition, may impose maximum of $3,000 fine.	YES, without consent
	Rape of a child	Class A felony	15-60 years and, in addition, may impose maximum of $50,000 fine.	NO
Texas {Tex. Penal Code Ann. § 21.01(Vernon 2005)}	Sexual Assault	2nd degree felony, except that it is a 1st degree felony if the victim was a person the actor was prohibited from marrying under Section 25.01.	2nd degree felony: 2-20 years and, in addition, may impose a maximum fine of $10,000 1st degree felony: 5-99 years and, in addition, may impose a maximum fine of $10,000	YES, without consent
* See Tex. Penal Code § 12.42 for repeat offenders	Aggravated Sexual Assault	1st degree felony	5-99 years and, in addition, may impose a maximum fine of $10,000	NO

State	Statute	Classification	Penalty	No Means No
	Indecency with a child	2nd degree felony if a person engages in sexual contact or causes the child to engage in sexual contact. 3rd degree felony if, with the intent to arouse any person, the actor exposes any part of own genitals or anus or causes the child to expose any part of his/her genitals or anus.	2nd degree felony: 2-20 years and, in addition, may impose a maximum fine of $10,000. 3rd degree felony: 2-10 years and, in addition, may impose a maximum fine of $10,000	NO
Utah {**Utah Code Ann. § 76-5-406 (2003)**}	Rape	1st degree felony	5 years-life	YES, without consent
* See Utah Code 76-3-203.1 for offenses committed with two or more persons where penalties are enhanced: class B misdemeanors become class A; class A misdemeanors become 3rd degree felonies; 3rd degree felonies become 2nd degree; 2nd degree felonies become 1st degree; 1st degree felonies enhanced to 9 years-life	Forcible Sexual Abuse	2nd degree felony	1-15 years	YES, without consent
	Object Rape	1st degree felony	5 years to life	NO
	Unlawful Sexual Conduct w/ 16-17 year old	3rd degree felony	Up to 5 years	YES
	Sexual Abuse of a minor	Class A misdemeanor	Up to 1 year	YES
* See Utah Code 76-3-407 for 3 years may be added to sentence for each prior conviction in addition to new sentence	Sexual Abuse of a child	2nd degree felony	1-15 years	YES
* See Code 76-3-408 for 3rd conviction defendant sentenced to life w/o parole	Aggravated sexual abuse of a child	1st degree felony	Mandatory prison sentence of 5 years to life	YES
*See Utah Code Ann. § 76-3-203.5 for habitual violent offender guidelines	Rape of a child	1st degree felony	Mandatory prison sentence of 6, 10, or 15 years or life	YES
* See Utah Code 76.3.203 for increase in sentence for use of a dangerous weapon	Object rape of a child	1st degree felony	Mandatory prison sentence of 6, 10, or 15 years or life	YES
	Sexual Battery	Class A misdemeanor	Up to 1 year	YES
*§ 76-5-406 - No Means No Statute that applies to all categories	Unlawful sexual activity with a minor	3rd degree felony; class B misdemeanor if actor is w/ in 4 years of victim's age	3rd degree felony: up to 5 years; Class B misdemeanor: up to 6 months	YES

State	Statute	Classification	Penalty	No Means No
	Aggravated Sexual Assault	1st degree felony	Mandatory prison sentence of 6, 10, or 15 years or life	NO
	Sodomy; forcible sodomy	Class B misdemeanor; 1st degree felony if committed by force	Class B misdemeanor: up to 6 months 1st degree felony: 5 years-life	NO
	Sodomy on a child	1st degree felony	not less than 6, 10, or 15 years or life	YES
Vermont {Vt. Stat. Ann. tit. 13, § 3251 (2005)}	Sexual Assault		Sentence of not more than 20 years or up to $10,000 fine, or both; if victim under 16 and actor is responsible for victim's welfare, sentence is not more than 35 years or fine up to $25,000, or both	YES
	Aggravated Sexual Assault		Maximum sentence of life in prison, fine of up to $50,000, or both	
Virginia {Va. Code Ann. § 18.2-67.10 (2005)}	Rape		5 years-life (rape of spouse convictions may be suspended upon completion of counseling)	
* See *Va Code 18.2-67.5:3* (2002) for subsequent convictions for rape, forcible sodomy, object sexual penetration, or conspiracy to commit these acts result in life in prison	Aggravated Sexual Battery	Felony	1-20 years; fine up to $100,000; or both	YES, without consent
* See *Va Code 18.2-67.5:2* for conviction for carnal knowledge of a child age 13-15, aggravated sexual battery, or conspiracy to commit results in maximum sentence	Sexual Battery	Class 1 misdemeanor	1 year; $1,000 fine	YES, non-consensual sexual acts
	Forcible Sodomy	Felony	5 years-life	YES, "against will"
	Attempted rape, forcible sodomy, object sexual penetration, aggravated sexual battery	Class 4 felony	2-10 years; up to $100,000 fine	YES, "against will"
* See *Va Code 18.2-67.5:1* for 3rd conviction of (attempted) sexual battery, defendant is guilty of class 6 felony		Class 6 felony: attempted aggravated sexual battery	1-5 years; up to $2,500 fine	YES, "against will"
		Class 1 misdemeanor: attempted sexual battery	Maximum 1 year; $2,500 fine	
	Carnal knowledge of child between 13-15	Class 4 felony. Class 6 felony if accused is a	Class 4 felony: 2-10 years; up to $100,000 fine Class 6 felony: 1-5 years; up to $2,500 fine Class	

State	Statute	Classification	Penalty	No Means No
	Object sexual penetration	Felony	Sentence of 5 years-life. If committed against a spouse, the court may suspend the sentence upon completion of counseling.	NO
Washington {**Wash. Rev. Code § 9A.44.010 (2005)**}	Rape—1st degree	Class A felony	*Felonies where a sentence is not*	
	Rape—2nd degree	Class A felony	*specifically stated within the statute*	
	Rape—3rd degree	Class C felony	*are assumed to be punishable by up*	under 13 = no consent (automatic)
	Rape of a child—1st degree	Class A felony	*to 10 years in prison and up to a $20,000 fine*	against will
	Rape of a child—2nd degree	Class A felony	*(Rev. Code Wash. (ARCW) § 9.92.010)*	NO
	Rape of a child—3rd degree	Class C felony		NO
	Sexual misconduct w/ a minor—1st degree	Class C felony		YES
	Sexual misconduct w/ a minor—2nd degree	Gross misdemeanor	Up to 1 year; $5,000 fine	NO
	Indecent liberties	Class B felony; if forcible compulsion involved, Class A felony	Up to 10 years	NO
West Virginia {**W. Va. Code § 61-8B-1 (2005)**} *Lack of consent defined § 61-8B-2 (applies to all categories)*	Sexual Assault—1st degree	Felony	State Prison 15-35 years, fine of $1,000-$10,000	NO
	Sexual Assault—2nd degree	Felony	Prison 10-25 years, fine of $1,000-$10,000	
	Sexual Assault - 3rd Degree	Felony	Prison 1-5 years; fine up to $10,000	NO
	Sexual Abuse—1st degree	Felony	Prison 1-5 years, fine up to $10,000	NO

State	Statute	Classification	Penalty	No Means No
	Sexual Abuse—2nd degree	Misdemeanor	Jail for up to 12 months; fined up to $500	YES
	Sexual Abuse—3rd degree	Misdemeanor	County jail for up to 90 days; or fined up to $500; or both	
Wisconsin {Wis. Stat. § 939.22 (2005)}	Sexual Assault—1st degree	Class B felony	maximum 60 years	YES, without consent
	Sexual Assault—2nd degree	Class C felony	maximum 40 years and/or $100,000 fine	YES, without consent
	Sexual Assault–3rd degree	Class G felony	maximum 5 years	
	Sexual Assault–4th degree	Class A misdemeanor	6 months - 1 year.	
	Sexual Assault of a child—1st degree	Class B felony (Wis. Stat. 948.025 (2002))	maximum 60 years	YES
	Sexual Assault of a child—2nd degree	Class C felony	maximum 40 years and/or $100,000 fine	YES, without consent
Wyoming {Wyo. Stat. § 6-2-301 (2005)}	Sexual Assault—1st degree	Felony	5-50 years	YES, without consent
* See Wyo. Stat. 6-2-306 (2005) for a person convicted of 2 of more 1st/2nd degree sexual assaults, sentenced to 5 years to life;	Sexual Assault—2nd degree	Felony	Up to 20 years	YES, without consent
3rd degree assault up to 20 years; life w/o parole for 3 convictions	Sexual Assault—3rd degree	Felony	Up to 15 years	NO
	Sexual Battery	Misdemeanor	Not more than 1 year; fine up to $1,000; or both	NO

State	Statute	Classification	Penalty	No Means No
Federal **18 USCS § 2241 et seq.**	Aggravated Sexual Abuse		Fine, sentence of any term of years, or both. If the crime involved a child under 12 and the defendant had been previously convicted under this subsection or a state law equivalent, unless the death penalty is imposed, the defendant shall be sentenced to life in prison.	YES, victim has not consented
	Sexual Abuse		fined, imprisoned for not more than 20 years, or both.	NO
Military **2005 MCM Article 120-45**	Rape		Death or such other punishment as a court-martial may direct	NO
	Carnal Knowledge		If the child had attained 12 years at the time of the offense, the maximum punishment is dishonorable discharge, forfeiture of all pay and allowances, and confinement of 20 years. If the child was under 12 at the time of the offense, the maximum punishment is dishonorable discharge, forfeiture of all pay and allowances, and confinement for life without eligibility for parole.	

Appendix B

State Definitions of Penetration for Sex Crimes

[Editors' note: Appendix B is provided as an overview and comparison for the reader of state definitions of rape and sexual assault. This chart was compiled in 2006, and readers should double check for any more recent changes to the law that may have been made in their state after the chart was created. The authors strongly recommend the reader seek legal counsel guidance for detailed interpretation of individual state definitions.]

STATE	PENETRATION TYPE FOR SEXUAL ACTS/ INTERCOURSE			DOES CRIME REQUIRE EMMISSION OF SEMEN?	PENETRATION TYPE FOR DEVIATE SEXUAL ACTS/CONTACT			THINGS INSERTED AS COVERED BY STATUTE					
	Vaginal	Anal	Oral		Vaginal	Anal	Oral	Penis	Tongue	Finger	Foreign object	Other	Any body part
ALABAMA	X			NO	X	X		X	X			X[1]	
ALASKA[2]													
ARIZONA[3]	X[4]	X	X					X	X		X	X	X
ARKANSAS	X[5]			NO	X[6]	X	X	X			X		X
CALIFORNIA	X	X	X	NO[7]				X	X		X[8]	X[9]	X
COLORADO	X	X	X	NO				X	X		X		
CONNECTICUT	X	X	X	NO				X	X		X		
DELAWARE	X	X	X	NO				X	X		X	X[10]	X
D.C.	X	X	X	NO				X	X	X	X		
FLORIDA	X	X	X					X	X		X		
GEORGIA	X			NO[11]	X[12]	X		X			X[13]		
HAWAII	X	X	X	NO				X	X		X		X
IDAHO	X	X	X	NO[14]				X				X[15]	
ILLINOIS	X	X	X	NO				X	X		X	X[16]	X
INDIANA	X				X	X		X	X		X		
IOWA	X	X	X					X	X	X		X[17]	
KANSAS	X				X[18]	X		X	X	X	X		
KENTUCKY	X			NO	X	X		X	X		X		

[1] In cases of sexual abuse, any "touching of intimate parts" is sexual contact.

[2] "Sexual act means sexual penetration or sexual contact." No other definition is provided (11.41.470).

[3] "Sexual intercourse" (penetration into the penis, vulva, or anus by any body part, object, or through masturbatory contact with the penis or vulva) and "oral sexual contact" (with the penis, vulva, or anus) are used in sexual assault statutes, while "sexual contact" is involved in sexual abuse (13-1401).

[4] Penetration of the vulva is sufficient (13-1401).

[5] Penetration of the labia majora is sufficient (5-14-101, 1B, 9).

[6] Specifically only the labia majora (5-14-101(1)(B)).

[7] Cal. Penal Code § 11165.1

[8] "Foreign object" includes "any part of the body except a sexual organ" (Section 289).

[9] See Section 289, part K(3) for definition of "unknown objects."

[10] "Sexual penetration" may also involve the placement of a "sexual device" inside the mouth of another person (Section 761).

[11] See Spraggins v. State, 255 Ga. 195, 336 S.E.2d 227 (1985)

[12] Anal/oral penetration is a crime of sodomy, not rape (16-6-2)

[13] Penetration with a foreign object is a crime of aggravated sexual battery (16-6-22.2)

[14] Idaho Code § 18-6103.

[15] Penetration in rape requires oral, vaginal, or anal penetration of a female by a penis (18-6101). For lewd conduct with a minor and sexual battery or a minor, sexual penetration may include, but is not limited to, genital-genital contact, oral-genital contact, anal-genital contact, oral-anal contact, manual-anal contact, or manual-genital contact (18-508 and 18-508A).

[16] "Sexual penetration" may also include the "intrusion, however slight" of an animal into the sex organ or anus of another person (721 ILCS 5/12-12).

[17] "Sexual act" also includes "use of artificial sexual organs or substitutes thereof in contact with the genitalia or anus" (702.17).

[18] This is sodomy (21-3505)

Reprinted with permission from the American prosecutor research Institute. © NCPVAW at APRI (2006). For more information, please contact the National Center for the Prosecution of Violence Against Women, APRI, 703-549-9222 or ncpvaw@ndaa-apri.org. This project war supported by Grant N. 2004-WT-AX-K047 awarded by the Office on Violence Against Women, U.S. Department of Justice. The opinions, findings, conclusions, and recommendations expressed in this publication are those of the authors and do not necessarily reflect the views of the Department of Justice, Office on Violence Against Women.

LOUISIANA	X	X	X	NO				X	X	X[19]		
MAINE	X	X	X					X	X	X	X[20]	
MARYLAND[21]	X	X	X	NO				X	X	X		
MASSACHUSETTS	X			NO	X	X		X	X[22]	X		X
MICHIGAN	X	X	X	NO				X	X	X		X
MINNESOTA	X	X	X	NO				X	X	X		X
MISSISSIPPI[23]	X	X	X					X	X	X		X
MISSOURI	X			NO	X	X		X	X	X		
MONTANA	X	X	X	NO[24]				X	X	X		X
NEBRASKA	X	X	X	NO				X	X	X		X[25]
NEVADA	X	X	X					X	X	X		X
NEW HAMPSHIRE	X	X	X	NO				X	X	X		X[26]
NEW JERSEY	X	X	X					X	X	X	X	X[27]
NEW MEXICO	X	X	X	NO				X	X	X		
NEW YORK	X	X	X					X	X	X[28]		
NORTH CAROLINA[29]	X	X	X	NO[30]				X	X	X		
NORTH DAKOTA	X	X	X	NO				X	X	X		X
OHIO	X	X	X					X	X	X		X
OKLAHOMA	X	X						X		X		X[31]
OREGON	X			NO	X	X		X	X	X[32]		
PENNSYLVANIA[33]	X	X	X	NO	X	X		X	X	X		

[19] While not included in the rape statutes, contact between the anus or genitals of one person and any "instrumentality or any part of the body" of another person is considered penetration during sexual battery (14:43.1).

[20] "Sexual act" also includes "any act between a person and an animal being used by another person which act involves direct physical contact between the genitals of one and the mouth or anus of the other, or direct physical contact between the genitals of one and the genitals of the other (Section 251).

[21] Maryland distinguishes between "vaginal intercourse" (genital copulation including penetration of the vagina) and "sexual acts" (analingus, cunnilingus, fellatio, anal intercourse, object penetration). The former is used in rape statutes, while the latter is used in laws against "sexual offenses" (3-301). See Section 22 for emission requirements for "sexual intercourse."

[22] Use of term "unnatural sexual intercourse" inserted by 1974 amendment refers to oral and anal intercourse, including fellatio, cunnilingus, and other intrusions of part of person's body or other objects into genital or oral opening of another person's body. *Commonwealth v. Gallant*, 373 Mass. 577, 369 NE2d 707 (1977).

[23] Penetration for rape requires intercourse, while penetration for sexual battery includes "cunnilingus, fellatio, buggery, or pederasty, any penetration of the genital or anal openings of another person's body" (97-3-97).

[24] *See St. v. Bouldin*, 153 M. 276, 456 P.2d 830 (1969).

[25] "Sexual penetration" also includes "any intrusion, however slight, of any part of the actor or victim's body" (28-318).

[26] "Sexual penetration" includes "any intrusion, however slight, of any part of the actor's body or any object manipulated by the actor into genital openings of the victim's body" and "any intrusion, however slight, of any part of the victim's body into genital or anal openings of the actor's body" (632-A:1).

[27] "Sexual penetration" also includes "insertion of the hand, finger, or object into the anus or vagina either by the actor or upon the actor's instruction" (2C:14-1).

[28] Insertion of a foreign object is considered aggravated 3rd degree sexual abuse (130.66). "Foreign object" is defined as "any instrument or article which, when inserted in the vagina, urethra, penis, or rectum, is capable of causing physical injury" (130.00).

[29] Rape requires vaginal intercourse, while "sexual offenses" require "sexual acts" which include cunnilingus, fellatio, analingus, anal intercourse, and penetration by any object into the genital or anal opening of another person (14-27.1).

[30] *See State v. Monds*, 130 N.C. 697, 41 S.E. 789 (1902).

[31] Rape by instrumentation involves "any inanimate object or any part of the human body" (21 Okla. Statute 1111.1).

[32] Penetration with "any object other than the penis or mouth of the actor" is considered unlawful sexual penetration (163.411).

RHODE ISLAND	X	X	X	NO					X	X	X[34]		X
SOUTH CAROLINA	X	X	X	NO[35]					X	X	X		X
SOUTH DAKOTA	X	X	X						X	X	X		X
TENNESSEE	X	X	X	NO					X	X	X		X[36]
TEXAS	X					X	X	X	X	X[37]			
UTAH	X			NO[38]		X[39]	X	X	X	X			
VERMONT	X	X	X						X	X	X		X
VIRGINIA	X			NO[40]		X[41]	X	X	X	X[42]			
WASHINGTON	X	X	X						X	X	X		
WEST VIRGINIA	X	X	X						X	X	X[43]		
WISCONSIN	X	X	X	NO					X	X	X		X[44]
WYOMING	X	X	X	NO					X	X	X		X
FEDERAL	X	X	X						X	X	X	X	
UCMJ[45]													

---

[33] "Sexual intercourse," in addition to its "ordinary meaning, includes intercourse per os or per anus. Deviate sexual intercourse" means intercourse "per per os or per anus between human beings and any form of sexual intercourse with an animal" as well as penetration of the genitals or anus of another person with a foreign object (18 Pa. C.S. 3101).

[34] "Sexual penetration" includes "intrusion, however slight, by any part of a person's body or of any object into the genital or anal openings of another person's body, or the victim's own body upon the accuser's instruction" (R.I. Gen.Laws 11-37-1).

[35] *State v. Worthy* (S.C. 1962) 239 S.C. 449, 123 S.E.2d 835 (decided under former statute).

[36] "Sexual penetration" includes "intrusion, however slight, by any part of a person's body or by any object into the genital or anal openings of the victim, defendant, or any other person's body" (Tenn. Code 39-13-501).

[37] Penetration of the genitals or the anus of another person with an object is considered deviate sexual intercourse (21.01).

[38] *See State v. Gehring*, 694 P.2d 599 (Utah 1984).

[39] Oral and anal intercourses are classified as sodomy (Utah Code 76-5-403).

[40] *See Commonwealth v. Thomas*, 3 Va. (1 Va. Cas.) 307 (1812).

[41] Oral and anal intercourses are classified as sodomy (Va. Code 18.2-67.1).

[42] Object sexual penetration includes both inanimate and animate objects (Va. Code 18.2-67.2).

[43] "Sexual intrusion" is defined as "any act between persons involving penetration, however slight, of the female sex organ or of the anus of any person by an object" in order to degrade, humiliate, or gratify desire (W.Va. Code 61-8B-1).

[44] "Sexual intercourse" also includes "intrusion, however slight, of any part of a person's body or of any object into the genital or anal opening either by the defendant or upon the defendant's instruction" (Wis. Statute 940.225).

[45] Sexual intercourse is not defined nor is penetration except to note that any penetration, however slight, constitutes an offense. (2005 MCM Article 120-45).

Appendix C

DOE Handbook for Campus Crime Reporting (Special Considerations: Policies Regarding Sex Offenses and Offenders)

[Editors' note: Appendix C is provided as a quick reference for the reader in determining the U.S. Department of Education's requirements for the reporting of sex offenses and offenders.]

[Editors' note: The following material is excerpted from U.S. Department of Education. (2005). *The handbook for campus crime reporting*, (pp. 103-110).]

What are the *Clery Act* requirements regarding policies and procedures for sex offenses? As mentioned in Chapter 8, the *Clery Act* requires you to provide policy statements regarding sex offenses and obtaining access to information regarding registered sex offenders in the campus community.

SEX OFFENSES

The FBI's National Incident-Based Reporting System (NIBRS) edition of the *UCR* defines a sex offense in general as *any sexual act directed against another person, forcibly and/or against that person's will; or not forcibly or against the person's will where the victim is incapable of giving consent.* (See Chapter 3 for definitions of forcible and non-forcible sex offenses.)

The *Clery Act* requires you to include a statement about your institution's sex offense policy, procedures and programs in your annual security report. Specifically, the regulation requires a statement of policy regarding **the institution's campus sexual assault programs to prevent sex offenses, and procedures to follow when a sex offense occurs.** The statement *must* include:

    a. A description of educational programs to promote the awareness of rape, acquaintance rape and other forcible and non-forcible sex offenses.

These programs are required by Section 485(f) of the *Higher Education Act*. We encourage your institution to contract with experts in the area of sex offense education to provide training to students and staff. Such experts include rape crisis intervention specialists, local law enforcement officials and social services personnel.

    b. Procedures students should follow if a sex offense occurs, including:
- Procedures concerning who should be contacted;
- The importance of preserving evidence for the proof of a criminal offense; and
- To whom the alleged offense should be reported.

Note that the *Clery Act* does not mandate whom to contact or to whom the offense should be reported. It requires only that your institution include this information in the procedures. Be specific with regard to this information. For example, if students are directed to a rape crisis counselor for support and the campus police department for reporting purposes, provide contact information. We encourage institutions to consult law enforcement about what constitutes "preserving evidence."

    c. Information on a student's option to notify appropriate law enforcement authorities, including:
- On-campus and local police; and
- A statement that institutional personnel *will* assist the student in notifying these authorities, if the student requests the assistance of these personnel.

Provide information so that students know what notifying law enforcement authorities entails. Be specific about both campus and local police, as applicable. The statement that your institution will comply with a student's request for assistance in notifying authorities is mandatory.

d. Notification to students of existing on- and off-campus counseling, mental health or other student services for victims of sex offenses.

Your statement should provide specific information identifying the appropriate available services for victims. Be sure to include both on- and off-campus services, as applicable. If there are no on-campus services or no off-campus services, state this.

e. Notification to students that the institution *will* change a victim's academic and living situations after an alleged sex offense, and the options for those changes if those changes are requested by the victim and are reasonably available.

An institution is obligated to comply with a student's request for a living and/or academic situation change following an *alleged* sex offense. The options should be identified.

These requirements allow an institution flexibility. For example, an institution could permit a victim to break a housing contract with the institution so that the student may seek off campus housing. But, it would not be reasonable to expect the institution to pay for the rental of a private apartment for the student.

f. Procedures for campus disciplinary action in cases of an alleged sex offense, *including a clear statement that*:
   i. The accuser and the accused are entitled to the same opportunities to have others present during a disciplinary proceeding; and
   ii. Both the accuser and the accused must be informed of the outcome of any institutional disciplinary proceeding that is brought alleging a sex offense. Compliance with this paragraph does not constitute a violation of the *Family Educational Rights and Privacy Act* (FERPA). For the purpose of this paragraph, the outcome of a disciplinary proceeding means only the institution's final determination with respect to the alleged sex offense and any sanction that is imposed against the accused.

Your statement regarding procedures for campus disciplinary action for alleged sex offenses must include both (i) and (ii). Add any other procedures as appropriate for your institution. The right to have others present and to be informed of the outcome apply to the institutional disciplinary proceedings, regardless of where the alleged sex offense occurred. Disclosure concerning the outcome of proceedings must be unconditional; a victim cannot be required to sign a nondisclosure agreement or to otherwise agree to a prohibition from discussing the case.

g. Sanctions the institution may impose following a final determination of an institutional disciplinary proceeding regarding rape, acquaintance rape or other forcible or non-forcible sex offenses.

Note that this does not require you simply to state that sanctions may be imposed. You are required to list the sanctions.

It is very important that you understand that:

- Simply stating the topic of a policy does not meet the requirements. All of the required components of a policy must be included in the policy statement.

- For the most part, institutions have discretion in the wording of these statements and how the policies and procedures are put into practice.

- It is imperative that an institution's policy statements accurately reflect what the institution does currently to prevent sex offenses, and the procedures that are followed when a sex offense occurs.

SAMPLE POLICY STATEMENT ADDRESSING SEX OFFENSES

Sexual Assault Prevention and Response

The University educates the student community about sexual assaults and date rape through mandatory freshman orientations each fall. The Police Department offers sexual assault education and information programs to University students and employees upon request. Literature on date rape education, risk reduction, and University response is available through the Office of Housing and Residential Education.

If you are a victim of a sexual assault at this institution, your first priority should be to get to a place of safety. You should then obtain necessary medical treatment. The University Police Department strongly advocates that a victim of sexual assault report the incident in a timely manner. Time is a critical factor for evidence collection and preservation. An assault should be reported directly to a University officer and/or to a Housing and Residential Education representative. Filing a police report with a University officer will not obligate the victim to prosecute, nor will it subject the victim to scrutiny or judgmental opinions from officers. Filing a police report will

> ➤ ensure that a victim of sexual assault receives the necessary medical treatment and tests, at no expense to the victim

> ➤ provide the opportunity for collection of evidence helpful in prosecution, which cannot be obtained later (ideally a victim of sexual assault should not wash, douche, use the toilet, or change clothing prior to a medical/legal exam)

> ➤ assure the victim has access to free confidential counseling from counselors specifically trained in the area of sexual assault crisis intervention.

When a sexual assault victim contacts the Police Department, the Metro Police Sex Crimes Unit will be notified as well. A representative from the Office of Housing and Residential Education will also be notified. The victim of a sexual assault may choose for the investigation to be pursued through the criminal justice system and the University Conduct Council, or only the latter.

A University representative from the Police Department or the Office of Housing and Residential Education will guide the victim through the available options and support the victim in his or her decision. Various counseling options are available from the University through the Student Health Center, the Women's Center, University Ministries, Employee Assistance, and the Psychological and Counseling Center. Counseling and support services outside the University system can be obtained through the Rape and Sexual Abuse Center and the Victim Intervention Program of the Metro Police Department.

University disciplinary proceedings, as well as special guidelines for cases involving sexual misconduct, are detailed in the *Student Handbook*. The *Handbook* provides, in part, that the accused and the victim will each be allowed to choose one person who has had no formal legal training to accompany them throughout the hearing. Both the victim and accused will be informed of the outcome of the hearing. A student found guilty of violating the University sexual misconduct policy could be criminally prosecuted in the state courts and may be suspended or expelled from the University for the first offense. Student victims have the option to change their academic and/or on-campus living situations after an alleged sexual assault, if such changes are reasonably available.

ADVISING THE CAMPUS COMMUNITY ABOUT SEX OFFENDERS

Upon release from prison, individuals convicted of sex crimes may be required to register with law enforcement agencies (under laws referred to as "Megan's Laws"). If registered sex offenders are enrolled at, or employed at a postsecondary institution, the offenders must also provide this information to the state. The information is then provided by the state to campus police departments or to other law enforcement authorities in the jurisdiction where the institution is located.

Your institution must provide a statement **advising the campus community where law enforcement agency information provided by a state concerning registered sex offenders may be obtained, such as the law enforcement office of the institution, a local law enforcement agency with jurisdiction for the campus, or a computer network address**.

You should know that:

- Institutions are not required to request this information from the state; rather, the state must provide this information to the campus police department or other law enforcement authorities in the school's jurisdiction.

- Institutions are required to provide the campus community with information that would enable them to obtain this public information about registered sex offenders on campus. The intention of this requirement is to afford a campus community the same availability of information about registered sex offenders as they would have in their home communities under Megan's Law.

- While institutions are required to inform the campus community where sex offender information can be *accessed*, the institution is not required to disseminate sex offender information throughout the community.

How FERPA Affects This Policy

Nothing in FERPA prohibits an educational institution from disclosing information about registered sex offenders. This includes the disclosure of personally identifiable, nondirectory information without prior written consent or other consent from the individual. Institutions also have authority to disclose information about registered sex offenders that may otherwise become available to educational institutions through the operation of state sex offender registration and community notification programs. However, state laws could limit disclosure of such information. Institutions are advised to contact their state authorities for guidance on this issue.

If the state in which your institution is located does not currently register sex offenders, or does not provide campus police or your local law enforcement agencies with this information, a statement in your annual security report should disclose this. However, you would be required to advise the campus community about obtaining registered sex offender information should the state provide it at a future date.

SAMPLE POLICY STATEMENT ADDRESSING SEX OFFENDER REGISTRATION (FOR INSTITUTIONS MAINTAINING A LIST OF REGISTERED SEX OFFENDERS ON-SITE)

Sexual Offender Registration

The Campus Sex Crimes Prevention Act (CSCPA) of 2000 is a federal law that provides for the tracking of convicted sex offenders enrolled at, or employed by, institutions of higher education. The CSCPA is an amendment to the Jacob Wetterling Crimes Against Children and Sexually Violent Offender Act. The federal law requires state law enforcement agencies (in Kansas, it is the Kansas Bureau of Investigation) to provide Dodge City Community College with a list of registered sex offenders who have indicated that they are either enrolled, employed or carrying on a vocation at Dodge City Community College.

Dodge City Community College is required to inform the campus community that a KBI registration list of sex offenders will be maintained and available at two campus locations: the Office of Campus Safety and Security in Shelden Hall and the Office of the Associate Dean of Students, located room 103 of the Student Union.

In addition, a list of all registered sex offenders in Kansas is available from the Kansas Bureau of Investigation at http://www.accesskansas.org/kbi/ro.htm. Dodge City is located in Ford County and the zip code is 67801.

The CSCPA further amends the Family Educational Rights and Privacy Act of 1974 (FERPA) to clarify that nothing in the Act can prohibit an educational institution from disclosing information provided to the institution concerning registered sex offenders.

This statement is provided in compliance with the Campus Sex Crimes Prevention Act of 2000 and the Kansas Offender Registration Act (KORA) of 2003, KSA 22-4902.

SAMPLE POLICY STATEMENT ADDRESSING SEX OFFENDER REGISTRATION (FOR INSTITUTIONS PROVIDING AN ELECTRONIC LINK TO REGISTERED SEX OFFENDER INFORMATION MAINTAINED BY AN OUTSIDE LAW ENFORCEMENT AGENCY)

In accordance with the "Campus Sex Crimes Prevention Act" of 2000, which amends the Jacob Wetterling Crimes Against Children and Sexually Violent Offender Registration Act, the Jeanne *Clery Act* and the Family Educational Rights and Privacy Act of 1974, the Virginia Tech Police Department is providing a link to the Virginia State Police Sex Offender Registry. This act requires institutions of higher education to issue a statement advising the campus community where law enforcement information provided by a State concerning registered sex offenders may be obtained. It also requires sex offenders already required to register in a State to provide notice of each institution of higher education in that State at which the person is employed, carries a vocation, or is a student. In the Commonwealth of Virginia, convicted sex offenders must register with the Sex Offender and Crimes Against Minors Registry maintained by the Department of State Police.

The Sex Offender and Crimes Against Minors Registry (SOR) for VIOLENT SEX OFFENDERS is available via Internet pursuant to Section 19.2-390.1 , (D), of the <u>Code of Virginia</u>. Registry information provided under this section shall be used for the purposes of the administration of criminal justice, screening of current or prospective employees, volunteers or otherwise for the protection of the public in general and children in particular. **Unlawful use of the information for purposes of intimidating or harassing another is prohibited and willful violation shall be punishable as a Class 1 misdemeanor.**

The Virginia State Police is responsible for maintaining this registry. Follow the link below to access the Virginia State Police website.

http://sex-offender.vsp.state.va.us/cool-ICE

Appendix D
Clery Act

[Editors' note: The Jeanne Clery Disclosure of Campus Security Policy and Campus Crime Statistics Act is provided in full as a comprehensive reference for the reader. The Campus Sexual Assault Victims' Bill of Rights is derived from the Clery Act and can be found in the shaded text on page D-5.]

20 U.S.C. § 1092(f)—Disclosure of Campus Security Policy and Campus Crime Statistics

(1) Each eligible institution participating in any program under this subchapter and part C of subchapter I of chapter 34 of Title 42 shall on August 1, 1991, begin to collect the following information with respect to campus crime statistics and campus security policies of that institution, and beginning September 1, 1992, and each year thereafter, prepare, publish, and distribute, through appropriate publications or mailings, to all current students and employees, and to any applicant for enrollment or employment upon request, an annual security report containing at least the following information with respect to the campus security policies and campus crime statistics of that institution:

(A) A statement of current campus policies regarding procedures and facilities for students and others to report criminal actions or other emergencies occurring on campus and policies concerning the institution's response to such reports.

(B) A statement of current policies concerning security and access to campus facilities, including campus residences, and security considerations used in the maintenance of campus facilities.

(C) A statement of current policies concerning campus law enforcement, including—

    (i) the enforcement authority of security personnel, including their working relationship with State and local police agencies; and

    (ii) policies which encourage accurate and prompt reporting of all crimes to the campus police and the appropriate police agencies.

(D) A description of the type and frequency of programs designed to inform students and employees about campus security procedures and practices and to encourage students and employees to be responsible for their own security and the security of others.

(E) A description of programs designed to inform students and employees about the prevention of crimes.

(F) Statistics concerning the occurrence on campus, in or on noncampus buildings or property, and on public property during the most recent calendar year, and during the 2 preceding calendar years for which data are available—

    (i) of the following criminal offenses reported to campus security authorities or local police agencies:

        (I) murder;

        (II) sex offenses, forcible or nonforcible;

        (III) robbery;

        (IV) aggravated assault;

        (V) burglary;

        (VI) motor vehicle theft;

        (VII) manslaughter;

        (VIII) arson; and

        (IX) arrests or persons referred for campus disciplinary action for liquor law violations, drug-related violations, and weapons possession; and

     (ii) of the crimes described in subclauses (I) through (VIII) of clause (i), and other crimes involving bodily injury to any person in which the victim is intentionally selected because of the actual or perceived race, gender, religion, sexual orientation, ethnicity, or disability of the victim that are reported to campus security authorities or local police agencies, which data shall be collected and reported according to category of prejudice.

  (G) A statement of policy concerning the monitoring and recording through local police agencies of criminal activity at off-campus student organizations which are recognized by the institution and that are engaged in by students attending the institution, including those student organizations with off- campus housing facilities.

  (H) A statement of policy regarding the possession, use, and sale of alcoholic beverages and enforcement of State underage drinking laws and a statement of policy regarding the possession, use, and sale of illegal drugs and enforcement of Federal and State drug laws and a description of any drug or alcohol abuse education programs as required under section 1011i of this title.

  (I) A statement advising the campus community where law enforcement agency information provided by a State under section 14071(j) of Title 42, concerning registered sex offenders may be obtained, such as the law enforcement office of the institution, a local law enforcement agency with jurisdiction for the campus, or a computer network address.

(2) Nothing in this subsection shall be construed to authorize the Secretary to require particular policies, procedures, or practices by institutions of higher education with respect to campus crimes or campus security.

(3) Each institution participating in any program under this subchapter and part C of subchapter I of chapter 34 of Title 42 shall make timely reports to the campus community on crimes considered to be a threat to other students and employees described in paragraph (1)(F) that are reported to campus security or local law police agencies. Such reports shall be provided to students and employees in a manner that is timely and that will aid in the prevention of similar occurrences.

(4) **(A)** Each institution participating in any program under this subchapter [20 U.S.C. § 1070 et seq.] and part C of subchapter I of chapter 34 of Title 42 [42 U.S.C. § 2751 et seq.] that maintains a police or security department of any kind shall make, keep, and maintain a daily log, written in a form that can be easily understood, recording all crimes reported to such police or security department, including—

    (i) the nature, date, time, and general location of each crime; and

    (ii) the disposition of the complaint, if known.

  (B) **(i)** All entries that are required pursuant to this paragraph shall, except where disclosure of such information is prohibited by law or such disclosure would jeopardize the confidentiality of the victim, be open to public inspection within two business days of the initial report being made to the department or a campus security authority.

    (ii) If new information about an entry into a log becomes available to a police or security department, then the new information shall be recorded in the log not later than two business days after the information becomes available to the police or security department.

      (iii) If there is clear and convincing evidence that the release of such information would jeopardize an ongoing criminal investigation or the safety of an individual, cause a suspect to flee or evade detection, or result in the destruction of evidence, such information may be withheld until that damage is no longer likely to occur from the release of such information.

(5) On an annual basis, each institution participating in any program under this subchapter and part C of subchapter I of chapter 34 of Title 42 [42 U.S.C. § 2751 et seq.] shall submit to the Secretary a copy of the statistics required to be made available under paragraph (1)(F). The Secretary shall—

    (A) review such statistics and report to the Committee on Education and the Workforce of the House of Representatives and the Committee on Labor and Human Resources of the Senate on campus crime statistics by September 1, 2000;

    (B) make copies of the statistics submitted to the Secretary available to the public; and

    (C) in coordination with representatives of institutions of higher education, identify exemplary campus security policies, procedures, and practices and disseminate information concerning those policies, procedures, and practices that have proven effective in the reduction of campus crime.

(6) **(A)** In this subsection:

    (i) The term "campus" means—

      (I) any building or property owned or controlled by an institution of higher education within the same reasonably contiguous geographic area of the institution and used by the institution in direct support of, or in a manner related to, the institution's educational purposes, including residence halls; and

      (II) property within the same reasonably contiguous geographic area of the institution that is owned by the institution but controlled by another person, is used by students, and supports institutional purposes (such as a food or other retail vendor).

    (ii) The term "noncampus building or property" means—

      (I) any building or property owned or controlled by a student organization recognized by the institution; and

      (II) any building or property (other than a branch campus) owned or controlled by an institution of higher education that is used in direct support of, or in relation to, the institution's educational purposes, is used by students, and is not within the same reasonably contiguous geographic area of the institution.

    (iii) The term "public property" means all public property that is within the same reasonably contiguous geographic area of the institution, such as a sidewalk, a street, other thoroughfare, or parking facility, and is adjacent to a facility owned or controlled by the institution if the facility is used by the institution in direct support of, or in a manner related to the institution's educational purposes.

    (B) In cases where branch campuses of an institution of higher education, schools within an institution of higher education, or administrative divisions within an institution are not within a reasonably contiguous geographic area, such entities shall be considered separate campuses for purposes of the reporting requirements of this section.

(7) The statistics described in paragraph (1)(F) shall be compiled in accordance with the definitions used in the uniform crime reporting system of the Department of Justice, Federal Bureau of Investigation, and the modifications in such definitions as implemented pursuant to the Hate Crime Statistics Act. Such statistics shall not identify victims of crimes or persons accused of crimes.

(8) **(A)** Each institution of higher education participating in any program under this subchapter and part C of subchapter I of chapter 34 of Title 42 shall develop and distribute as part of the report described in paragraph (1) a statement of policy regarding—

  (i) such institution's campus sexual assault programs, which shall be aimed at prevention of sex offenses; and
  (ii) the procedures followed once a sex offense has occurred.

(B) The policy described in subparagraph (A) shall address the following areas:

  (i) Education programs to promote the awareness of rape, acquaintance rape, and other sex offenses.
  (ii) Possible sanctions to be imposed following the final determination of an on-campus disciplinary procedure regarding rape, acquaintance rape, or other sex offenses, forcible or nonforcible.
  (iii) Procedures students should follow if a sex offense occurs, including who should be contacted, the importance of preserving evidence as may be necessary to the proof of criminal sexual assault, and to whom the alleged offense should be reported.
  (iv) Procedures for on-campus disciplinary action in cases of alleged sexual assault, which shall include a clear statement that—

    (I) the accuser and the accused are entitled to the same opportunities to have others present during a campus disciplinary proceeding; and
    (II) both the accuser and the accused shall be informed of the outcome of any campus disciplinary proceeding brought alleging a sexual assault.

  (v) Informing students of their options to notify proper law enforcement authorities, including on-campus and local police, and the option to be assisted by campus authorities in notifying such authorities, if the student so chooses.
  (vi) Notification of students of existing counseling, mental health or student services for victims of sexual assault, both on campus and in the community.
  (vii) Notification of students of options for, and available assistance in, changing academic and living situations after an alleged sexual assault incident, if so requested by the victim and if such changes are reasonably available.

(C) Nothing in this paragraph shall be construed to confer a private right of action upon any person to enforce the provisions of this paragraph.

(9) The Secretary shall provide technical assistance in complying with the provisions of this section to an institution of higher education who requests such assistance.

(10) Nothing in this section shall be construed to require the reporting or disclosure of privileged information.

(11) The Secretary shall report to the appropriate committees of Congress each institution of higher education that the Secretary determines is not in compliance with the reporting requirements of this subsection.

(12) For purposes of reporting the statistics with respect to crimes described in paragraph (1)(F), an institution of higher education shall distinguish, by means of separate categories, any criminal offenses that occur—

    (A) on campus;

    (B) in or on a noncampus building or property;

    (C) on public property; and

    (D) in dormitories or other residential facilities for students on campus.

(13) Upon a determination pursuant to section 1094(c)(3)(B) of this title that an institution of higher education has substantially misrepresented the number, location, or nature of the crimes required to be reported under this subsection, the Secretary shall impose a civil penalty upon the institution in the same amount and pursuant to the same procedures as a civil penalty is imposed under section 1094(c)(3)(B) of this title.

(14) **(A)** Nothing in this subsection may be construed to—

        (i) create a cause of action against any institution of higher education or any employee of such an institution for any civil liability; or

        (ii) establish any standard of care.

    (B) Notwithstanding any other provision of law, evidence regarding compliance or noncompliance with this subsection shall not be admissible as evidence in any proceeding of any court, agency, board, or other entity, except with respect to an action to enforce this subsection.

(15) This subsection may be cited as the "Jeanne Clery Disclosure of Campus Security Policy and Campus Crime Statistics Act".

Appendix E

New Jersey Campus Sexual Assault Victim's Bill of Rights

[Editors' note: Appendix E is provided as an example of one state's legislation and how it may impact on the provision of services within a particular state.]

State of New Jersey:
Campus Sexual Assault Victim's Bill of Rights
(Updated Through P.L. 2007, ch. 41 and J.R. 4)

TITLE 18A EDUCATION

18A:61E-2. "Campus Sexual Assault Victim's Bill of Rights"; development; content

2. The Commission on Higher Education shall appoint an advisory committee of experts which shall develop a "Campus Sexual Assault Victim's Bill of Rights" which affirms support for campus organizations which assist sexual assault victims and provides that the following rights shall be accorded to victims of sexual assaults that occur on the campus of any public or independent institution of higher education in the State and where the victim or alleged perpetrator is a student at the institution or when the victim is a student involved in an off-campus sexual assault.

a. The right to have any allegation of sexual assault treated seriously; the right to be treated with dignity; and the right to be notified of existing medical, counseling, mental health or student services for victims of sexual assault, both on campus and in the community whether or not the crime is reported to campus or civil authorities.

"Campus authorities" as used in this act shall mean any individuals or organizations specified in an institution's statement of campus security policy as the individuals or organizations to whom students and employees should report criminal offenses.

b. The right to have any allegation of sexual assault investigated and adjudicated by the appropriate criminal and civil authorities of the jurisdiction in which the crime occurred, and the right to the full and prompt cooperation and assistance of campus personnel in notifying the proper authorities. The provisions of this subsection shall be in addition to any campus disciplinary proceedings which may take place.

c. The right to be free from pressure from campus personnel to refrain from reporting crimes, or to report crimes as lesser offenses than the victims perceive the crimes to be, or to report crimes if the victim does not wish to do so.

d. The right to be free from any suggestion that victims are responsible for the commission of crimes against them; to be free from any suggestion that victims were contributorily negligent or assumed the risk of being assaulted; to be free from any suggestion that victims must report the crimes to be assured of any other right guaranteed under this policy; and to be free from any suggestion that victims should refrain from reporting crimes in order to avoid unwanted personal publicity.

e. The same right to legal assistance, and the right to have others present, in any campus disciplinary proceeding, that the institution permits to the accused; and the right to be notified of the outcome of any disciplinary proceeding against the accused.

f. The right to full, prompt, and victim-sensitive cooperation of campus personnel in obtaining, securing, and maintaining evidence, including a medical examination if it is necessary to preserve evidence of the assault.

g. The right to be informed of, and assisted in exercising, any rights to be confidentially or anonymously tested for sexually transmitted diseases or human immunodeficiency virus; the right to be informed of, and assisted in exercising, any rights that may be provided by law to compel and disclose the results of testing of sexual assault suspects for communicable diseases.

h. The right to have access to counseling under the same terms and conditions as apply to other students seeking such counseling from appropriate campus counseling services.

i. The right to require campus personnel to take reasonable and necessary action to prevent further unwanted contact of victims with their alleged assailants, including but not limited to, notifying the victim of options for and available assistance in changing academic and living situations after an alleged sexual assault incident if so requested by the victim and if such changes are reasonably available.

L.1994, c.160, s.2.

18A:61E-3. Implementation of bill of rights

3. In developing the "Campus Sexual Assault Victim's Bill of Rights," established by P.L.1994, c.160 (C.18A:61E-1 et seq.), the committee created pursuant to section 2 of P.L.1994, c.160 (C.18A:61E-2) shall review existing policies and procedures of public and independent institutions of higher education within the State and shall, as appropriate, incorporate those policies into a proposed bill of rights. The committee shall make a recommendation to the commission which incorporates a proposed "Campus Sexual Assault Victim's Bill of Rights." The commission following consultation with the New Jersey Presidents' Council, established pursuant to section 7 of P.L.1994, c.48 (C.18A:3B-7), shall adopt a "Campus Sexual Assault Victim's Bill of Rights." The commission shall make the "Campus Sexual Assault Victim's Bill of Rights "available to each institution of higher education within the State. The governing boards of the institutions shall examine the resources dedicated to services required on each campus to guarantee that this bill of rights is implemented, and shall make appropriate requests to increase or reallocate resources where necessary to ensure implementation.

L.1994, c.160, s.3.

18A:61E-4. Distribution to students

4. Every public and independent institution of higher education within the State shall make every reasonable effort to ensure that every student at that institution receives a copy of the "Campus Sexual Assault Victim's Bill of Rights."

Appendix F
Web Site Resources

[Editors' note: Appendix F offers a selection of Internet resources for further research in the campus SART development process. All the Web sites listed are commonly recognized in the provision of accurate, comprehensive information and are therefore offered for the reader's convenience. This does not imply that the authors are in any way affiliated with or endorse the information provided at each site.]

Alcohol and Drug Abuse	http://www.higheredcenter.org
American College Health Association	http://www.acha.org
California Coalition Against Sexual Assault	http://calcasa.org/
Community Oriented Policing Services	http://www.cops.usdoj.gov
Crime Victims Rights	http://www.victimlaw.info
Disabilities Information	http://www.thearc.org
End Violence International	http://www.evawintl.org
Enforcement Administrators	http://www.iaclea.org
Federal Grant Resources	http://www.grants.gov
Florida Coalition Against Sexual Violence	http://www.fcasv.org
International Association of Campus Law	
International Association of Chiefs of Police	http://www.iacp.org
International Association of Forensic Nurses	http://www.iafn.org
Male Survivors of Sexual Violence	http://www.malesurvivor.org
National Center for Victims of Crime	http://www.ncvc.org
National Criminal Justice Reference Service	http://www.ncjrs.org
National District Attorneys Association	http://www.ndaa.org
National Sexual Violence Resource Center	http://www.nsvrc.org
Office on Violence Against Women	http://www.ovw.usdoj.gov
Pennsylvania Coalition Against Rape	http://www.pcar.org
Rape, Abuse and Incest National Network	http://www.rainn.org
Security on Campus, Inc.	http://www.securityoncampus.org
Sexual Assault Resource Center	http://sane-sart.com/
Sexual Assault Training and Investigation	http://www.mysati.com
World Institute on Disability	http://www.wid.org

Appendix G

ACHA Sexual Assault Response Team Survey 2008

[Editors' note: Appendix G offers complete survey results from the American College Health Association Sexual Assault Response Team Survey completed in 2008. This can be a useful tool in "benchmarking" schools with similar demographics and structure.]

Sexual Assault Response Team Survey 2008 is reprinted courtesy of the American College Health Association.

Responses Received: 154

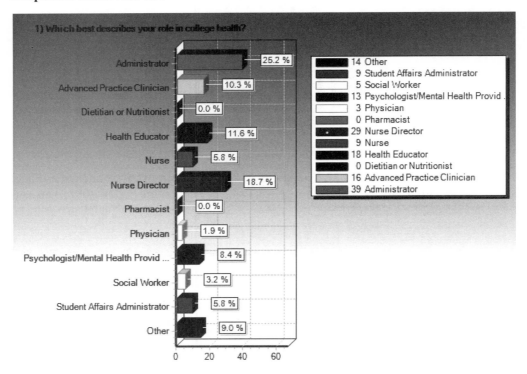

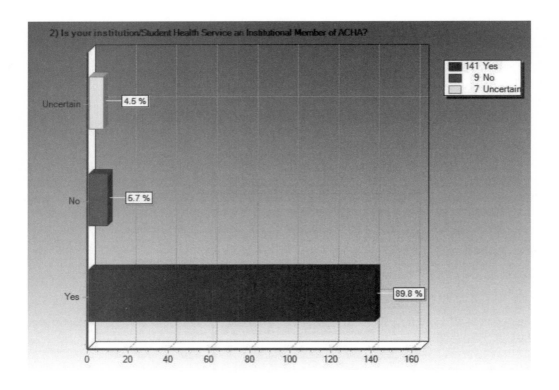

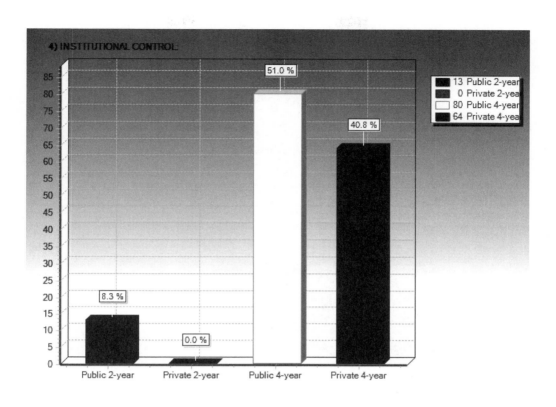

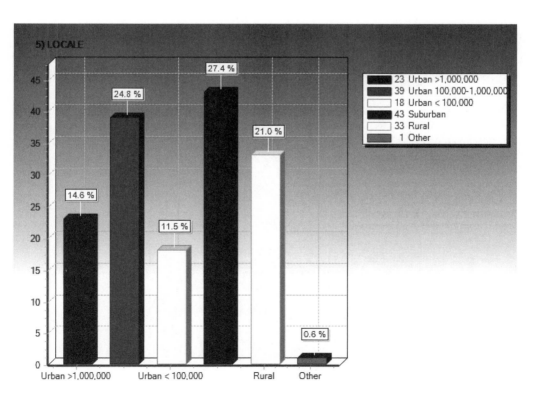

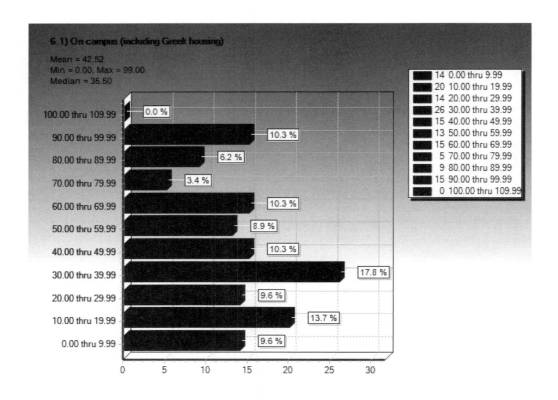

6.1) On campus (including Greek housing)

Mean = 42.52
Min = 0.00, Max = 99.00
Median = 35.50

14	0.00 thru 9.99
20	10.00 thru 19.99
14	20.00 thru 29.99
26	30.00 thru 39.99
15	40.00 thru 49.99
13	50.00 thru 59.99
15	60.00 thru 69.99
5	70.00 thru 79.99
9	80.00 thru 89.99
15	90.00 thru 99.99
0	100.00 thru 109.99

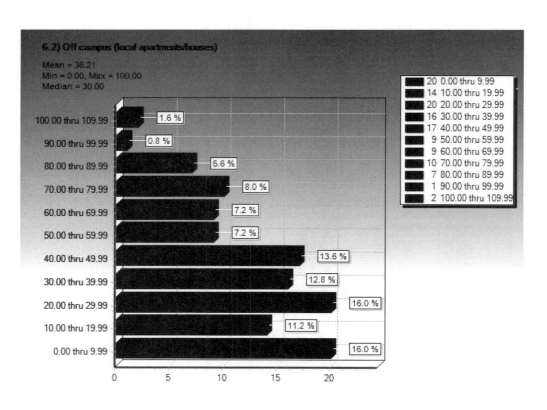

6.2) Off campus (local apartments/houses)

Mean = 36.21
Min = 0.00, Max = 100.00
Median = 30.00

20	0.00 thru 9.99
14	10.00 thru 19.99
20	20.00 thru 29.99
16	30.00 thru 39.99
17	40.00 thru 49.99
9	50.00 thru 59.99
9	60.00 thru 69.99
10	70.00 thru 79.99
7	80.00 thru 89.99
1	90.00 thru 99.99
2	100.00 thru 109.99

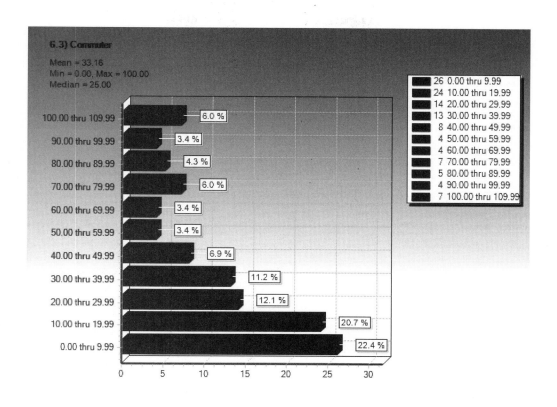

6.3) Commuter

Mean = 33.16
Min = 0.00, Max = 100.00
Median = 25.00

26	0.00 thru 9.99
24	10.00 thru 19.99
14	20.00 thru 29.99
13	30.00 thru 39.99
8	40.00 thru 49.99
4	50.00 thru 59.99
4	60.00 thru 69.99
7	70.00 thru 79.99
5	80.00 thru 89.99
4	90.00 thru 99.99
7	100.00 thru 109.99

- 100.00 thru 109.99 — 6.0 %
- 90.00 thru 99.99 — 3.4 %
- 80.00 thru 89.99 — 4.3 %
- 70.00 thru 79.99 — 6.0 %
- 60.00 thru 69.99 — 3.4 %
- 50.00 thru 59.99 — 3.4 %
- 40.00 thru 49.99 — 6.9 %
- 30.00 thru 39.99 — 11.2 %
- 20.00 thru 29.99 — 12.1 %
- 10.00 thru 19.99 — 20.7 %
- 0.00 thru 9.99 — 22.4 %

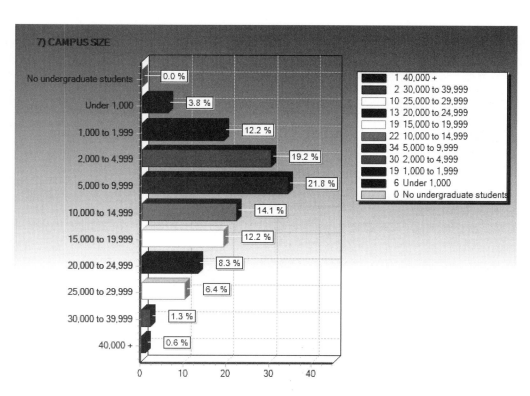

7) CAMPUS SIZE

1	40,000 +
2	30,000 to 39,999
10	25,000 to 29,999
13	20,000 to 24,999
19	15,000 to 19,999
22	10,000 to 14,999
34	5,000 to 9,999
30	2,000 to 4,999
19	1,000 to 1,999
6	Under 1,000
0	No undergraduate students

- No undergraduate students — 0.0 %
- Under 1,000 — 3.8 %
- 1,000 to 1,999 — 12.2 %
- 2,000 to 4,999 — 19.2 %
- 5,000 to 9,999 — 21.8 %
- 10,000 to 14,999 — 14.1 %
- 15,000 to 19,999 — 12.2 %
- 20,000 to 24,999 — 8.3 %
- 25,000 to 29,999 — 6.4 %
- 30,000 to 39,999 — 1.3 %
- 40,000 + — 0.6 %

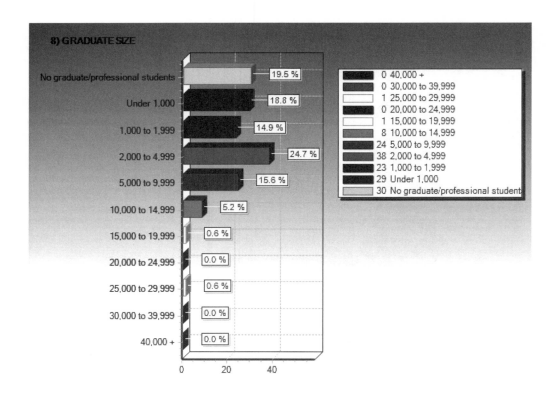

8) GRADUATE SIZE

Category	Percent
No graduate/professional students	19.5 %
Under 1,000	18.8 %
1,000 to 1,999	14.9 %
2,000 to 4,999	24.7 %
5,000 to 9,999	15.6 %
10,000 to 14,999	5.2 %
15,000 to 19,999	0.6 %
20,000 to 24,999	0.0 %
25,000 to 29,999	0.6 %
30,000 to 39,999	0.0 %
40,000 +	0.0 %

Legend:
- 0   40,000 +
- 0   30,000 to 39,999
- 1   25,000 to 29,999
- 0   20,000 to 24,999
- 1   15,000 to 19,999
- 8   10,000 to 14,999
- 24   5,000 to 9,999
- 38   2,000 to 4,999
- 23   1,000 to 1,999
- 29   Under 1,000
- 30   No graduate/professional student

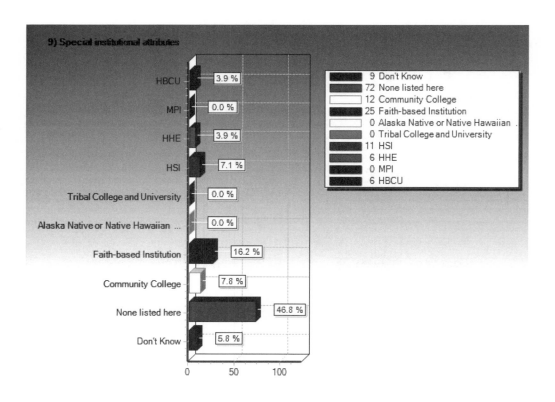

9) Special institutional attributes

Category	Percent
HBCU	3.9 %
MPI	0.0 %
HHE	3.9 %
HSI	7.1 %
Tribal College and University	0.0 %
Alaska Native or Native Hawaiian ...	0.0 %
Faith-based Institution	16.2 %
Community College	7.8 %
None listed here	46.8 %
Don't Know	5.8 %

Legend:
- 9   Don't Know
- 72   None listed here
- 12   Community College
- 25   Faith-based Institution
- 0   Alaska Native or Native Hawaiian ..
- 0   Tribal College and University
- 11   HSI
- 6   HHE
- 0   MPI
- 6   HBCU

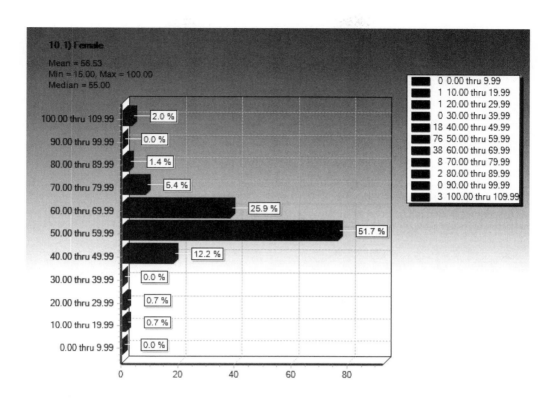

10.1) Female

Mean = 58.53
Min = 15.00, Max = 100.00
Median = 55.00

Legend:
- 0   0.00 thru 9.99
- 1   10.00 thru 19.99
- 1   20.00 thru 29.99
- 0   30.00 thru 39.99
- 18   40.00 thru 49.99
- 76   50.00 thru 59.99
- 38   60.00 thru 69.99
- 8   70.00 thru 79.99
- 2   80.00 thru 89.99
- 0   90.00 thru 99.99
- 3   100.00 thru 109.99

- 100.00 thru 109.99 — 2.0 %
- 90.00 thru 99.99 — 0.0 %
- 80.00 thru 89.99 — 1.4 %
- 70.00 thru 79.99 — 5.4 %
- 60.00 thru 69.99 — 25.9 %
- 50.00 thru 59.99 — 51.7 %
- 40.00 thru 49.99 — 12.2 %
- 30.00 thru 39.99 — 0.0 %
- 20.00 thru 29.99 — 0.7 %
- 10.00 thru 19.99 — 0.7 %
- 0.00 thru 9.99 — 0.0 %

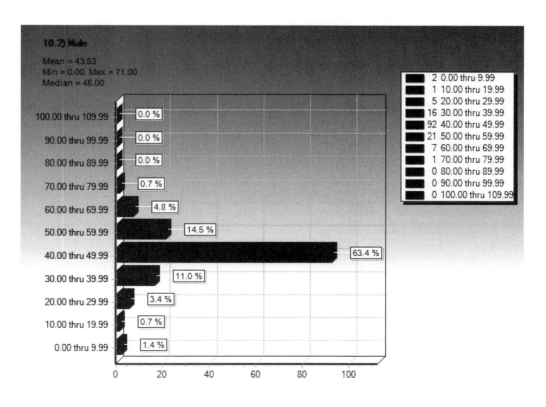

10.2) Male

Mean = 43.53
Min = 0.00, Max = 71.00
Median = 45.00

Legend:
- 2   0.00 thru 9.99
- 1   10.00 thru 19.99
- 5   20.00 thru 29.99
- 16   30.00 thru 39.99
- 92   40.00 thru 49.99
- 21   50.00 thru 59.99
- 7   60.00 thru 69.99
- 1   70.00 thru 79.99
- 0   80.00 thru 89.99
- 0   90.00 thru 99.99
- 0   100.00 thru 109.99

- 100.00 thru 109.99 — 0.0 %
- 90.00 thru 99.99 — 0.0 %
- 80.00 thru 89.99 — 0.0 %
- 70.00 thru 79.99 — 0.7 %
- 60.00 thru 69.99 — 4.8 %
- 50.00 thru 59.99 — 14.5 %
- 40.00 thru 49.99 — 63.4 %
- 30.00 thru 39.99 — 11.0 %
- 20.00 thru 29.99 — 3.4 %
- 10.00 thru 19.99 — 0.7 %
- 0.00 thru 9.99 — 1.4 %

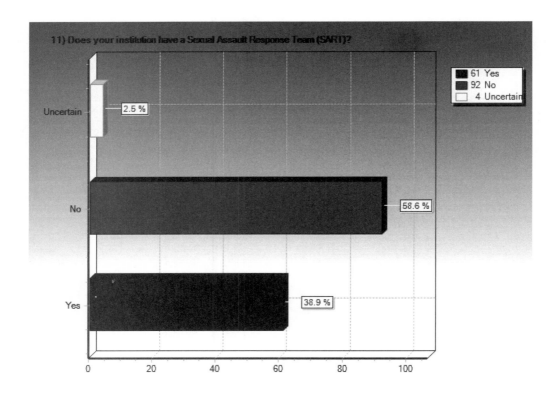

11) Does your institution have a Sexual Assault Response Team (SART)?

Legend:
- 61 Yes
- 92 No
- 4 Uncertain

- Uncertain: 2.5 %
- No: 58.6 %
- Yes: 38.9 %

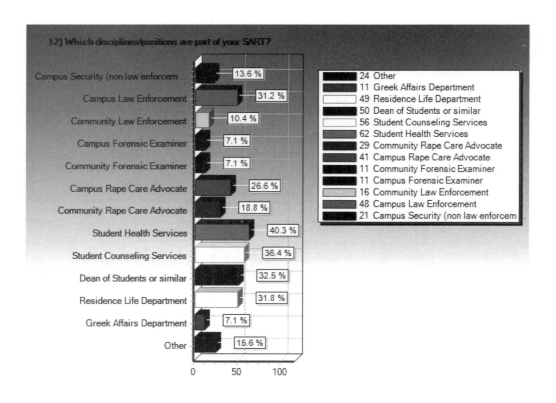

12) Which disciplines/positions are part of your SART?

- Campus Security (non law enforcem ...): 13.6 %
- Campus Law Enforcement: 31.2 %
- Community Law Enforcement: 10.4 %
- Campus Forensic Examiner: 7.1 %
- Community Forensic Examiner: 7.1 %
- Campus Rape Care Advocate: 26.6 %
- Community Rape Care Advocate: 18.8 %
- Student Health Services: 40.3 %
- Student Counseling Services: 36.4 %
- Dean of Students or similar: 32.5 %
- Residence Life Department: 31.8 %
- Greek Affairs Department: 7.1 %
- Other: 15.6 %

Legend:
- 24 Other
- 11 Greek Affairs Department
- 49 Residence Life Department
- 50 Dean of Students or similar
- 56 Student Counseling Services
- 62 Student Health Services
- 29 Community Rape Care Advocate
- 41 Campus Rape Care Advocate
- 11 Community Forensic Examiner
- 11 Campus Forensic Examiner
- 16 Community Law Enforcement
- 48 Campus Law Enforcement
- 21 Campus Security (non law enforcem ...

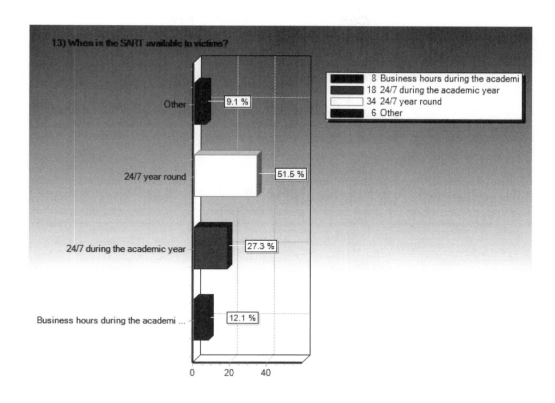

13) When is the SART available to victims?

Legend:
- 8 Business hours during the academi
- 18 24/7 during the academic year
- 34 24/7 year round
- 6 Other

- Other — 9.1 %
- 24/7 year round — 51.5 %
- 24/7 during the academic year — 27.3 %
- Business hours during the academi ... — 12.1 %

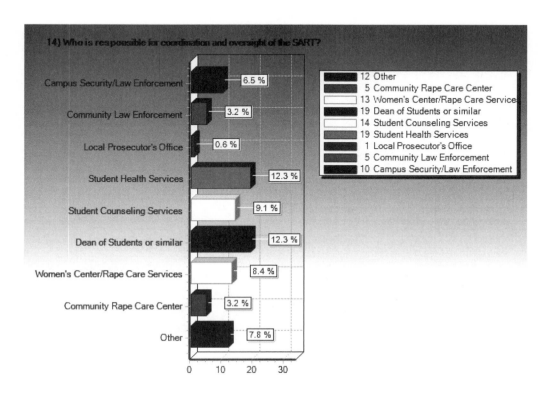

14) Who is responsible for coordination and oversight of the SART?

Legend:
- 12 Other
- 5 Community Rape Care Center
- 13 Women's Center/Rape Care Service
- 19 Dean of Students or similar
- 14 Student Counseling Services
- 19 Student Health Services
- 1 Local Prosecutor's Office
- 5 Community Law Enforcement
- 10 Campus Security/Law Enforcement

- Campus Security/Law Enforcement — 6.5 %
- Community Law Enforcement — 3.2 %
- Local Prosecutor's Office — 0.6 %
- Student Health Services — 12.3 %
- Student Counseling Services — 9.1 %
- Dean of Students or similar — 12.3 %
- Women's Center/Rape Care Services — 8.4 %
- Community Rape Care Center — 3.2 %
- Other — 7.8 %

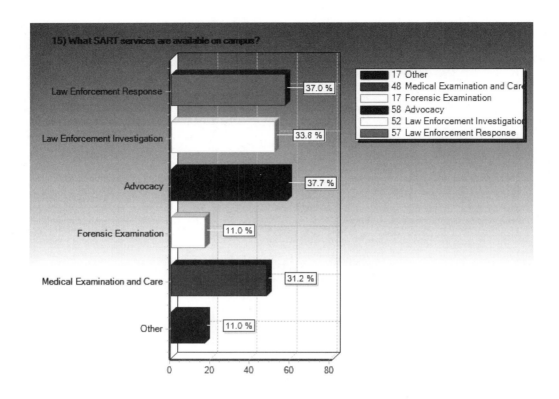

15) What SART services are available on campus?

Legend:
- 17 Other
- 48 Medical Examination and Care
- 17 Forensic Examination
- 58 Advocacy
- 52 Law Enforcement Investigation
- 57 Law Enforcement Response

- Law Enforcement Response — 37.0 %
- Law Enforcement Investigation — 33.8 %
- Advocacy — 37.7 %
- Forensic Examination — 11.0 %
- Medical Examination and Care — 31.2 %
- Other — 11.0 %

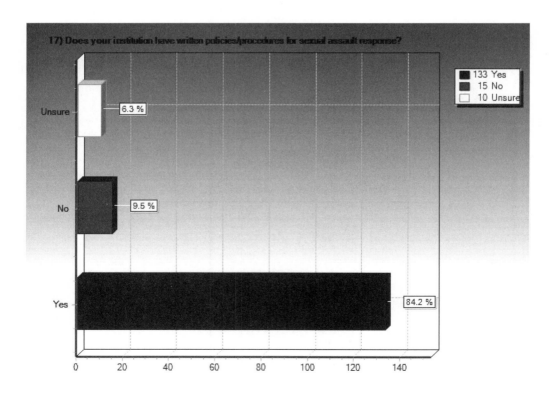

17) Does your institution have written policies/procedures for sexual assault response?

Legend:
- 133 Yes
- 15 No
- 10 Unsure

- Unsure — 6.3 %
- No — 9.5 %
- Yes — 84.2 %

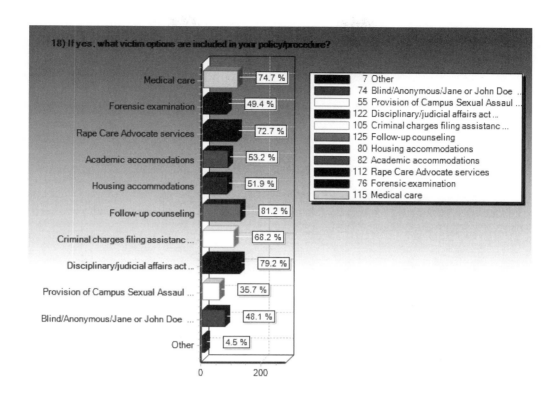

18) If yes, what victim options are included in your policy/procedure?

Legend	
7	Other
74	Blind/Anonymous/Jane or John Doe ...
55	Provision of Campus Sexual Assaul ...
122	Disciplinary/judicial affairs act ...
105	Criminal charges filing assistanc ...
125	Follow-up counseling
80	Housing accommodations
82	Academic accommodations
112	Rape Care Advocate services
76	Forensic examination
115	Medical care

Medical care — 74.7 %
Forensic examination — 49.4 %
Rape Care Advocate services — 72.7 %
Academic accommodations — 53.2 %
Housing accommodations — 51.9 %
Follow-up counseling — 81.2 %
Criminal charges filing assistanc ... — 68.2 %
Disciplinary/judicial affairs act ... — 79.2 %
Provision of Campus Sexual Assaul ... — 35.7 %
Blind/Anonymous/Jane or John Doe ... — 48.1 %
Other — 4.5 %

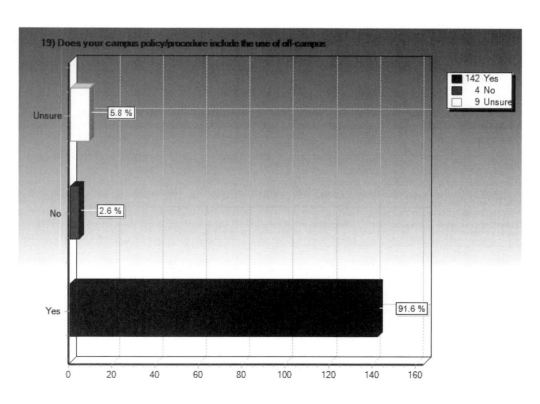

19) Does your campus policy/procedure include the use of off-campus

Legend	
142	Yes
4	No
9	Unsure

Unsure — 5.8 %
No — 2.6 %
Yes — 91.6 %

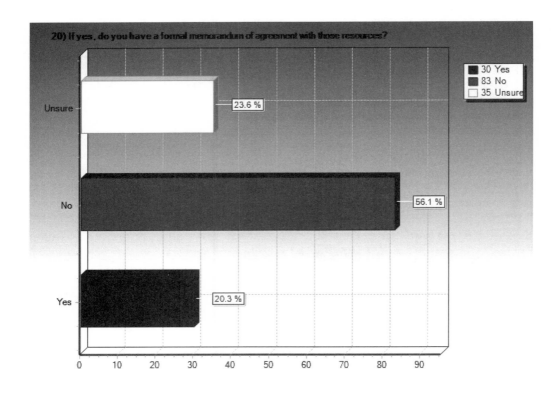

20) If yes, do you have a formal memorandum of agreement with those resources?

- 30 Yes
- 83 No
- 35 Unsure

- Unsure — 23.6 %
- No — 56.1 %
- Yes — 20.3 %

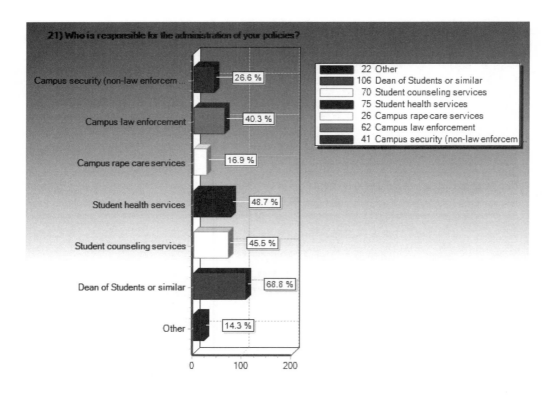

21) Who is responsible for the administration of your policies?

- 22 Other
- 106 Dean of Students or similar
- 70 Student counseling services
- 75 Student health services
- 26 Campus rape care services
- 62 Campus law enforcement
- 41 Campus security (non-law enforcem...)

- Campus security (non-law enforcem... — 26.6 %
- Campus law enforcement — 40.3 %
- Campus rape care services — 16.9 %
- Student health services — 48.7 %
- Student counseling services — 45.5 %
- Dean of Students or similar — 68.8 %
- Other — 14.3 %

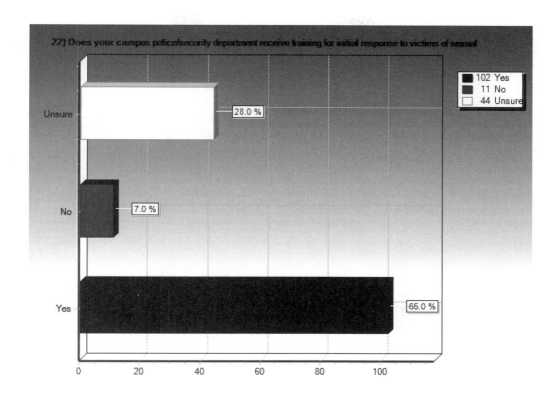

22) Does your campus police/security department receive training for initial response to victims of sexual

Legend:
- 102 Yes
- 11 No
- 44 Unsure

- Unsure: 28.0 %
- No: 7.0 %
- Yes: 65.0 %

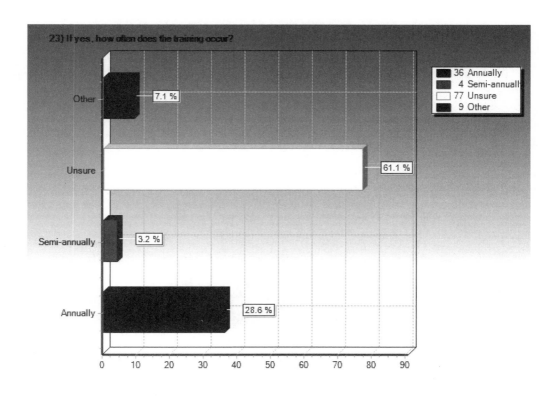

23) If yes, how often does the training occur?

Legend:
- 36 Annually
- 4 Semi-annually
- 77 Unsure
- 9 Other

- Other: 7.1 %
- Unsure: 61.1 %
- Semi-annually: 3.2 %
- Annually: 28.6 %

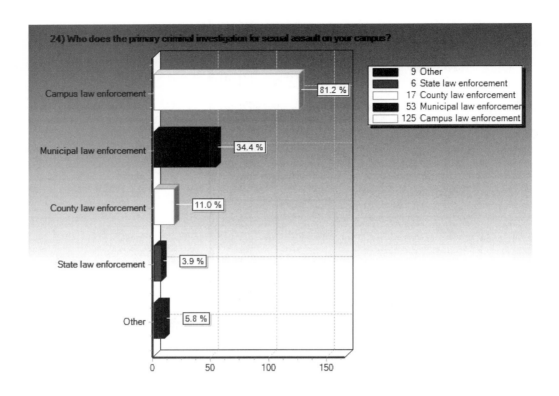

24) Who does the primary criminal investigation for sexual assault on your campus?

Legend:
- 9 Other
- 6 State law enforcement
- 17 County law enforcement
- 53 Municipal law enforcement
- 125 Campus law enforcement

- Campus law enforcement: 81.2 %
- Municipal law enforcement: 34.4 %
- County law enforcement: 11.0 %
- State law enforcement: 3.9 %
- Other: 5.8 %

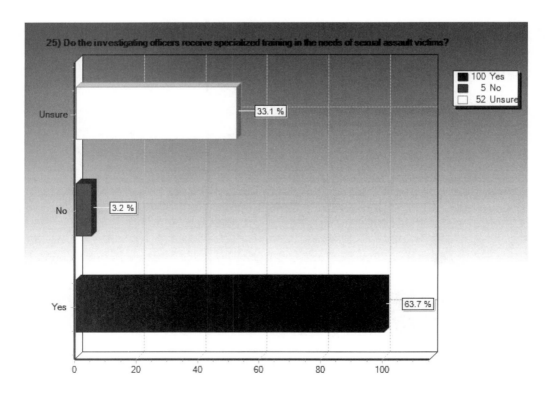

25) Do the investigating officers receive specialized training in the needs of sexual assault victims?

Legend:
- 100 Yes
- 5 No
- 52 Unsure

- Unsure: 33.1 %
- No: 3.2 %
- Yes: 63.7 %

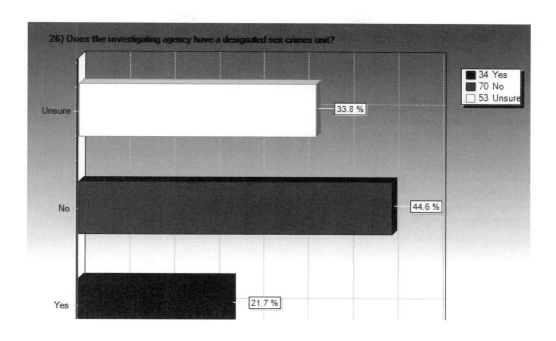

26) Does the investigating agency have a designated sex crimes unit?

- 34 Yes
- 70 No
- 53 Unsure

Category	Percentage
Unsure	33.8 %
No	44.6 %
Yes	21.7 %

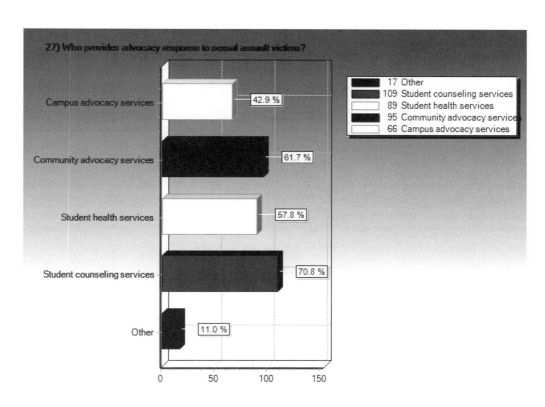

27) Who provides advocacy response to sexual assault victims?

- 17 Other
- 109 Student counseling services
- 89 Student health services
- 95 Community advocacy services
- 66 Campus advocacy services

Category	Percentage
Campus advocacy services	42.9 %
Community advocacy services	61.7 %
Student health services	57.8 %
Student counseling services	70.8 %
Other	11.0 %

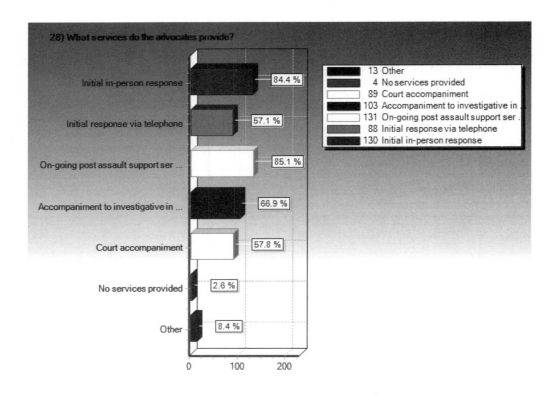

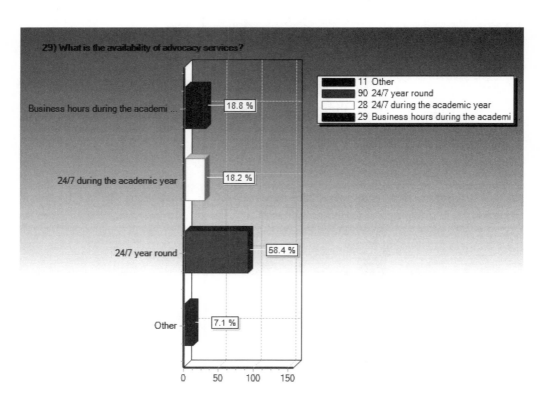

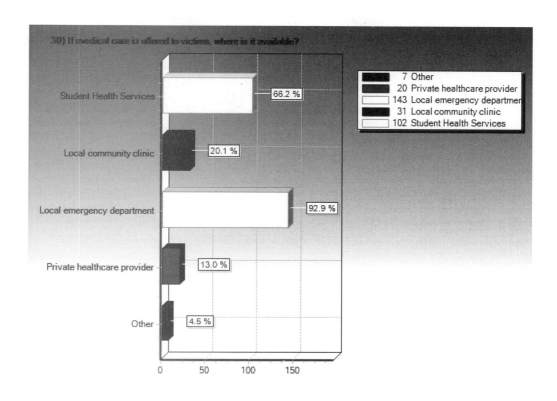

30) If medical care is offered to victims, where is it available?

Student Health Services	66.2 %
Local community clinic	20.1 %
Local emergency department	92.9 %
Private healthcare provider	13.0 %
Other	4.5 %

Legend:
- 7 Other
- 20 Private healthcare provider
- 143 Local emergency department
- 31 Local community clinic
- 102 Student Health Services

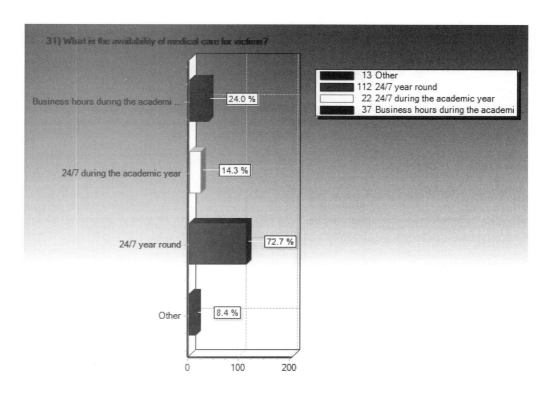

31) What is the availability of medical care for victims?

Business hours during the academi ...	24.0 %
24/7 during the academic year	14.3 %
24/7 year round	72.7 %
Other	8.4 %

Legend:
- 13 Other
- 112 24/7 year round
- 22 24/7 during the academic year
- 37 Business hours during the academi

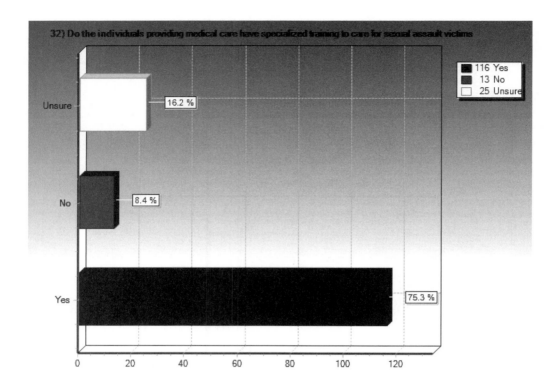

32) Do the individuals providing medical care have specialized training to care for sexual assault victims

Legend:
- 116 Yes
- 13 No
- 25 Unsure

- Unsure: 16.2 %
- No: 8.4 %
- Yes: 75.3 %

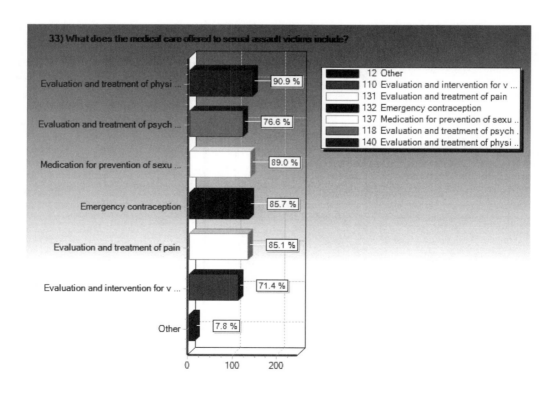

33) What does the medical care offered to sexual assault victims include?

Legend:
- 12 Other
- 110 Evaluation and intervention for v ...
- 131 Evaluation and treatment of pain
- 132 Emergency contraception
- 137 Medication for prevention of sexu ...
- 118 Evaluation and treatment of psych ...
- 140 Evaluation and treatment of physi ...

- Evaluation and treatment of physi ...: 90.9 %
- Evaluation and treatment of psych ...: 76.6 %
- Medication for prevention of sexu ...: 89.0 %
- Emergency contraception: 85.7 %
- Evaluation and treatment of pain: 85.1 %
- Evaluation and intervention for v ...: 71.4 %
- Other: 7.8 %

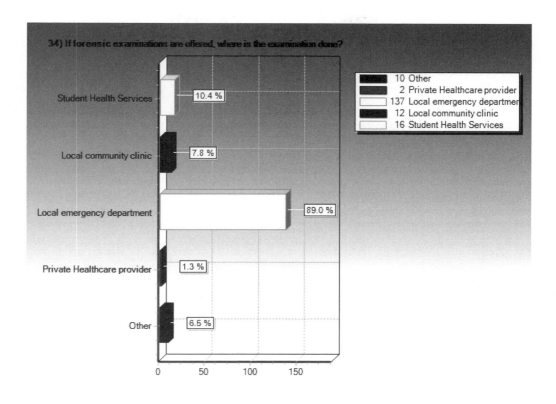

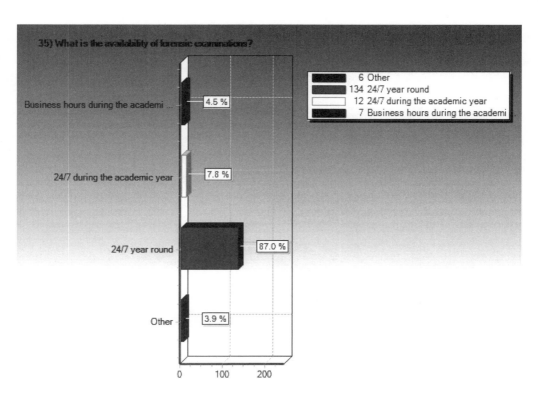

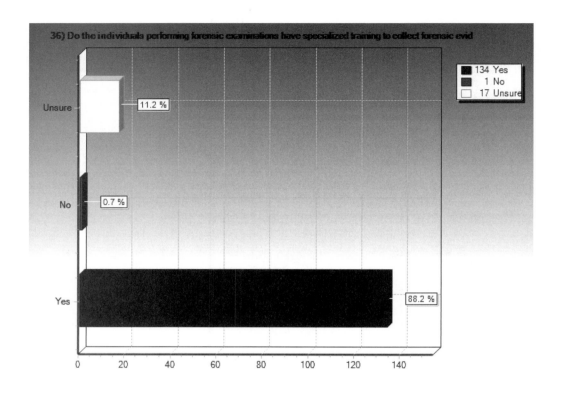

36) Do the individuals performing forensic examinations have specialized training to collect forensic evid

- 134 Yes
- 1 No
- 17 Unsure

Unsure 11.2 %

No 0.7 %

Yes 88.2 %

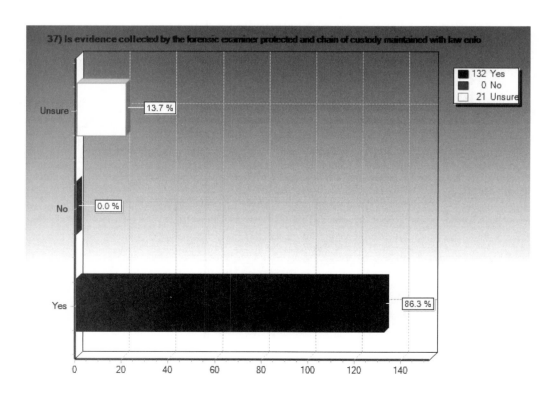

37) Is evidence collected by the forensic examiner protected and chain of custody maintained with law enfo

- 132 Yes
- 0 No
- 21 Unsure

Unsure 13.7 %

No 0.0 %

Yes 86.3 %

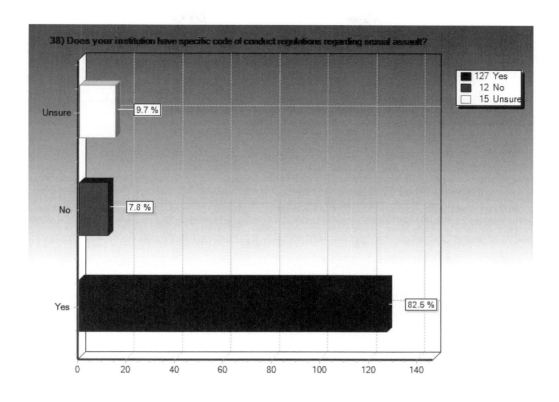

38) Does your institution have specific code of conduct regulations regarding sexual assault?

	127	Yes
	12	No
	15	Unsure

- Unsure: 9.7 %
- No: 7.8 %
- Yes: 82.5 %

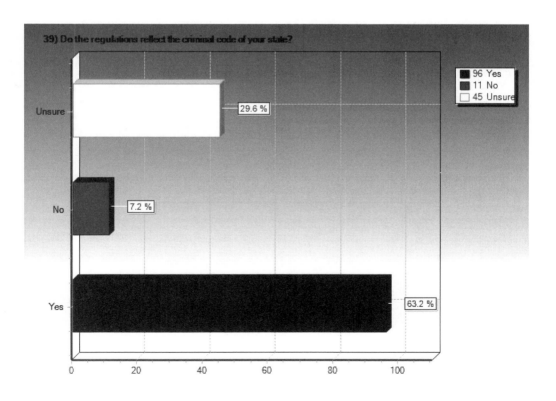

39) Do the regulations reflect the criminal code of your state?

	96	Yes
	11	No
	45	Unsure

- Unsure: 29.6 %
- No: 7.2 %
- Yes: 63.2 %

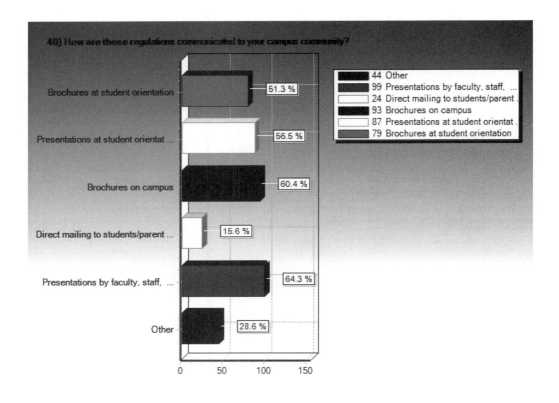

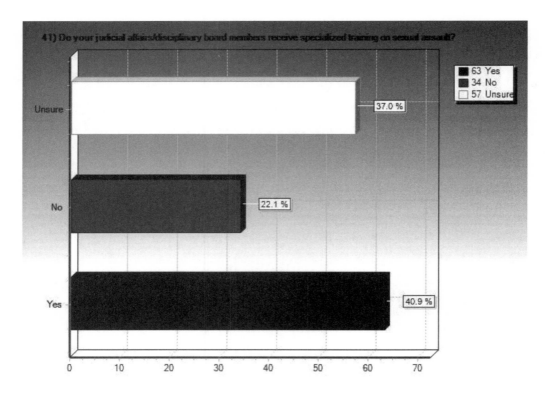

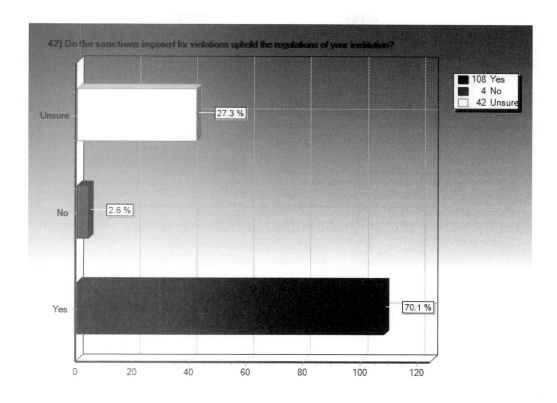

42) Do the sanctions imposed for violations uphold the regulations of your institution?

- 108 Yes
- 4 No
- 42 Unsure

Unsure — 27.3 %
No — 2.6 %
Yes — 70.1 %

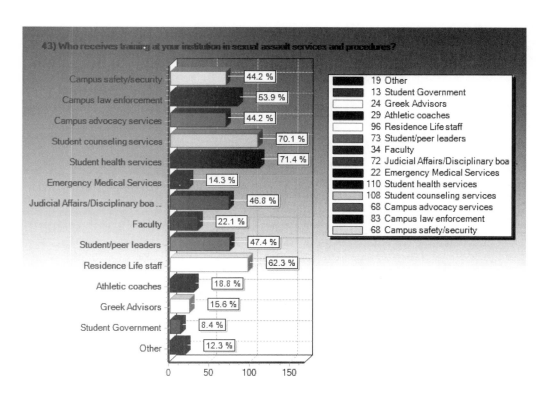

43) Who receives training at your institution in sexual assault services and procedures?

Campus safety/security — 44.2 %
Campus law enforcement — 53.9 %
Campus advocacy services — 44.2 %
Student counseling services — 70.1 %
Student health services — 71.4 %
Emergency Medical Services — 14.3 %
Judicial Affairs/Disciplinary boa ... — 46.8 %
Faculty — 22.1 %
Student/peer leaders — 47.4 %
Residence Life staff — 62.3 %
Athletic coaches — 18.8 %
Greek Advisors — 15.6 %
Student Government — 8.4 %
Other — 12.3 %

- 19 Other
- 13 Student Government
- 24 Greek Advisors
- 29 Athletic coaches
- 96 Residence Life staff
- 73 Student/peer leaders
- 34 Faculty
- 72 Judicial Affairs/Disciplinary boa .
- 22 Emergency Medical Services
- 110 Student health services
- 108 Student counseling services
- 68 Campus advocacy services
- 83 Campus law enforcement
- 68 Campus safety/security

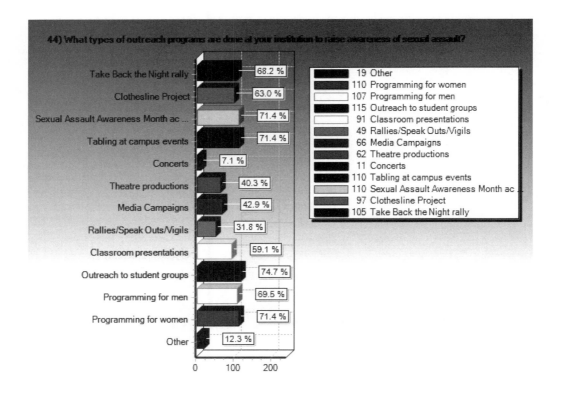

44) What types of outreach programs are done at your institution to raise awareness of sexual assault?

Take Back the Night rally	68.2 %	
Clothesline Project	63.0 %	
Sexual Assault Awareness Month ac ...	71.4 %	
Tabling at campus events	71.4 %	
Concerts	7.1 %	
Theatre productions	40.3 %	
Media Campaigns	42.9 %	
Rallies/Speak Outs/Vigils	31.8 %	
Classroom presentations	59.1 %	
Outreach to student groups	74.7 %	
Programming for men	69.5 %	
Programming for women	71.4 %	
Other	12.3 %	

Legend:
19 Other
110 Programming for women
107 Programming for men
115 Outreach to student groups
91 Classroom presentations
49 Rallies/Speak Outs/Vigils
66 Media Campaigns
62 Theatre productions
11 Concerts
110 Tabling at campus events
110 Sexual Assault Awareness Month ac ...
97 Clothesline Project
105 Take Back the Night rally

x-axis: 0   100   200

Appendix H

Twenty-First Century Model Student Conduct Code

[Editors' note: Appendix H is a valuable tool for the evaluation and revision of institutional conduct codes to be effective codes for sexual assault violations.]

NAVIGATING PAST THE "SPIRIT OF INSUBORDINATION":

A TWENTY-FIRST CENTURY MODEL STUDENT CONDUCT CODE WITH A MODEL HEARING SCRIPT*

EDWARD N. STONER II**
AND JOHN WESLEY LOWERY***

"The article of discipline is the most difficult in American education. Premature ideas of independence, too little repressed by parents, beget a spirit of insubordination, which is the greatest obstacle to science with us, and a principal cause of its decay since the revolution. I look to it with dismay in our institution, as a breaker ahead, which I am far from being confident we shall be able to weather."

—Thomas Jefferson[1]

---

* The authors are indebted to Dr. Dennis C. Golden, president of Fortbonne University and past president of the National Association of Student Personnel Administrators; three past presidents of the National Association of College and University Attorneys, Pamela J. Bernard, vice president and general counsel of the University of Florida, William R. Kauffman, vice president and general counsel of Saint Louis University, and Mary Elizabeth Kurz, vice chancellor and general counsel of North Carolina State University, to Dr. Donald D. Gehring, first president of the Association for Student Judicial Affairs; and Robert D. Bickel, professor of law at Stetson University Law School and former general counsel of Florida State University. Their consistent and compassionate leadership in student affairs and higher education law has inspired both our efforts and the careers of countless colleagues.

** B.A., DePauw University, 1969; J.D., University of Virginia, 1972; Attorney, Reed Smith LLP, Pittsburgh, Pennsylvania. Mr. Stoner is a past president and chairman of the board of directors of the National Association of College and University Attorneys, a charter member of the Association for Student Judicial Affairs, and a member of the bars of Pennsylvania, Florida, and the United States Supreme Court.

*** B.A., University of Virginia, 1990; M.Ed. University of South Carolina, 1992; Ph.D., Bowling Green State University, 2000. Dr. Lowery is a former member of the board of directors of the Association for Student Judicial Affairs and of the board of directors of the National Association of Student Personnel Administrators. Dr. Lowery is an assistant professor of Educational Leadership and Policies at the University of South Carolina.

1. Letter from Thomas Jefferson to Thomas Cooper (Nov. 2, 1822), *in* THOMAS JEFFERSON: WRITINGS 1463, 1465 (M. Patterson, ed., The Library of America) (1984) [hereinafter Letter to Cooper].

"[Higher] education deserves the highest respect and the fullest protection of the courts in the performance of its lawful mission. . . . If it is true, as it well may be, that man is in a race between education and catastrophe, it is imperative that educational institutions not be limited in the performance of their lawful missions by unwarranted judicial interference."

—U.S. District Judges Becker, Oliver, Collinson, and Hunter sitting en banc[2]

"[S]chool regulations are not to be measured by the standards which prevail for criminal law and for criminal procedure."

—Harry A. Blackmun, then, Eighth Circuit judge, later, Associate Justice of the U.S. Supreme Court[3]

Since the era when Thomas Jefferson wrote to Mr. Cooper,[4] higher education administrators have struggled with the task of responding to the spirit of insubordination of college and university students in ways that were not only developmentally sound but that also were effective to create an environment in which all members of the academic community could live, work, and learn together.

In recent years, the job has been complicated by the need to avoid judicial interference with the efforts of professional educators to guide the academic community. Some, even after Justice Blackmun's admonition not to do so, continue to analyze student conduct codes as if they were parsing a criminal code. As a result, commentators concerned that the moral and intellectual development of students not be lost observe, with concern, that: "Student affairs is at a crossroads. Contemporary administration of higher education often reflects a litigious and legalistic society on a collision course with developmental approaches to college and university administration. Student affairs should stand at the center of that intersection."[5]

Thus, today, it remains as important as ever that college and university administrators continue to guide students through their era of development on

---

2.   *General Order on Judicial Standards of Procedure and Substance in Review of Student Discipline in Tax Supported Institutions of Higher Education*, 45 F.R.D. 133, 136, 141, (W.D. Mo. 1968) (en banc) [hereinafter *General Order*]. This General Order is recommended reading to anyone seeking to understand the relationship between judicial systems and campus systems regulating student conduct.

3.   Esteban v. Cent. Mo. State Coll., 415 F.2d 1077, 1090 (8th Cir. 1969), *cert. denied* 398 U.S. 965 (1970), *aff'g* 290 F. Supp. 622 (W.D. Mo. 1968), *following new hearing order*, 277 F. Supp. 649 (W.D. Mo. 1967).

4.   Thomas Cooper was the second President (1820-1835) of South Carolina College, later renamed the University of South Carolina. Mr. Jefferson was, according to his self-authored epitaph, the "Author of the Declaration of American Independence, of the Statute of Virginia for Religious Freedom and Father of the University of Virginia." JEFFERSON, WRITINGS, *supra* note 1, at 706.

5.   James M. Lancaster & Diane L. Cooper, *Standing at the Intersection: Reconsidering the Balance in Administration,* 82 NEW DIRECTIONS FOR STUDENT SERVICES 95, 100 (1998).

campus. Just as in Mr. Jefferson's day, the issue of discipline remains the most difficult in American higher education, for both the students and for the academy itself. It also remains the most important. As Supreme Court Justice Hugo Black once observed, "School discipline, like parental discipline, is an integral important part of training our children to be good citizens—to be better citizens."[6]

It is not an easy task. This new model code, however, is an attempt to aid the practitioner not only in navigating past the shoals of the spirit of insubordination but also in weathering the breakers of judicial processes followed by courts.

In contemplating how to provide a good living/learning environment for college and university students, our instincts today are the same as Mr. Jefferson's. When some students rioted on the early nineteenth century University of Virginia Lawn, Mr. Jefferson wrote that "we wished to trust very much to the discretion of the students themselves for their own government. With about four-fifths of them this did well, but there were about fifteen or twenty bad subjects who were disposed to try whether our indulgence was without limit."[7] From this experience, Mr. Jefferson learned one lesson that all college and university administrators know: we cannot hope that all students will behave themselves simply because they are adults.

Since then, generations of higher education administrators have tried both to give educational leadership to those wishing to develop into good citizens and, at the same time, to respond appropriately to aberrant behavior that damages the living/learning environment on campus, even if the unwanted behavior is prompted by the "spirit of insubordination."[8]

---

6. Tinker v. Des Moines Indep. Cmty. Sch. Dist., 393 U.S. 503, 524 (1969) (Black, J., dissenting).

7. Letter from Thomas Jefferson to Ellen W. Coolidge *in* 18 THE WRITINGS OF THOMAS JEFFERSON 346–47 (The Thomas Jefferson Memorial Ass'n ed., memorial ed. 1904), *quoted in General Order*, *supra* note 2, at 140 n.4 [hereinafter Letter to Coolidge].

8. Many recent resources exist, including other model codes and articles on issues peculiar to college and university student discipline including: Fernand N. Dutile, *Disciplinary Versus Academic Standards in Higher Education: A Doomed Dichotomy?*, 29 J.C. & U.L. 619 (2003); Lucien Capone III, *Jurisdiction Over Off Campus Offenses: How Long is the University's Arm?*, 43rd Annual Conf., Nat'l Ass'n of Coll. & Univ. Att'ys (2003) (on file with author); Nona L. Wood, *Due Process in Disciplinary Proceedings: Classic Cases and Recent Trends in Case Law*, Ass'n for Student Judicial Affairs, Donald D. Gehring Training Inst. of the Ass'n for Student Judicial Affairs (2003) (on file with author); William Fischer & Lori Fox, *The Sexual Assault Case and the Student Judiciary*, 42nd Annual Conf., Nat'l Ass'n of Coll. & Univ. Att'ys (2002) (on file with author); Lee E. Bird & Edward N. Stoner, *Lessons Learned from Student Conduct Hearings*, Univ. of Vt. Legal Issues in Higher Educ. Conf. (2002) (on file with author); Fernand N. Dutile, *Students and Due Process In Higher Education: Of Interests and Procedures*, 2 FLA. COASTAL L. REV. 243 (2001); Lisa Tenerowicz, *Student Misconduct at Private Colleges and Universities: A Roadmap for "Fundamental Fairness" in Disciplinary Proceedings*, 42 B.C. L. REV. 653 (2001); Melinda W. Grier & Edward N. Stoner, *Student Misconduct in Instructional or Research Environments*, 21st Annual Nat'l Conf. on Law & Higher Educ., Stetson Univ. Sch. of Law (2000) (on file with author); Thomas R. Baker, *Judicial Complaint Resolution Models and Schemes: An Administrator's Reference Guide for Self-Assessment*, 12th Annual Conf. of the Ass'n for Student Judicial Affairs (2000) (on file with author); Gary Pavela, *Applying the Power of Association on Campus: A Model Code of Student Conduct*, 11 SYNTHESIS 817 (2000); Robert Bienstock, STUDENT DISCIPLINE PRIMER (Nat'l Ass'n of Coll. & Univ. Attys, pub. 1999); WILLIAM A. KAPLIN & BARBARA A. LEE, THE LAW OF HIGHER EDUCATION §§ 4.5–4.6.2, 4.8.1–

Working toward these goals, college and university administrators strive to provide a living/learning environment with standards far exceeding the law of the streets regulated by the criminal law.[9] This factor alone illustrates why, as then-Judge Blackmun wrote in *Esteban v. Central Missouri State College*,[10] criminal

---

4.8., 4.10 (3rd ed. 1995 & 2001 Supp.); Edward N. Stoner, Pamela J. Bernard & Patricia Grunder, *Legal Issues Involved in the Processing of Student Grievances and the Revision of Student Conduct Codes or Policies*, 17th Annual Nat'l Conf. on Law & Higher Educ., Stetson Univ. Sch. of Law (1996) (on file with author); Pamela J. Bernard, *Academic Dismissals of Students Involved in Clinical, Internship or Externship Activities*, 16th Annual Nat'l Conf. on Law & Higher Educ., Stetson Univ. Coll. of Law (1995) (on file with author). *Compare* HARVEY A. SILVERGLATE & JOSH GEWOLB, DUE PROCESS AND FAIR PROCEDURE ON CAMPUS 3, 4 (2003) (noting that the book was written "to help accused students" from perspective that "campus courts lack the kinds of basic fact-finding mechanisms and procedural safeguards that a decent society should provide"); Curtis J. Berger & Vivian Berger, *Academic Discipline: A Guide to Fair Process for the University Student*, 99 COLUM. L. REV. 289 (1999).

9. Commentators have explained why colleges and universities seek to have higher behavioral standards than what the criminal justice system provides:

> The college, the university, the community of scholars, the academy, is a very special place. The town and gown are different. Teaching and learning go on in a very special atmosphere. Educators attempt to create environments where dialogue, debate, and the exchange of ideas can proceed unfettered, environments in which there is concern about preserving the sanctity of the classroom and protecting academic freedom. These are the assumptions that educators have made when asserting the need to establish rules.

Donald D. Gehring & William R. Bracewell, *Standards of Behavior and Disciplinary Proceeding*, RIGHTS, FREEDOMS, AND RESPONSIBILITIES OF STUDENTS 89, 90 (1992). The district court in *Esteban v. Central Missouri State College* offered the following explanation:

> The discipline of students in the educational community is, in all but the case of irrevocable expulsion, a part of the teaching process. In the case of irrevocable expulsion for misconduct, the process is not punitive or deterrent in the criminal law sense, but the process is rather the determination that the student is unqualified to continue as a member of the educational community. Even then, the disciplinary process is not equivalent to the criminal law processes of federal or state criminal law. For, while the expelled student may suffer damaging effects, sometimes irreparable, to his educational, social and economic future, he or she may not be imprisoned, fined, disenfranchised, or subjected to probationary supervision. The attempted analogy of student discipline to criminal proceedings against adults and juveniles is not sound.

290 F. Supp. 622, 628 (W.D. Mo. 1968).

10. 415 F.2d 1077 (8th Cir. 1969). Then-Judge Blackmun's opinion noted:

> College attendance, whether it be a right or a privilege, very definitely entails responsibility. This is fundamental. It rests upon the fact that the student is approaching maturity. His elementary and secondary education is behind him. He already knows, or should know, the basics of decent conduct, of nonviolence, and of respect for the rights of others. . . . These plaintiffs are no longer children. While they may have been minors, they were beyond the age of [eighteen]. Their days of accomplishing ends and status by force are at an end. It was time they assumed at least the outward appearance of adulthood and of manhood. The mass denial of rights of others is irresponsible and childish. So is the defiance of proper college administrative authority ("I have the right to be here"; "I refuse to identify myself"; gutter abuse of an official; the dumping of a trash can at a resident's feet; "I plan on turning this school into Berkeley if. . ."; and being part of the proscribed college peace-disturbing and property-destroying demonstration). One might expect this from the spoiled child of tender years. One rightly does not expect it from the college student who has had two decades of life and who, in theory, is close to being "grown up."

codes are not good models for student conduct codes.[11]   Unlike society, our institutions are voluntary associations of scholars who demand and deserve a positive—and special—living/learning environment, as well as a special approach for enforcing the academic community's standards. This perspective is a common one.[12] As the judges of the United States District Court for the Western District of Missouri, sitting en banc, stated:

> Attendance at a tax supported educational institution of higher learning is not compulsory. The federal constitution protects the equality of opportunity of all qualified persons to attend. Whether this protected opportunity be called a qualified "right" or "privilege" is unimportant. It is optional and voluntary.
>
> The voluntary attendance of a student in such institution is a voluntary entrance into the academic community. By such voluntary entrance, the student voluntarily assumes obligations of performance and behavior reasonably imposed by the institution of choice relevant to its lawful missions, processes, and functions. *These obligations are generally much higher than those imposed on all citizens by the civil and criminal law.* So long as there is no invidious discrimination, no deprival of due process, no abridgement of a right protected in the circumstances, and no capricious, clearly unreasonable or unlawful action employed, the institution may discipline students to secure compliance with these higher obligations as a teaching method or to sever the student from the academic community.[13]

Accordingly, colleges and universities also desire to use a student discipline process that, itself, will help to educate students about their responsibilities as members of an academic community and to impose educational sanctions when student conduct is beyond the limit of the community's indulgence.[14]

Id. at 1089.

11.   *Id.*

12.   Mr. Justice Frankfurter's concurring opinion in Sweezy v. New Hampshire, 354 U.S. 234, 263 (1957) captured this point:

> It is the business of a university to provide that atmosphere which is most conducive to speculation, experiment and creation. It is an atmosphere in which there prevail "the four essential freedoms" of a university—to determine for itself on academic grounds who may teach, what may be taught, how it shall be taught, and who may be admitted to study.

13.   *General Order*, *supra* note 2, at 141. (emphasis added). This same conclusion is reached even by commentators whose view of student discipline is that, "Unfortunately, campus judicial systems are not always fair and decent." SILVERGLATE & GEWOLB, *supra* note 8, at 57. The authors advise:

> Because attendance at public colleges and universities is a privilege extended only to a select group of citizens, institutions may require that their students demonstrate superior moral or ethical standards. Even if courts think a university's rules to be unwise, they do not have the authority to strike them down if these unwise rules nonetheless conceivably relate to legitimate behavioral or academic objectives.

Id. at 71–72.

14.   Mr. Jefferson is not the only one who felt that the tendency of young adults to test the limits of insubordination was "too little repressed by parents." A contemporary commentator put

Our effort, in 1990, to set forth some of this guidance in our first model student conduct code reflected evolution in the legal cases and began to explain three trends that are more obvious today.[15]

There is, first, continuing deference by the judiciary to efforts by educators when they are exercising their educational judgment,[16] including when they are dealing with student misconduct. For example, the Massachusetts Superior Court recently explained: "Courts are generally reluctant about second-guessing academic and disciplinary decisions made by private schools. This deference derives from a commendable respect for the independence of private educational institutions and a well-justified laissez-faire attitude toward the internal affairs of such institutions."[17] Likewise, the Arkansas Court of Appeals has been "reluctant to allow the judiciary to encroach upon disciplinary proceedings of an educational institution."[18]

Second, the judiciary understands that, as Justice Blackmun observed,[19] courtroom procedures including rules of evidence and numerous criminal law

---

it this way: "One senses, however, that some activist parents see college not 'in the place of the parent,' but simply *as* parent, enforcing standards that were never articulated or upheld at home." Gary Pavela, *Parents and Student Conduct*, SYNFAX WEEKLY REPORT 828–29 (March 15, 1999).

15.   Edward N. Stoner & Kathy L. Cerminara, *Harnessing the "Spirit of Insubordination": A Model Student Conduct Code*, 17 J.C. & U.L. 89 (1990).

16.   *See* Edward N. Stoner & J. Michael Showalter, *Judicial Deference to Educational Judgment: Justice O'Connor's Opinion in* Grutter *Reapplies Longstanding Principles, As Shown by Rulings Involving College Students in the Eighteen Months before* Grutter, 30 J.C. & U.L. 583 (2004).

17.   Morris v. Brandeis Univ., No. CA002161, 2001 WL 1470357 at *4 (Sept. 4. 2001 Mass. Super. Ct. 2001) ("Great deference is extended to university decision-making in academic and disciplinary matters.") *aff'd*, 804 N.E.2d 961, tbl. op. *available at* No. 01-P-1573, 2004 WL 369106 (Mass. App. Ct. Feb. 27, 2004). The Massachusetts Supreme Judicial Court had the same sentiment, a year earlier when it stated: "[C]ourts are chary about interfering with academic and disciplinary decisions made by private colleges and universities. A university is not required to adhere to the standards of due process guaranteed to criminal defendants or to abide by rules of evidence adopted by courts." Schaer v. Brandeis Univ., 735 N.E.2d 373, 381 (Mass. 2000) (internal citations omitted). A typical articulation of this judicial perspective was set forth a decade earlier, in Illinois:

> Courts have adopted this deferential standard because of a reluctance to interfere with the academic affairs and regulation of student conduct at a private university. A private university may prescribe the moral, ethical and academic standards that its students must observe; it is not the court's function to decide whether student misbehavior should be punished or to select the appropriate punishment for transgressions of an educational institution's ethical or academic standards.

Holert v. Univ. of Chi., 751 F. Supp. 1294, 1301 (N.D. Ill. 1990) (internal citations omitted).

18.   Lyon Coll. v. Gray, 999 S.W.2d 213, 216 (Ark. Ct. App. 1999).

19.   See *supra*, note 3 and accompanying text. Justice Blackmun's comments echoed the conclusions of the Missouri federal judges:

> The nature and procedures of the disciplinary process in such cases should not be required to conform to federal processes of criminal law, which are far from perfect, and designed for circumstances and ends unrelated to the academic community. By judicial mandate to impose upon the academic community in student discipline the intricate, time consuming, sophisticated procedures, rules and safeguards of criminal law would frustrate the teaching process and render the institutional control impotent.

General Order, *supra* note 2, at 142.

principles not only do not control the efforts of educators to deal with student rule violators but also they are bad models for achieving a positive college or university environment for studying and learning. As the Missouri federal judges explained, "Standards so established [on campus] may require scholastic attainments higher than the average of the population and may require superior ethical and moral behavior. In establishing standards of behavior, the institution is not limited to the standards or the forms of criminal laws."[20]

Third, there is evolving recognition that educational models need to be applied when fact finding occurs in the student conduct arena. Accepting the wisdom of jurists that criminal principles are the wrong model, professional educators are challenged to create a fact finding atmosphere designed to reflect the values of the academic community itself.[21]

These trends did not happen in a vacuum. Since the publication of our first model student conduct code, nearly a generation of college and university students and administrators has passed through our institutions. Students have developed new ways to display their spirit of insubordination:[22] from rioting because their school's athletics team won or lost some now forgotten "important" sporting event,[23] to abusing drugs not even invented in the century now passed. At the

---

20. *General Order, supra* note 2, at 145. Another federal judge observed, more recently, "[Student disciplinary proceedings] are not criminal in nature as they only regulate the relationship between the student and the university, and have no bearing on a student's legal rights or obligations under state or federal criminal laws." United States v. Miami Univ., 91 F. Supp. 2d 1132, 1157 (S.D. Ohio 2000), *aff'd.* 294 F.3d 797 (6th Cir. 2002). Similarly, Professor Wright wrote: "[C]ourts will reach right results if they do not allow themselves to be distracted by analogies from criminal law or administrative law or elsewhere and keep their gaze fastened on the twin requirements of fairness and reasonableness as these apply in that unique institution, the academic community." Charles Alan Wright, *The Constitution on the Campus,* 22 VAND. L. REV. 1027, 1082 (1969). Educators, as well as legal scholars, agree that today's challenge is "to go beyond the minimalism of law and policy and strive for the possibilities of our highest expectations for success on behalf of our students and our institutions." James M. Lancaster & Diane L. Cooper, *Standing at the Intersection: Reconsidering the Balance in Administration,* 82 NEW DIRECTIONS FOR STUDENT SERVICES 95, 104–05 (1998).

21. As one commentator noted, "There is no indication courts will be obstacles to the on-going reduction of proceduralism in college disciplinary proceedings." Gary Pavela, *Disciplinary and Academic Decisions Pertaining to Students: A Review of the 1995 Decisions,* 23 J.C. & U.L. 391, 393 (1997).

22. One judge had the spirit of insubordination too. When a varsity basketball player at the University of Missouri was suspended for a semester for stealing from the university bookstore, a federal district judge reviewed the discipline by exercising constitutional review. He revoked the suspension, explaining that it was a "damned outrage" that "sticks in my craw." Coleman v. Monroe, 977 F.2d 442, 443 (8th Cir. 1992). The Court of Appeals for the Eighth Circuit, Justice Blackmun's former court, reinstated the suspension. *Id.* at 444. It wrote, "Finding no 'sticks in my craw' test in the Constitution, we reverse.'" *Id* at 843.

23. Hill v. Michigan State Univ., 182 F. Supp. 2d 621 (W.D. Mich. 2001) (upholding student suspension issued for participation in riot after men's basketball team lost an National Collegiate Athletic Association ("NCAA") tournament game). Post-sports rioting is not unique to Michigan State University. In its *Report on the Sportsmanship and Fan Behavior Summit,* the NCAA identified twelve serious incidents between 1999 and early 2003 (report available online at http://www.ncaa.org/sportsmanship/sportsmanshipFanBehavior/report.pdf) (Feb. 20, 2003). Nor is such behavior limited to evenings after losing a game. In 2004, students and other fans rioted after the University of Maryland won the Atlantic Coast Conference men's basketball

same time, administrators have developed student conduct codes that fit the unique environment of their campuses[24] and that respond to the needs of their students— such as responding to sexual violence—in order to address issues that profoundly impact the living and learning environment.

As this process has developed on campus, judicial treatment of the legal relationship between a college or university and its students has not fit neatly within one legal doctrine.[25] During the first part of the twentieth century, the concept of in loco parentis[26] predominated. Under this doctrine, courts viewed institutions as standing in the place of students' parents. Courts tended to give colleges and universities a great deal of discretion when they viewed the institutions as standing in loco parentis to the students. [27]

During the 1960s, however, courts began to move away from the concept of in loco parentis. Instead, courts viewed the relationship between students and institutions as contractual. Under this view, institutions enter into contracts with their students to provide them with educational services in exchange for students' paying certain fees and obeying certain rules.[28] In addition, beginning with the

---

tournament and after the University of Connecticut won the NCAA men's basketball championship. Jon Ward & Judith Person, *Students Could Be Expelled for Post Game "Riot" at U Md,* WASHINGTON TIMES, March 16, 2004, at B1; Grace E. Merritt, *Rioting May Be the End; UConn Students Face Expulsion,* HARTFORD COURANT, April 9, 2004, at B9.

24. *General Order, supra* note 2, at 146: "Different standards, scholastic and behavioral, may be established for different divisions, schools, colleges, and classes or an institution if the differences are reasonably relevant to the missions, processes, and functions of the particular divisions, schools, colleges, and classes concerned." Student conduct codes go by a variety of names but have the same purposes. *E.g.,* "Code of Student Conduct" (Univ. of Florida); "Student Responsibilities" (Univ. of Iowa); "Standards of Conduct and Rules of Procedures" (Univ. of Missouri); "Community Standards" (Loyola Coll.); "Student Code of Conduct" (Normandale Community Coll.); "Code of Student Rights and Responsibilities" (Northern Kentucky Univ.); "Standards of Conduct" (Univ. of Virginia).

25. Donald R. Fowler, *The Legal Relationship Between the American College Student and the College: An Historical Perspective and the Renewal of a Proposal,* 13 J.L. & EDUC. 401 (1984).

26. Literally, "in the place of a parent." BLACK'S LAW DICTIONARY 803 (8th ed. 2004).

27. Gott v. Berea Coll., 161 S.W. 204 (Ky. App. 1913) ("College authorities stand in loco parentis concerning the physical and moral welfare, and mental training of the pupils, and we are unable to see why to that end they may not make any rule or regulation for the government or betterment of their pupils that a parent could for the same purpose."); Anthony v. Syracuse Univ., 231 N.Y.S. 435 (N.Y. App. Div. 1928) (permitting expulsion of student from private school for not being "a typical Syracuse girl"). *See* William A. Kaplin, *Law on the Campus 1960-1985: Years of Growth and Challenge,* 12 J.C. & U.L. 269, 272 (1985); Note, *Reasonable Rules, Reasonably Enforced—Guidelines for University Disciplinary Proceedings,* 53 MINN. L. REV. 301, 310 (1968).

28. Elizabeth M. Baldizan, *Development, Due Process, and Reduction: Student Conduct in the 1990's,* 82 NEW DIRECTIONS FOR STUDENT SERVICES 29, 3–31 (1998) (tracing the demise of in loco parentis and noting, "The issues students face today cry out not for less but for more moral and ethical reflection. Rather than stepping away in a neutral zone, hiding behind legal rationales, administrators of student policies desperately need to be addressing life and learning experiences that lead to ethical and moral outcomes."); See, *e.g.,* Prusack v. New York, 498 N.Y.S.2d 455 (N.Y. App. Div. 1986); Corso v. Creighton Univ., 731 F.2d 529 (8th Cir. 1984); Cloud v. Trs. of Boston Univ., 720 F.2d 721 (1st Cir. 1983). *See also* E.K. Jennings, *Breach of Contract Suits by Students Against Postsecondary Education Institutions: Can They Succeed?,* 7

landmark case of Dixon v. Alabama Board of Education,[29] in 1961, courts have required public institutions of higher learning to afford students minimal procedural due process[30] before taking disciplinary action.[31]

J.C. & U.L. 191 (1981) (discussing the incorporation and development of principles of contract law in cases between students and universities).

29.   294 F.2d 150 (5th Cir. 1961). *Dixon* was referred to as a "landmark" decision by the Supreme Court in *Goss v. Lopez*, 419 U.S. 565, 576 n.8 (1975). For a discussion of the importance of *Dixon*, see Donald Reidhaar, *The Assault on the Citadel: Reflections on a Quarter Century of Change in the Relationships Between the Student and the University*, 12 J.C. & U.L. 343, 346 (1985) and Wright, *supra* note 20, at 1031–32.

30.   The Fourteenth Amendment to the United States Constitution provides in part: "No State shall . . . deprive any person of life, liberty or property, without due process of law." U.S. CONST. amend. XIV, § 1. This provision regulates governmental action. It does not apply to private parties, such as private colleges and universities. *See* Al-Khadra v. Syracuse Univ., 737 N.Y.S.2d 491 (N.Y. App. Div. 2002) (holding that judicial inquiry was complete once the institution demonstrated that it had complied with its own rules). In Harwood v. Johns Hopkins Univ., 747 A.2d 205, 209–10 (Md. Ct. Spec. App. 2000) (internal citations and quotations omitted), the court explained:

> School discipline is not an area in which courts lay claim to any expertise. Consequently, courts will not generally interfere in the operations of colleges and universities. Courts must enter the realm of school discipline with caution . . . . Although the actions of public universities are subject to due process scrutiny, private institutions are not bound to provide students with the full range of due process protections. . . . [W]hen reviewing a private university's decision to discipline a student, Constitutional due process standards should not be used to judge the College's compliance with contractual obligations.

See also Boehm v. Univ. of Pa. Sch. of Veterinary Med., 573 A.2d 575, 579 (Pa. Super. Ct. 1990) ("[S]tudents [of private institutions] who are being disciplined are entitled only to those procedural safeguards which the school specifically provides."), *quoted in* Centre Coll. v. Trzop, 127 S.W.3d 562 (Ky. 2003); In re Rensselaer Soc. of Eng. v. Rensselaer Poly. Inst., 689 N.Y.S.2d 292, 295 (N.Y. App. Div. 1999) ("[J]udicial scrutiny of the determination of disciplinary matters between a university and its students, or student organizations, is limited to determining whether the university substantially adhered to its own published rules and guidelines for disciplinary proceedings so as to ascertain whether its actions were arbitrary or capricious."); Holert v. Univ. of Chi., 751 F. Supp. 1294, 1301 (N.D. Ill. 1990) ("Holert was entitled only to those procedural safeguards that the University agreed to provide.").

Thus, only public schools, or schools which have the requisite amount of interaction with the state to constitute "state action," are required to provide minimal constitutional procedural due process for their students. Hankins v. Temple Univ. Health Sciences Ctr., 829 F.2d 437, 444 n.8 (3d Cir. 1987); VanLoock v. Curran, 489 So.2d 525, 528 (Ala. 1986). *See generally* H.L. Silets, *Of Students' Rights and Honor: The Application of the Fourteenth Amendment's Due Process Strictures to Honor Code Proceedings at Private Colleges and Universities*, 64 DEN. U. L. REV. 47 (1987) (discussing the application of due process principles to the enforcement of college and university honor codes); Richard Thigpen, *The Application of Fourteenth Amendment Norms to Private Colleges and Universities*, 11 J.L. & EDUC. 171 (1982) (discussing various jurisprudential theories used to apply due process requirements to colleges and universities); Annotation, *Action of Private Institution of Higher Education as Constituting State Action or Action Under Color of Law for Purposes of the Fourteenth Amendment and 42 U.S.C.S. § 1983*, 37 A.L.R. FED. 601 (1978) (examining circumstances in which action by colleges and universities constitutes state action or action under color of law under the Fourteenth Amendment and related statutory provisions). Students at private colleges and universities, however, have attempted to bring these minimal procedural due process and other constitutional cases against private institutions without success. *See, e.g.*, Albert v. Carovano, 851 F.2d 561 (2d Cir. 1988) (en banc) (affirming dismissal of due process claims against Hamilton College);

Although twenty-first century courts no longer merely rubber-stamp college or university decisions, as they once may have done under the doctrine of in loco parentis, courts continue to afford institutions of higher education a great deal of discretion.[32] Nevertheless, when colleges and universities do specify the process they will follow for student discipline, courts expect them to follow the process they select.[33] Because institutions will be held by judicial reviewers to comply

---

Cummings v. Va. Sch. of Cosmetology, 466 F. Supp. 780 (E.D. Va. 1979); Miller v. Long Island Univ., 380 N.Y.S.2d 917 (N.Y. Sup. Ct. 1976) (dismissing lawsuit). *But see* Powe v. Miles, 407 F.2d 73 (2d Cir. 1968) (holding that there was no "state action" as to students at one college of the private university but that there was "state action" at another of its colleges which was separately funded by the state).

A case sometimes miscited for the proposition that requirements akin to those of minimal Constitutional procedural due process were required at Dickinson College, a private institution, in the nineteenth century does not stand for this proposition after all. Instead, *Commonwealth v. McCauley*, 2 Pa. C.C. 459 (Pa. Com. Pl. 1887) merely holds that the court should inquire further as to whether a private school's faculty had conscientiously determined to expel the student, notwithstanding the faculty's blanket denial that it had done anything wrong. *Id.* at *5. There is no subsequent report as to whether the court made further rulings but it imposed no due process-like requirements.

In addition, of course, state law should be consulted to see whether state "due process" requirements apply. Centre Coll. v. Trzop, 127 S.W.3d 562 (Ky. 2003) (reversing holding that Kentucky state law required even private colleges to apply statutory due process to student disciplinary proceedings).

31.   Immediate action may be taken in exceptional cases. Wright, *supra* note 20, at 1074. *See* Model Code, *infra* pp. 59–60, at art. IV(C).

32.   *See* Schulman v. Franklin & Marshall Coll., 538 A.2d 49, 52 (Pa. Super. Ct. 1988).

33.   Under Florida law, a student from a private law school stated a claim of violation of implied contract by alleging that the university did not follow its own disciplinary procedures, although it was subject to proof. Jarzynka v. Saint Thomas Univ. Sch. of Law, 310 F. Supp. 2d (S.D. Fla. 2004); Ebert v. Yeshiva Univ., 780 N.Y.S.2d 283 (N.Y. Sup. Ct. 2004) (granting rehearing to remedy defective notice). A college was required to reinstate a student until it provided the Community Standards Board Hearing mandated by its policy rather than suspending the student using a Procedural Interview. Ackerman v. President & Trs. of the Coll. of the Holy Cross, 16 Mass. L. Rptr. 108 at *1 (Mass. Super. Ct. 2003). While institutions have wide discretion in selecting the process to provide, *Ackerman* illustrates that a university must provide the specified process. Another University was ordered to provide a student with a new hearing when it did not give him the opportunity to "hear and question adverse witnesses" as specified in its Code of Conduct. Morfit v. Univ. of So. Fla., 794 So.2d 655, 656 (Fla. Dist. Ct. App. 2001); Wolff v. Vassar College, 932 F. Supp. 88 (S.D.N.Y. 1996); Gruen v. Chase, 626 N.Y.S.2d 261 (N.Y. Sup. Ct. 1995) (new hearing ordered when process not followed); Weidemann v. State Univ. of N.Y. at Cortland, 592 N.Y.S.2d 99 (N.Y. Sup. Ct. 1992) (new hearing ordered when specified period of notice not given and new information was obtained after the hearing without notice to the student); Tedeschi v. Wagner Coll., 404 N.E.2d 1302, 1305–6 (N.Y. 1980); VanLoock v. Curran, 489 So.2d 525, 528 (Ala. 1986); Woody v. Burns, 188 So.2d 56, 59 (Fla. 1966) (finding that faculty committee at the University of Florida failed to follow specified process); Warren v. Drake Univ., 886 F.2d 200, 202 (8th Cir. 1989).

One may speculate that this is *not* the law in Kentucky, at least as to private institutions when a student admits conduct that violates a campus rule. In *Centre College*, the Kentucky Supreme Court stated that a college's obligation, under its handbook, to provide a disciplinary process was void once a rules violation was "admitted." It explained:

A contract between an educational institution and a student is only enforceable so long as the student complies with the college's rules and regulations. Therefore, even if Centre had guaranteed Trzop's due process, such was rendered unenforceable after

with their own choices about process, language must be selected carefully. There must not be a commitment—even a vague one—to observe murky general "legal sounding" ideals like "due process" or "fundamental fairness."[34] A better practice is to state exactly what process is provided without using such platitudes.

In this environment, it is now normal practice for colleges and universities to have written student disciplinary codes. Such a written code is one step toward educating students about how to behave appropriately as members of an academic community.[35] The process of drafting or re-drafting a student conduct code[36] allows members of the academic community to evaluate what choices they believe are educationally appropriate—away from the heat of a specific incident. It may also provide a bulwark against charges of arbitrary action; for example, allegations that the school singled out one student for particularly unfair treatment or applied processes or sanctions that were inconsistent from case to case. This consideration applies to private institutions, as well as public ones even though the constitutional concepts of minimal procedural due process apply only to public institutions.[37] Thus, a written student code can benefit both public and private institutions, as

---

Trzop failed to comply with Centre's rules. When Trzop intentionally possessed a knife in violation of Centre's express prohibition, he breached his contract with Centre and therefore excused any further performance on the college's behalf.

127 S.W.3d at 568 (internal citations omitted).

The above statement, it must be noted, is *dicta*, because the Kentucky Supreme Court also held that the college did not guarantee the student the state law due process at issue in that case.

34. The term "fundamental fairness" that a college used in its student conduct code was construed against the college because it had not defined what the term meant. *Ackerman*, 16 Mass. L. Rptr. at 108. Another college was denied summary judgment when sued over whether it complied with the processes it designated for its conduct code. Goodman v. President & Trs. of Bowdoin Coll., 135 F. Supp. 2d 40, 40 (D. Me. 2001). It had promised to "conduct judicial procedures which reflect fundamental fairness" but did not define what it meant by "fundamental fairness," although it could easily have done so or could have chosen not to use the ambiguous term at all. *Id.* at 57. But the judge left it for a jury to decide what "fundamental fairness" meant. *Id* at 43–44. Fortunately for the college, after a seven day trial, a jury determined that the college had provided "fundamental fairness" and the court of appeals affirmed the trial court's instructions to the jury on how it should interpret and apply the phrase "fundamental fairness." Goodman v. President and Trs. of Bowdoin Coll., 380 F.3d 33, 42, 47 (1st Cir. 2004). The use of the undefined term "fundamental fairness" prevented another court from granting a university's motion to dismiss. Gomes v. Univ. of Me. Sys., 304 F. Supp. 2d 117 (D. Me. 2004). A case illustrating the folly of promising to provide "due process" without defining what, exactly, the institution meant when it used the term is Fellheimer v. Middlebury Coll., 869 F. Supp. 238 (D. Vt. 1994).

35. In a legal sense, it also gives them "notice" of campus policies, procedures, and rules.

36. For a discussion of many considerations involved in drafting a code, including how to involve various campus constituencies in the process, see Edward N. Stoner, *A Model Code for Student Discipline*, in THE ADMINISTRATION OF CAMPUS DISCIPLINE: STUDENT, ORGANIZATIONAL AND COMMUNITY ISSUES 3 (Brent G. Paterson & William L. Kibler eds., 1998).

37. *See* Wright, *supra* note 20, at 1035 ("A wise university may well make a prudential judgment that it ought to give its students greater freedom, or more procedural protections, than the Constitution demands of it."). *See also* KAPLIN & LEE, *supra* note 8, at 464–65 (arguing that while private institutions are not required to incorporate principles of constitutional due process into their codes of student conduct, they may wish to include these principles as a matter of good administration).

well as students.[38]

What follows is a model student conduct code that college or university counsel and administrators may use in creating or revising their own written student disciplinary code. Of course, decisions with regard to certain topics will depend upon the preference of each individual college or university. Such topics include choosing a person at the institution to administer student conduct code policies and procedures, establishing a minimum amount of notice of the alleged violation, setting a maximum period between the time students are notified of charges against them and the day on which those charges are heard, and deciding who will determine responsibility and sanctions. Nevertheless, the following model is a sound beginning upon which to build a student disciplinary code.

College or university counsel and administrators may wish to keep a few principles in mind when drafting their own student disciplinary codes.[39]

First, the institution, whether public or private, should try to follow the general requirements of minimal procedural due process. As the Supreme Court has indicated, these requirements vary, depending upon the circumstances, but do, at least, require some kind of notice and some kind of hearing.[40] If an institution is public, it is required to grant minimal procedural due process.[41] If the institution is

---

38. There is one negative aspect to the promulgation of a written student code. "Although the trend toward written codes is a sound one, legally speaking, because it gives students fairer notice of what is expected from them and often results in a better-conceived and administered system, written rules also provide a specific target to aim at in a lawsuit." KAPLIN & LEE, *supra* note 37, at 462.

39. Many of the judicial decisions mentioned in this article are analyzed in more detail in earlier articles in this Journal. *See* Stoner & Showalter, *supra* note 16: Edward N. Stoner & Maraleen D. Shields, *Disciplinary and Academic Decisions Pertaining to Students in Higher Education—2001*, 29 J.C. & U.L. 287 (2003); Edward N. Stoner & Bradley J. Martineau, *Disciplinary and Academic Decisions Pertaining to Students in Higher Education*, 28 J.C. & U.L. 311 (2002); Edward N. Stoner & Bradley J. Martineau, *Disciplinary and Academic Decisions Pertaining to Students in Higher Education,* 27 J.C. & U.L. 313 (2000); Edward N. Stoner & Corey A. Detar, *Disciplinary and Academic Decisions Pertaining to Students in Higher Education,* 26 J.C. & U.L. 273 (1999); Edward N. Stoner & Susan P. Schupansky, *Disciplinary and Academic Decisions Pertaining to Students: A Review of the 1997 Judicial Decisions*, 25 J.C. & U.L. 293 (1998); Gary Pavela, *Disciplinary and Academic Decisions Pertaining to Students: A Review of 1996 Judicial Decisions*, 24 J.C. & U.L. 213 (1997); Pavela, *supra* note 21; Elizabeth L. Grossi & Terry D. Edwards, *Student Misconduct: Historical Trends in Legislative and Judicial Decision-Making in American Universities,* 23 J.C. & U.L. 829 (1997).

40. *See* Goss v. Lopez, 419 U.S. 565, 579 (1975). *See, e.g.,* Clayton v. Trs. of Princeton Univ., 608 F. Supp. 413, 435–36 (D.N.J. 1985) (private institution). In applying a very minimal standard of "fundamental fairness," the court concluded:

> Princeton places great reliance in the Honor Code and attaches considerable sanctity to it. It does not behoove this court to tell any private institution how they should handle alleged cheaters as long as the dictates of fundamental fairness are met. Clayton knew about the Honor Code when he arrived, and he was found to have violated it. If the Code needs correction, it is for Princeton to correct, and not this court.

Id. at 440.

41. *See supra* note 29, and accompanying text; Albert S. Miles, *The Due Process Rights of Students in Public School or College Disciplinary Hearings.* 48 ALA. LAW. 144, 146 (1987) ("[I]t is a good idea for a school or college to grant as much due process as it thinks is allowable, given a balance between the circumstances, the educational mission of the school and the rights of the student.").

private, such constitutional minimal procedural due process is not required,[42] but the institution's actions may appear more fair and more reasonable both to a court and to campus constituencies if it gives students the minimal procedural due process that would apply at a public institution.

As the *Dixon* court explained, the minimal procedural due process that public institutions are required to provide is, indeed, minimal. The Indiana Court of Appeals gave a typical contemporary description:

> When a sanction is imposed for disciplinary reasons, the fundamental requirements of due process are notice and an opportunity for a hearing appropriate to the nature of the case. In order to be fair in the due process sense, the hearing must afford the person adversely affected the opportunity to respond, explain, and defend. For school expulsion, due process requires an informal give-and-take between the student and the disciplinarian, where the student is given an opportunity to explain his version of the facts. Due process further requires that a university base an expulsion on substantial evidence. [43]

Second, then-Judge Blackmun's observation that college and university conduct codes need not be "measured by the standards which prevail for the criminal law and for criminal procedure"[44] remains as accurate today as when he wrote those words two generations ago. The Missouri federal judges made the same point.[45]

There is no general requirement that procedural due process in student disciplinary cases provide for legal representations, a public hearing, confrontation and cross-examination of witnesses, warnings about privileges, self-incrimination, application of principles of former or double jeopardy,[46] compulsory production of

---

42.　*See supra* note 29 and accompanying text.

43.　Gagne v. Indiana Univ., 692 N.E.2d 489, 493 (Ind. Ct. App. 1998). The *Gagne* Court carefully tracked the instructions of the Supreme Court in *Goss v. Lopez,* 419 U.S. 565, 583–84 (1975) and of the Missouri federal judges in the General Order, *supra* note 2, at 147. *See also* Nawaz v. State Univ. of N.Y. at Buffalo Sch. of Medicine, 744 N.Y.S.2d 590, 591–92 (N.Y. App. Div. 2002) ("Due process requires that the petitioners be given the names of the witnesses against them, the opportunity to present a defense, and the results and finding of the hearing."); Reilly v. Daly, 666 N.E.2d 439, 444–45 (Ind. Ct. App. 1996) (following Professor Wright's description of the *Dixon* requirements of minimal procedural due process in cases implicating a possible serious penalty) "The student must be advised of the grounds of the charge, he must be informed of the nature of the evidence against him, he must be given an opportunity to be heard in his own defense, and he must not be punished except on the basis of substantial evidence." Wright, *supra*, note 20, at 1071–72.

44.　Esteban v. Central Mo. State Coll., 415 F.2d 1077, 1090 (8th Cir. 1969).

45.　*General Order*, *supra* note 2, at 147–48.

46.　As one commentator concluded, "The prohibition against double jeopardy has *zero* application to this situation. Double jeopardy only applies to criminal prosecutions within the same jurisdiction. By definition, adjudication of an offense under a student conduct code is not a criminal prosecution." Capone III, *supra* note 8, at 7. Professor Wright noted, "When a student's conduct leads both to a criminal charge and to disciplinary proceedings within the university . . . claims of 'double jeopardy' are not uncommon, but are utterly without merit." Wright, *supra*, note 20, at 1077–78. Judicial decisions uniformly reach the same conclusion. *See* Missouri v. Mullenix, 73 S.W.3d 32, 33 (Mo. Ct. App. 2002) (holding that student driving drunk on campus of Northwest Missouri State University could be subject both to university discipline and to criminal prosecution); Oklahoma v. Kauble, 948 P.2d 321 (Okla. Crim. App. 1997); Maine v.

witnesses, or any of the remaining features of federal criminal jurisprudence.

Thus, student disciplinary codes need not be drafted with the specificity of criminal statutes.[47] Nor do technical judicial hearing rules, like rules of evidence, apply on campus. The Supreme Court of Massachusetts recently joined others in emphasizing that student conduct code proceedings need not mirror courtroom proceedings. It approved a provision from the Brandeis University rules that stated, "[A]t a disciplinary hearing, '[t]he technical rules of evidence applicable to civil and criminal cases shall not apply.'"[48] A sentence like this one *must* appear in every well-drafted twenty-first century student conduct code.[49]

Similarly, in order to avoid implying that it expects its student code to be treated like a criminal statute, a college or university should avoid criminal law

---

Sterling, 685 A.2d 432 (Me. 1996); City of Oshkosh v. Winkler, 557 N.W.2d 464, 466 (Wis. Ct. App. 1996) ("This case primarily concerns whether student disciplinary action under University of Wisconsin System rules constitutes 'punishment' which triggers double jeopardy protection. We conclude that it does not."); Ohio v. Wood, 679 N.E.2d 735, 741 (Ohio Ct. App. 1996) (holding that alumnus of Kent State University who was subject to University "persona non grata" proceeding could also be prosecuted for disorderly conduct in municipal court); Paine v. Bd. of Regents of the Univ. of Tex. Sys., 355 F. Supp. 199, 203 (W.D. Tex. 1972), *aff'd per curium*, 474 F.2d 1397 (5th Cir. 1973). For an enlightened discussion of the need to keep in mind the educational purposes of campus sanctions in the double jeopardy context, see Pavela, *supra* note 39, at 222–24.

47. Lisa L. Swem, Note, *Due Process Rights in Student Disciplinary Matters*, 14 J.C. & U.L. 359, 367 n.43 (1987). Justice Blackmun's response to the claims of college students that college rules were not as specific as criminal statutes resonates today:

> Roberds was disciplined because he had participated in the demonstrations in the face of specific warning delivered by personal interview with the dean. This was defiance of proper college authority. Esteban was disciplined because of his refusal to comply with an appropriate request by Doctor Meverden and because of his childish behavior and obscenity toward college officials. This, too, was defiance of proper college authority. There was no confusion or unawareness in either case. The exercise of common sense was all that was required. Each plaintiff knew the situation very well, knew what he was doing, and knew the consequences. Each, we might note, had had prior disciplinary experience. Their respective protestations of young and injured innocence have a hollow ring. . . . [W]e agree with Judge Hunter that it is not sound to draw an analogy between student discipline and criminal procedure . . . . [W]e do not find the regulation at all difficult to understand and we are positive the college student, who is appropriately expected to possess some minimum intelligence, would not find it difficult. It asks for the adherence to standards of conduct which befit a student and it warns of the danger of mass involvement. We must assume Esteban and Roberds can read and that they possess some power of comprehension. Their difficulty was that they chose not to read or not to comprehend.

Esteban, 415 F.2d at 1088.

48. Schaer v. Brandeis Univ., 735 N.E.2d 373, 380 n.15 (Mass. 2000). The Massachusetts Supreme Judicial Court explained that the college student discipline fact finding process is quite different from a judicial process:

> Although these statements would be excluded from a courtroom under the rules of evidence, a university is not required to abide by the same rules. Brandeis may choose to admit all statements by every witness or it may choose to exclude some evidence. It is not the business of lawyers and judges to tell universities what statements they may consider and what statements they must reject.

Id. at 380.

49. *See infra* Model Code, art. IV(A)(4)(j).

language.[50]

The cardinal error of this type is the practice of calling student discipline proceedings "judicial." This misnomer is unfortunate because rulings from members of the *real* judiciary have consistently held, when so urged by college and university officials, that campus proceedings are *not* "judicial" proceedings. Much confusion has been caused by calling the campus process a "judicial" one when it is not. Frequently, a college or university attorney's explanation that judicial structures and technical judicial rules are not applicable on campuses has been derailed by a judge's observation that, "The College itself calls it a 'judicial' process." Luckily, most such derailments have been only temporary. The use of the term "judicial" may also contribute to similar confusion of elected officials and to the development of confusing legislation based upon a misunderstanding of the purpose and role of campus conduct codes. For these reasons, a sound twenty-first century student conduct code should eschew the word "judicial."

While college and university rules should not use the wording of criminal statutes and are not required to be as specific as a criminal code, a student conduct code should be sufficiently specific to make the rules clear.[51]

Third, whatever process it adopts, the institution will want to remember the basic student affairs precept that it is important to treat all students with equal care, concern, honor, fairness, and dignity. For example, in student-on-student violence cases, the rights of the accused student, the student claiming to be the victim, and the academic community are equally important. It is helpful to judge potential process choices against this filter. The student who claims s/he is the victim of campus violence has the same rights to fair treatment as does the student accused of violating campus rules—and these expectations of both students spring from the same source: their honored status as students.

Fourth, student code drafters should be aware that, as in any generic document,

---

50. A college or university would not want to use terms such as "guilty" or "beyond a reasonable doubt," for example. Instead, students who do violate rules are found "responsible" for violating institutional rules, using a "more likely than not standard." *See infra* Model Code, art. IV(A)(4)(i). Nor would it want to describe its fact finding process as a "trial," the person presenting information (if it uses that model) as a "prosecutor" (s/he may be called a "presenter" or a "witness"), the consequences of misbehavior a "sentence" (instead, a "sanction"), the persons who determine what happened and/or recommend sanctions "judges" (they are "board members"), what fact finders consider "evidence" (instead, "information"), the students who allegedly violated the conduct code as "defendant" (instead, "Accused Student" or "student respondent"), or the person who alleges s/he was violated by another student's misconduct a "victim" (instead, "student" or "witness"). *See also infra* note 152 (concerning the use of the word "victim").

　　　Similarly, one would want to avoid using criminal laws or criminal law words as, or in, institutional rules. *See* Hardison v. Florida Agric. and Mech. Univ., 706 So. 2d 111 (Fla. Dist. Ct. App. 1998) (vacating student conduct panel's finding of "assault and battery" because it did not find a violation of state criminal law offense by the same name).

51. James M. Picozzi, *University Disciplinary Process: What's Fair, What's Due, and What You Don't Get*, 96 YALE L.J. 2132, 2155 (1987) (arguing that a written code ensures that both the administrator and the student know what process is due an accused student). Wright, *supra* note 20, at 1062–65 (noting that specific rules are desirable although not constitutionally required). On the other hand, a college or university will want to include some broadly worded rules in its student code in order to preserve as much flexibility as possible.

the principles set forth in the model student code represent the generally prevailing law and practice. In some instances, courts disagree. In others, administrators hold opposing views. In many cases, the model either offers the drafters alternative choices or advocates the position taken by the majority of courts or institutions, while noting that the position taken is not unanimously held. As with any form document, college or university counsel should review case law in his or her own jurisdiction to ensure that the institution is not bound by opposing precedent.

Finally, although such a section is not included in this model student code, the college or university may wish to emphasize, in addition to its prohibitions, rights that it recognizes. This can be included in a preamble to the student code[52] or in the college or university handbook.[53] The institution thereby assures its students that it does not intend to take away rights, but intends merely to control action going beyond, as Mr. Jefferson put it, "whether our indulgence was without limit."[54] The institution can thus help to insulate itself from criticisms that the student code takes away some constitutional right.

The following model student code is organized so that all concerned—students, administrators and faculty members—can understand the concepts embodied therein. It progresses from a general definition section to a section outlining the authority of the institution's student conduct bodies, a description of standards of conduct covered by the code, an outline of the procedures for bringing charges, holding hearings and deciding appeals and, finally, a section on interpretation and revision of the code. The commentary following various provisions sets forth not only the practical reason for including each section within the code, but also the legal support for each provision and, in some cases, suggestions on how the college or university official could approach certain situations.

The model student conduct code is followed by a model Student Conduct Board Hearing script. This script follows the model student conduct code and illustrates how a Student Conduct Board Hearing can be conducted effectively and in compliance with the dictates of minimal procedural due process, without using criminal law or courtroom models. Instead, the board chair runs the meeting of a committee—of which there are many in higher education—whose charge is to determine what the student did and to recommend the type of sanction that might be imposed if the student's conduct violated institutional rules. The model and the atmosphere are educational, not adversarial.

Throughout the model code and script appear detailed discussions of thorny issues. For example, there is a discussion of the legal points to consider when a student who believes s/he was victimized by another student does not want to

---

52. *See, e.g.*, LOYOLA COLL. OF MD., COMMUNITY STANDARDS 2004–2005, at 5–8, *available at* http://www.loyola.edu/campuslife/studentlife/42018%20Text.pdf (2004); TEXAS A&M UNIV., STUDENT RULES AT TEXAS A&M UNIV. *available at* http://student-rules.tamu.edu/ (last visited Oct. 12, 2004).

53. *See, e.g.*, UNIV. OF S.C, 2003–2004 STUDENTS RIGHTS AND FREEDOMS WITHIN THE ACADEMIC COMMUNITY, *available at* http://www.sa.sc.edu/carolinacommunity/rights.htm (last visited Oct. 12, 2004); UNIV. OF FLA., DEAN OF STUDENTS OFFICE, STUDENT GUIDE, *available at* http://www.dso.ufl.edu/studentguide/studentconductcode.html#studentrights (last visited Oct. 12, 2004).

54. *See* Letter to Coolidge, *supra* note 7, *quoted in* General Order, *supra* note 2, at 140 n.4.

confront her/his alleged attacker in an institutional process.[55] What options may we consider? A physical screen? Remote testimony by television? Another section proposes an educational solution to a problem created on some campuses: reporting process results to alleged student victims.[56] In these, as in many other issues, the answer fortunately lies in our educational leaders exercising their education judgment to the advantage of both their students and the entire academic community.

As we noted in our first model student conduct code, even the adoption of a sound student code, applied with compassionate educational judgment, will not eliminate the "spirit of insubordination" that Thomas Jefferson saw as such a significant problem for higher education nearly two centuries ago.[57]

For this reason, the captains who navigate our ships of higher education know that the calm waters of consistently proper student behavior are unlikely ever to be reached. Instead, as Mr. Jefferson once feared, the challenges of student discipline are likely always to loom as breakers ahead. Nevertheless, a sound student code following this model, like a sound ship under a sailing captain of old, will enable college and university administrators to navigate confidently past the dangers of the spirit of insubordination, even when those dangers are accompanied, as they often are, by storm clouds of public concern and lightning bolts of campus unrest.

With luck, twenty-first century navigators of the spirit of insubordination will be as successful as Mr. Jefferson was. After responding to the University of Virginia riots by expelling four students,[58] submitting the matter to a criminal grand jury, and reprimanding the rest of the students involved, he wrote to Ellen Wayles Randolph Coolidge on November 14, 1825:

> [The imposition of student discipline] determined the well-disposed among them to frown upon everything of the kind hereafter, and the ill-disposed returned to order from fear, if not from better motives. A perfect subordination has succeeded, entire respect towards the professors, and industry, order, and quiet the most exemplary, has prevailed ever since. Every one is sensible of the strength which the institution has derived from what appeared at first to threaten its foundation. We have no further fear of any thing of the kind from the present set, but as at the next term their numbers will be more than doubled by the accession of an additional band, as unbroken as these were, we mean to be prepared . . . .[59]

---

55. *See infra* Model Code, art. IV(A)(7).

56. *See infra* Model Code, art. IV(B)(3)(b).

57. *See* Letter to Cooper, *supra* note 1, at 1463.

58. Just as modern student affairs officers face unusual challenges, Mr. Jefferson expelled his own great-great nephew, Wilson Miles Carey, from the University of Virginia. D. MALONE, 6 JEFFERSON AND HIS TIME: THE SAGE OF MONTICELLO 463–68 (Little & Brown, eds., 1977).

59. Letter to Coolidge, *supra* note 7, *quoted in General Order*, *supra* note 2, at 140 n.4. Mr. Jefferson was quite a dreamer, wasn't he!?

A TWENTY-FIRST CENTURY
MODEL STUDENT CONDUCT CODE

PREAMBLE

Commentary. A preamble could precede Article I reflecting the institution's mission, the principles that its faculty, students, and administrators value, and the community's commitment to establishing a special living/learning environment— all of which are intended to be reflected in the Student Conduct Code. These statements may, and do, take many forms and are worth the effort required to create one that reflects the culture of the institution.[60]

ARTICLE I: DEFINITIONS[61]

1. The term [College] [University] means [name of institution].
2. The term "student" includes all persons taking courses at the [College] [University], either full-time or part-time, pursuing undergraduate, graduate, or professional studies. Persons who withdraw after allegedly violating the

---

60.   John Wesley Lowery, *Institutional Policy and Individual Responsibility: Communities of Justice and Principle*, 82 NEW DIRECTIONS FOR STUDENT SERVICES 15, 21–24 (1998). One example is "The Carolinian Creed" from the University of South Carolina. It is a general statement of values and is not a part of the student code per se:

> The community of scholars at the University of South Carolina is dedicated to personal and academic excellence. Choosing to join the community obligates each member to a code of civilized behavior. As a Carolinian . . . I will practice personal and academic integrity; I will respect the dignity of all persons; I will respect the rights and property of others; I will discourage bigotry, while striving to learn from differences in people, ideas, and opinions; I will demonstrate concern for others, their feelings, and their need for conditions which support their work and development. Allegiance to these ideals requires each Carolinian to refrain from and discourage behaviors which threaten the freedom and respect every individual deserves.

UNIV. OF S.C., CAROLINIAN CREED, *available at* http://www.sa.sc.edu/creed/ (last visited Oct. 12, 2004).

A second example is from at the University of Delaware:

> [T]o adjudicate violations of the Student Code of Conduct. As such it functions as an aspect of the University's educational process. The goals of the [student discipline] System are (1) to promote a campus environment that supports the overall educational mission of the University; (2) to protect the University community from disruption and harm; (3) to encourage appropriate standards of individual and group behavior; (4) to foster ethical standards and civic virtues.

UNIV. OF DEL., OFFICE OF JUDICIAL AFFAIRS, MISSION STATEMENT, *available at* http://www.udel.edu/judicialaffairs/ (last visited Oct. 12, 2004).

61.   The authors recommend that, as in every good legal document, a student code should contain a section in which the code's drafters define all the terms of art that will appear throughout the code. The following is a partial list of definitions recommended for use with a college or university's student code. Definitions of some terms will, of course, vary with the type of disciplinary system established, and with the institution's traditional definitions of certain concepts.

Student Code, who are not officially enrolled for a particular term but who have a continuing relationship with the [College] [University] or who have been notified of their acceptance for admission are considered "students" as are persons who are living in [College] [University] residence halls, although not enrolled in this institution. This Student Code [does][does not] apply at all locations of the [College][University], including the campus in [e.g., a foreign country or another state].

Commentary. This definition is intended to include persons not enrolled for a particular term but who were considered "students" when the conduct at issue occurred and could otherwise return. Such persons would be responsible for complying with the Student Code even between periods of their actual enrollment. Similarly, the Student Code would apply to students who have been accepted for admission but who are on campus prior to the beginning of their first semester. Also, under this model, students residing at one institution while enrolled at another would face the possibility of discipline at each institution for misbehavior in the institution of residence. The institution of residence should make sure that, if it follows this model, such visiting students are informed of the terms of the Code when they begin their residence. Similarly, it would be a good practice to advise students, in their letter of acceptance for admission or when they come to campus for events such as orientation, of the applicability of the student code (as well as other student affairs policies of importance, for example, a "three strikes and you're out" alcohol policy, if the institution has one). This definition would also include students enrolled in courses delivered by some form of distance education. Institutions will have to consider carefully, however, the ramifications and possible adjustments necessary to the student conduct process to accommodate students who reside some distance from the physical campus.

3. The term "faculty member" means any person hired by the [College] [University] to conduct classroom or teaching activities or who is otherwise considered by the [College] [University] to be a member of its faculty.
4. The term "[College] [University] official" includes any person employed by the [College] [University], performing assigned administrative or professional responsibilities.
5. The term "member of the [College] [University] community" includes any person who is a student, faculty member, [College] [University] official or any other person employed by the [College] [University]. A person's status in a particular situation shall be determined by [title of appropriate college or university administrator].[62]
6. The term "[College] [University] premises" includes all land, buildings, facilities, and other property in the possession of or owned, used, or controlled by the [College] [University] (including adjacent streets and sidewalks).

---

62. The college or university must designate a person within its administration to oversee the operation of the student code and to be responsible for its administration. *See infra* Model Code art. I(13). The person designated should be the same person assigned under art. V(A), to resolve other questions of interpretation.

7. The term "organization" means any number of persons who have complied with the formal requirements for [College] [University] [recognition/registration].

8. The term "Student Conduct Board" means any person or persons authorized by the [title of administrator identified in Article I, number 13][63] to determine whether a student has violated the Student Code and to recommend sanctions that may be imposed when a rules violation has been committed.

Commentary. A "Student Conduct Board," sometimes called a "hearing board," need not be comprised of any particular number of persons. A single person could be authorized to serve as the Student Conduct Board. Concerns recur about the composition of such bodies. An impartial decision maker is essential.[64] Courts have recognized, however, that in the college or university context it is often impossible to assemble a group who has not in some way heard of the charges at issue or who do not know the person(s) involved.[65] Frequently, a "Student Conduct Board" that determines whether the Student Code has been violated includes both students and faculty members or administrators.[66] In this model, the student conduct administrator defines the composition of hearing boards but, if the history or social system on campus dictates otherwise, the composition may be defined in more detail in the Student Code.

A critical point in naming the boards and job titles of persons involved in student discipline is not to fall into the old pattern of using criminal law or civil law sound-alike words, such as "judicial" (as in "student judicial board"). Use of such language creates the false impression that the Student Code is intended to "model" courtroom or judicial procedures. Instead, the process is an educational one by which the institution applies its values to establishing the best possible living/learning environment for students. It is not a "judicial" process at all and does not either enforce outside criminal or civil law or intend to mimic such

---

63. The person who authorizes the Student Conduct Board should be the same person designated to be responsible for the administration of the student code. *See infra* Model Code art. I(13).

64. Henry J. Friendly, *Some Kind of Hearing*, 123 U. PA. L. REV. 1267, 1279 (1975).

65. "Members of the college community, including students, usually comprise the hearing board. Given the nature of the academic community, members of the hearing board may know the student outside the context of the disciplinary proceeding." Swem, *supra* note 47, at 371. Holert v. Univ. of Chi., 751 F. Supp. 1294, 1301 (N.D. Ill. 1990) ("In a University setting, prior contact among the faculty and students is likely; that fact alone does not indicate bias or partiality."). *See* Henderson State Univ. v. Spadoni, 848 S.W.2d 951, 954 (Ark. Ct. App. 1993) (holding that it was not a deprivation of procedural due process for fraternity brother of victim to serve on student conduct board that suspended student for one year); Nash v. Auburn Univ., 812 F.2d 655, 666 (11th Cir. 1987) (finding that participation of a student on the student conduct board who had prior knowledge of the charge did not indicate bias).

66. There are many permutations on the composition of such boards. For example, Washington University's Judicial Board is comprised of six student members, six faculty/administrative staff members, and a chairperson. WASHINGTON UNIV. IN ST. LOUIS, POLICIES AND PROCEDURES: UNIV. JUDICIAL CODE, § IV *available at* http://www.wustl.edu/policies/judicial.html (last visited Oct. 12, 2004). The panel selected to meet in individual cases is comprised of at least three student members and three faculty/staff members and the chairperson. *Id.*

judicial processes.[67]

9.   The term "Student Conduct Administrator" means a [College] [University] official authorized on a case-by-case basis by the [title of administrator identified in Article I, number 13] to impose sanctions upon any student(s) found to have violated the Student Code. The [title of administrator identified in Article I, number 13] may authorize a Student Conduct Administrator to serve simultaneously as a Student Conduct Administrator and the sole member or one of the members of the Student Conduct Board.   The [title of administrator identified in Article I, number 13] may authorize the same Student Conduct Administrator to impose sanctions in all cases.

Commentary. Just as courts have recognized that persons comprising a Student Conduct Board may have prior knowledge of the events at issue or the person(s) involved, they have recognized that it is not always easy to avoid having one person occupy multiple roles with respect to disciplinary proceedings, even when suspension or expulsion is a possible outcome.[68] *While it is not improper for student affairs professionals to serve in multiple roles, whenever possible the college or university should avoid putting someone in the position of "wearing two hats." If the size of the institution's staff permits, it is preferable to have the functions of informal investigating and/or mediating separated from that of determining whether a violation has occurred and setting the sanction. Thus, this model recognizes the advisability of separating the functions when possible, while preserving the flexibility to combine functions—which usually will be a fact of life*

---

67.   *See supra* text following note 50.

68.   In *Gorman v. University of Rhode Island*, 837 F.2d 7, 15 (1st Cir. 1987), the court explained:

> Nor do the various roles of Weisinger, while inappropriate in a judicial setting, necessarily violate the requirement of fairness. As Justice Blackmun noted in *Richardson v. Perales*, 402. U.S. 389 (1971), 'the advocate-judge-multiple hat suggestion . . . assumes too much and would bring down too many procedures designed, and working well. . . ." *Id* at 410. Gorman's contention that Weisinger's various roles or 'multiple hats' are evidence of bias and undue influence, also 'assumes too much.' The University procedures are designed to give students an opportunity to respond and defend against the charges made, and there is no evidence which would show that Gorman was denied a fair hearing because of Weisinger's multiple roles.

See also Nash, 812 F.2d at 666 (11th Cir. 1987) ("In *Duke*, we refused 'to establish a *per se* rule that would disqualify administrative hearing bodies . . . solely for the reason that . . . some of [the members] participated in the initial investigation of the incident and initiation of the cause under consideration."); Winnick v. Manning, 460 F.2d 545, 548 (2d Cir. 1972) (holding that accused students' due process right to an impartial decision-maker did not preclude the dean from the office which brought disciplinary action against students from serving as decision-maker); Hillman v. Elliott, 436 F. Supp. 812, 816 (W.D. Va. 1977) (holding that principal should be permitted to serve as hearing officer despite his prior involvement in the disciplinary matter in question). *Cf.* Megill v. Bd. of Regents, 541 F.2d 1073, 1079 (5th Cir. 1976) (holding that mere familiarity with the facts of the case gained by school board members in the performance of their statutory role did not disqualify them as decision-makers); Alex v. Allen, 409 F. Supp. 379, 387–88 (W.D. Pa. 1976) (stating that unless the record indicates partiality, it is assumed that the administrative body is unbiased).

at many institutions.

A student challenging a Student Conduct Board's decision on the grounds of bias must demonstrate actual bias or that the board acted improperly.[69] There is, however, nothing improper about a college or university official advising the Student Conduct Board during the disciplinary process.[70] This model anticipates that a college or university official will determine sanctions after a violation has been found. In some systems sanctions are set by the same Student Conduct Board which determines whether a violation has occurred.[71]

10. The term "Appellate Board" means any person or persons authorized by the [title of administrator identified in Article I, number 13] to consider an appeal from a Student Conduct Board's determination as to whether a student has violated the Student Code or from the sanctions imposed by the Student Conduct Administrator.

11. The term "shall" is used in the imperative sense.

12. The term "may" is used in the permissive sense.

13. The [title of appropriate administrator] is that person designated by the [College] [University] President to be responsible for the administration of the Student Code.

14. The term "policy" means the written regulations of the [College] [University] as found in, but not limited to, the Student Code, Residence Life Handbook, the [College] [University] web page and computer use policy, and Graduate/Undergraduate Catalogs.

Commentary. Listed herein is a sampling of the types of other sources of rules and regulations governing colleges or universities. The institution should include here a list of the primary places where such rules and regulations may be found.

15. The term "cheating" includes, but is not limited to: (1) use of any unauthorized assistance in taking quizzes, tests, or examinations; (2) use of

---

69.   *Holert*, 751 F. Supp. at 1301 ("The disciplinary committee, which included a student representative, is entitled to a presumption of honesty and integrity, absent a showing of actual bias, such as animosity, prejudice, or a personal or financial stake in the outcome."); *Gorman*, 837 F.2d at 15 (1st Cir. 1988) ("In the intimate setting of a college or university, prior contact between the participants is likely, and does not *per se* indicate bias or partiality."); *Nash*, 812 F.2d at 666 (finding no bias where student conduct board member had prior knowledge of the incident); Duke v. N. Tex. State Univ., 469 F.2d 829, 834 (5th Cir. 1972) ("Alleged prejudice of university hearing bodies must be based upon more than mere speculation and tenuous inferences."); Barker v. Hardway, 283 F. Supp. 228, 237 (S.D. W.Va. 1968) ("[T]he law indulges the presumption that school authorities act reasonably and fairly and in good faith in exercising the authority with which it clothes them, and casts the burden on him who calls their conduct into question to show that they have not been actuated by proper motives.").

70.   Morris v. Brandeis Univ., 804 N.E.2d 961, 964 (Mass. App. Ct. 2004) ("There was no fiduciary relationship between [an accused] student and a university administrator/advisor like Tenser in these circumstances [serving as the advisor to the student conduct board during the discipline process].").

71.   *See infra* note 163, and accompanying text.

sources beyond those authorized by the instructor in writing papers, preparing reports, solving problems, or carrying out other assignments; (3) the acquisition, without permission, of tests or other academic material belonging to a member of the [College] [University] faculty or staff (4) engaging in any behavior specifically prohibited by a faculty member in the course syllabus or class discussion.

16. The term "plagiarism" includes, but is not limited to, the use, by paraphrase or direct quotation, of the published or unpublished work of another person without full and clear acknowledgment. It also includes the unacknowledged use of materials prepared by another person or agency engaged in the selling of term papers or other academic materials.

Commentary. Cheating and plagiarism are the two most common types of academic misconduct.[72] Faculty should be strongly encouraged to discuss academic misconduct in the course syllabus and their course web page if they have one, so that it is in writing, and in class discussion. The courts' views about institutional decisions regarding such academic misconduct will be discussed in greater detail hereafter.[73] In any event, drafters must assure that the possible overlap between faculty response and student affairs' response to academic misbehavior be addressed directly and thoughtfully so that there is no confusion as to the process that applies to such situations.

17. The term "Complainant" means any person who submits a charge alleging that a student violated this Student Code. When a student believes that s/he has been a victim of another student's misconduct, the student who believes s/he has been a victim will have the same rights under this Student Code as are provided to the Complainant, even if another member of the [College][University] community submitted the charge itself.

Commentary. Normally, a student who believes s/he has been the victim of another student's misconduct becomes the Complainant. This is not always the case. For example, a member of campus security may be the technical Complainant if a matter begins with a security report. In that event, this provision preserves for the student who believes s/he was a victim the same rights (such as to attend the entire hearing or to appeal) as are also accorded to the Complainant.

18. The term "Accused Student" means any student accused of violating this Student Code.

---

72. William Kibler, *Addressing Academic Dishonesty and Promoting Academic Integrity*, in THE ADMINISTRATION OF CAMPUS DISCIPLINE: STUDENT, ORGANIZATIONAL, AND COMMUNITY ISSUES 161 (Brent G. Paterson & William L. Kibler, eds., 1998).

73. *See infra,* notes 91–92, and accompanying text; Dutile, *supra* note 8; Grier & Stoner, *supra* note 8; Bernard, *supra* note 8. *See also* CENTER FOR ACADEMIC INTEGRITY KENAN INSTITUTE FOR ETHICS AT DUKE UNIVERSITY, *at* http://www.academicintegrity.org (providing links to member institution honor codes) (last visited Oct. 12, 2004).

ARTICLE II: STUDENT CODE AUTHORITY

1. The Student Conduct Administrator shall determine the composition of Student Conduct Boards and Appellate Boards and determine which Student Conduct Board, Student Conduct Administrator and Appellate Board shall be authorized to hear each matter.

2. The [title of appropriate administrator] shall develop policies for the administration of the student conduct system and procedural rules for the conduct of Student Conduct Board Hearings that are not inconsistent with provisions of the Student Code.

Commentary. This provision is intended to allow the institution to adopt and to revise operating procedures in a nimble fashion, not invoking the more complicated formal process used to review and to revise the Student Code itself.

3. Decisions made by a Student Conduct Board and/or Student Conduct Administrator shall be final, pending the normal appeal process.

ARTICLE III: PROSCRIBED CONDUCT

A. Jurisdiction of the [College] [University] Student Code

The [College] [University] Student Code shall apply to conduct that occurs on [College] [University] premises, at [College] [University] sponsored activities, and to off-campus conduct that adversely affects the [College] [University] Community and/or the pursuit of its objectives. Each student shall be responsible for his/her conduct from the time of application for admission through the actual awarding of a degree, even though conduct may occur before classes begin or after classes end, as well as during the academic year and during periods between terms of actual enrollment (and even if their conduct is not discovered until after a degree is awarded).[74] The Student Code shall apply to a student's conduct even if the student withdraws from school while a disciplinary matter is pending. The [title of administrator identified in Article I, number 13] shall decide whether the Student Code shall be applied to conduct occurring off campus, on a case by case basis, in

---

74. Inappropriate conduct occurring, for example, during on-campus visits by applicants or by students who have completed classes awaiting graduation ceremony are covered by this student conduct code. Dinu v. Harvard Coll., 56 F. Supp. 2d 129, 133 (D. Mass. 1999) (rejecting assertion that college rules did not apply between completion of course work and graduation day); O'Sullivan v. N.Y. Law Sch., 22 N.Y.S. 663, 665 (N.Y. Sup. Ct. 1893):

> It cannot be that a student having passed all examinations necessary for a degree can, before his graduation, excite disturbance and threaten injury to the school or college without being amenable to some punishment. No course would seem open except to forthwith expel him or refuse his degree. . . . The faculties of educational institutions having power to confer degrees . . . are necessarily vested with a broad discretion as to the persons who shall receive those honors. . . . Any other rule would be subversive of all discipline in the schools. . . . We see no reason why the right to discipline is not as great between the final examination and the graduation as before.

See infra Model Code, art. IV(B)(1)(k).

his/her sole discretion.

Commentary.[75] *The college or university should state in general terms the conduct which the institution intends to reach. A college or university has jurisdiction to impose sanctions upon a student for activities that take place off campus when those activities adversely affect the interests of the college or university community. School officials have wide latitude in determining whether an activity adversely affects the interests of the college or university community.*[76]

In 1968, one court noted the demise of 'in loco parentis' and opined that it foresaw "a trend to reject the authority of university officials to regulate 'off-campus' activity of students."[77] *The actual trend was to embrace and to encourage institutions that worked to regulate off-campus student misbehavior. The Missouri federal judges concluded that it was appropriate for institutions to regulate such off-campus behavior and even to expect "superior ethical and moral behavior."*[78] *So did the courts in Esteban v. Central Missouri State College,*[79] *Krasnow v. Virginia Polytechnic Inst. & State Univ.,*[80] *Hill v. Michigan State University,*[81] *Ray*

---

75. An excellent discussion of both legal and practical considerations involved in dealing with "off-campus" student behavior is set forth in, Capone III *supra* note 8; KAPLIN & LEE, *supra* note 8, §4.12.2.

76. *See* Wright, *supra* note 20, at 1068. In *Kusnir v. Leach*, 439 A.2d 223 (Pa. Commw. Ct. 1982), a college disciplinary board suspended a student for two semesters for participating in misconduct at a private party at a private off-campus residence. *Id.* at 225. The student asserted in part that the college lacked jurisdiction to punish students for off-campus misconduct. *Id.* The court disagreed, saying the argument had "no merit." *Id.* at 226. "Obviously, a college has a vital interest in the character of its students, and may regard off-campus behavior as a reflection of a student's character and his fitness to be a member of the student body." *Id.*

77. Buttny v. Smiley, 281 F. Supp. 280, 286 (D. Colo. 1968).

78. *General Order, supra* note 2, at 145:

Standards so established may apply to student behavior on and off campus when relevant to any lawful mission, process, or function of the institution. By such standards of student conduct the institution may prohibit any action or omission which impairs, interferes with, or obstructs the missions, processes and functions of the institution.

79. 290 F. Supp. 622 (W.D. Mo. 1968) (holding that the college had substantial justification for subjecting to discipline students involved in demonstrations which blocked traffic on and near campus).

80. 414 F. Supp. 55, 57 (D. Va. 1976), (off-campus drug possession) (upholding higher standards of morals and behavior despite questioning whether the off-campus acts had "little to do with university life").

81. 182 F. Supp. 2d 621 (W.D. Mich. 2001). The court found:

Hill fails to cite any case holding that a university violates the Constitution by suspending a student for off-campus acts. This Court doubts such a case exists because universities typically take into consideration many off-campus acts in deciding whether to admit or retain a student. For example, if a student sold drugs across the street from campus, or committed arson one block from campus, such acts could certainly be taken into account in determining whether to retain a person on campus. These acts raise legitimate concern, even fear, as to the safety of the property and persons on campus—i.e., if he does it off-campus, he is as likely to do it on campus. Likewise, encouraging fires, rocking vehicles, and kicking telephone booths, even though occurring off-campus, shows a disregard for the property and safety of others that raises a legitimate concern as to the safety of the property and persons on-campus.

v. Wilmington College,[82] *numerous other cases,*[83] *and, even a state attorney general.*[84]

Under this Model Student Code, when an activity occurs off campus, that is not at a college or university sponsored event, it would be the responsibility of the administrator designated in Article I, number 13, to determine whether college or university jurisdiction should be asserted.[85] *Utilizing this procedure on a case-by-case basis allows the institution to consider the unique facts of each situation without the impossible problem of drafting language to cover every possible situation.*

Id. at 637.

82.   667 N.E.2d 39 (Ohio Ct. App. 1995) (approving application of student conduct code to off-campus sexual conduct, under language from the 1990 Model Code).   The *Ray* court explained: "An educational institution's authority to discipline its students does not necessarily stop at the physical boundaries of the institution's premises. The institution has the prerogative to decide that certain types of off-campus conduct are detrimental to the institution and to discipline a student who engages in that conduct." *Id.* at 41.

83.   Gomes v. Univ. of Me. Sys., 304 F. Supp. 2d 117 (D. Me. 2004) (stating that accused student's argument that University could not deal with alleged sexual assault because it occurred off campus was "simply frivolous."); Reliford v. Univ. of Akron, 610 N.E.2d 521 (Ohio Ct. App. 1991); Slaughter v. Brigham Young Univ., 514 F.2d 622 (10th Cir. 1975) (upholding expulsion of graduate student for fraud in publications); Cornette v. Aldridge, 408 S.W.2d 935 (Tex. Civ. App. 1966) (upholding suspension of student after multiple driving offenses in city). *See* Hart v. Ferris State Coll., 557 F. Supp. 1379 (W.D. Mich. 1983); Sohmer v. Kinnard, 535 F. Supp. 50 (D. Md. 1982); Wallace v. Florida A&M Univ., 433 So. 2d 600 (Fla. Dist. Ct. App. 1983); Dale R. Agthe, Annotation, *Misconduct of College or University Student Off Campus As Grounds for Expulsion, Suspension, or Other Disciplinary Action*, 28 A.L.R. 4th 463 (1984).

84.   Referring to the University of Maryland College Park, Maryland Attorney General J. Joseph Curan, Jr. concluded that "it is constitutionally permissible for a public college or university to impose disciplinary sanctions on students for misconduct that occurs off-campus." 74 Op. Md. Atty. Gen. 147 at *4 (1989). He added, "Any statute or university rule authorizing an institution to sanction such conduct . . . must limit disciplinary actions to misconduct that is detrimental to the institution's interests. *Id.*

85.   *See infra* Model Code, art. V(A). University of Florida Rule 6C1-4.018 gives guidance on when and how it deals with off-campus conduct:

> When a student violates city, state or federal law, by an offense committed off campus and which is not associated with a University-connected activity, the disciplinary authority of the University will not be used merely to duplicate the penalty awarded for such an act under applicable ordinances and laws.   The University will take disciplinary action against a student for such an off-campus offense only when it is required by law to do so or when the nature of the offense is such that in the judgment of the Director of Student Judicial Affairs, the continued presence of the student on campus is likely to interfere with the educational process or the orderly operation of the University; the continued presence of the student on campus is likely to endanger the health, safety or welfare of the University community or is intimidating or threatening to another individual within the University community; or the offense committed by the student is of such a serious nature as to adversely affect the student's suitability as a member of the University community.   If the Director of Student Judicial Affairs determines that disciplinary action is warranted, the Director of Student Judicial Affairs shall so notify the student . . . . The action of the University with respect to any such off-campus conduct shall be taken independently of any off-campus authority.

RULES OF FLA. DEPT. OF EDUC., DIV. OF UNIVS., UNIV. OF FLA., Rule 6C1-4.018, *available at* http://www.generalcounsel.ufl.edu/Rules/Chapter%204/4018.pdf (last visited Oct. 12, 2004).

Institutions with multiple, remote or overseas locations will wish to state here whether the student code applies in those locations.

B.   Conduct—Rules and Regulations

Any student found to have committed or to have attempted to commit the following misconduct is subject to the disciplinary sanctions outlined in Article IV:

1.   Acts of dishonesty, including but not limited to the following:

    a.   Cheating, plagiarism, or other forms of academic dishonesty.

    b.   Furnishing false information to any [College] [University] official, faculty member, or office.

    c.   Forgery, alteration, or misuse of any [College] [University] document, record, or instrument of identification.

2.   Disruption or obstruction of teaching, research, administration, disciplinary proceedings, other [College] [University] activities, including its public service functions on or off campus, or of other authorized non- [College] [University] activities when the conduct occurs on [College] [University] premises.

3.   Physical abuse, verbal abuse, threats, intimidation, harassment, coercion, and/or other conduct which threatens or endangers the health or safety of any person.[86]

---

86.   While this language is appropriate for a private university or college which need not worry unduly about due process requirements under federal or state constitutional or statutory law, persons drafting a code at a public institution should review with their institutional counsel whether more specific language is required in their situation. One court, however, noted that this language was not too vague to enforce, noting that, "Any ordinary reasonable person could understand the [college] code. . . ." Cady v. S. Suburban Coll., 310 F. Supp. 2d 447 (N.D. Ill. 2004).

    A broadly worded provision such as this one would bring within the Student Code incidents of alleged sexual misconduct, hazing and, when coupled with rule number 4, "riots." There are many more specific definitions of inappropriate sexual conduct in Student Codes. Here are two approaches, defining inappropriate sexual conduct:

Sexual misconduct that involves:

    i.   Deliberate touching of another's sexual parts without consent;

    ii.   Deliberate sexual invasion of another without consent;

    iii.   Deliberate constraint or incapacitation of another, without that person's knowledge or consent, so as to put another at substantially increased risk of sexual injury; or

    iv.   Unwelcome sexual advances, requests for sexual favors, or other verbal or physical conduct of a sexual nature that expressly or implicitly imposes conditions upon, threatens, interferes with, or creates an intimidating, hostile, or demeaning environment for an individual's (I) academic pursuits, (II) University employment; (III) participation in activities sponsored by the University or organizations or groups related to the University, or (IV) opportunities to benefit from other aspects of University life.

UNIV. OF N.C. AT CHAPEL HILL, INSTRUMENT OF STUDENT JUDICIAL GOVERNANCE II.C.1.b., *available at* http://instrument.unc.edu/instrument.text.html#IIOffenses (July 1, 2003);

Sexual misconduct.

    1.   Any sexual act that occurs without the consent of the victim, or that occurs when the victim is unable to give consent.

Commentary. It is very important to include a broadly worded rule, such as this one, so that there are no gaps of misconduct between the areas covered by more specific rules.[87]

4.   Attempted or actual theft of and/or damage to property of the [College] [University] or property of a member of the [College] [University] community or other personal or public property, on or off campus.

5.   Hazing,[88] defined as an act which endangers the mental or physical health or safety of a student, or which destroys or removes public or private property, for the purpose of initiation, admission into, affiliation with, or as a condition for continued membership in, a group or organization.[89]   The express or

---

2.   Obscene or indecent behavior, which includes, but is not limited to, exposure of one's sexual organs or the display of sexual behavior that would reasonably be offensive to others.

3.   Conduct of a sexual nature that creates an intimidating, hostile, or offensive campus, educational, or working environment for another person. This includes unwanted, unwelcome, inappropriate, or irrelevant sexual or gender-based activities or comments.

FLA. STATE UNIV., STUDENT CONDUCT CODE 5(a), *available at* http://www.fsu.edu/Books/Student-Handbook/2003codes/conduct.html (last visited Oct. 12, 2004).

For opposing resources on dealing with sexual assault on college and university campuses, compare CAL. COALITION AGAINST SEXUAL ABUSE, *at* http://www.calcasa.org (last visited Oct. 12, 2004) (focusing on protecting victims of sexual assault) *with* FOUND. FOR INDIVIDUAL RIGHTS IN EDUC., *at* http://www.thefire.org/issues.php (last visited Oct. 12, 2004) (focusing on rights of students accused of misconduct).

In Mallory v. Ohio Univ., 76 Fed. Appx. 634, 634 (6th Cir. 2003), a student's expulsion was upheld despite his Title IX lawsuit. He had been found in violation of the university's sexual assault policy, with the disciplinary board stating that the female student's "degree of intoxication was such 'that the victim's judgment was so impaired that she would not have been capable of making rational decisions about her welfare; as such she could not have given consent to engage in sexual intercourse with the accused student.'" *Id.* at 637.

87.   It would be impossible for any committee of administration, faculty and students to compose rules and regulations so specific as to cover every possible offense, which the fertile imagination of present day students might conceive or perpetuate. Herman v. Univ. of S.C., 341 F. Supp. 226, 232 (D.S.C. 1971).

88.   An excellent discussion of legal and practical considerations involved in dealing with Greek organization hazing is Melinda W. Grier, *Regulating and Disciplining Fraternities and Sororities*, 38th Annual Conf., Nat'l Ass'n of Coll. & Univ. Att'ys (1998) (on file with author).

89.   *See* PA. STAT. ANN. tit. 24, §5352 (West 1992). In Pennsylvania, the legislature has promulgated an anti-hazing law, PA. STAT. ANN. tit. 24, §§ 5351–5354 (West 1992), requiring all public or private institutions of higher education to adopt a written anti-hazing policy and to establish rules for enforcement of the policy and punishment of offenders. As part of this law, the legislature has defined what it considers to be hazing. Student code drafters would be well advised to determine whether applicable state law provides a definition of hazing and, if so, to use that definition as a reference when drafting the language of their student code in order to make the provision self-executing, i.e., to provide a free standing rule which prohibits hazing whether it constitutes a precise violation of the criminal law, or not. In so doing, the drafter must take care not simply to make reference to the state statute, so that there is no implication that there is no college or university rule violated unless or until the state criminal law processes first find a violation of the criminal law. For a link to forty-two state laws on hazing, see http://www.stophazing.org/laws.html (last visited Oct. 12, 2004).

implied consent of the victim will not be a defense. Apathy or acquiescence in the presence of hazing are not neutral acts; they are violations of this rule.[90]

6. Failure to comply with directions of [College] [University] officials or law enforcement officers acting in performance of their duties and/or failure to identify oneself to these persons when requested to do so.

7. Unauthorized possession, duplication or use of keys to any [College] [University] premises or unauthorized entry to or use of [College] [University] premises.

8. Violation of any [College] [University] policy, rule, or regulation published in hard copy or available electronically on the [College][University] website.

9. Violation of any federal, state or local law.[91]

Two other groups' explanations of conduct prohibited as hazing include:

Any action taken or situation created, intentionally, whether on or off fraternity premises, to produce mental or physical discomfort, embarrassment, harassment, or ridicule. Such activities may include but are not limited to the following: use of alcohol; paddling in any form; creation of excessive fatigue; physical and psychological shocks; quests, treasure hunts, scavenger hunts, road trips or any other such activities carried on outside or inside of the confines of the chapter house; wearing of public apparel which is conspicuous and not normally in good taste; engaging in public stunts and buffoonery; morally degrading or humiliating games and activities; and any other activities which are not consistent with academic achievement, fraternal law, ritual or policy or the regulations and policies of the educational institution or applicable state law.

FRATERNITY INSURANCE PROTECTION GROUP, RISK MANAGEMENT MANUAL, 45 *available at* http://www.fipg.org/media/FIPGRiskMgmtManual.pdf (last updated Dec. 2003).

"Hazing" refers to any activity expected of someone joining a group (or to maintain full status in a group) that humiliates, degrades or risks emotional and/or physical harm, regardless of the person's willingness to participate. In years past, hazing practices were typically considered harmless pranks or comical antics associated with young men in college fraternities. Today we know that hazing extends far beyond college fraternities and is experienced by boys/men and girls/women in school groups, university organizations, athletic teams, the military, and other social and professional organizations. Hazing is a complex social problem that is shaped by power dynamics operating in a group and/or organization and within a particular cultural context. Hazing activities are generally considered to be: physically abusive, hazardous, and/or sexually violating. The specific behaviors or activities within these categories vary widely among participants, groups and settings. While alcohol use is common in many types of hazing, other examples of typical hazing practices include: personal servitude; sleep deprivation and restrictions on personal hygiene; yelling, swearing and insulting new members/rookies; being forced to wear embarrassing or humiliating attire in public; consumption of vile substances or smearing of such on one's skin; brandings; physical beatings; binge drinking and drinking games; sexual simulation and sexual assault.

STOPHAZING.ORG, *at* http://www.stophazing.org/definition.html (last visited Oct. 12, 2004):

90. Pavela, *supra* note 8 at 830, n.18.

91. This language is not too vague to enforce. Woodis v. Westark Comm. Coll., 160 F.3d 435, 440 (8th Cir. 1998) (holding that student who pled nolo contendere to misdemeanor controlled substances charge was in violation of rule requiring her to "obey all federal, state and local laws" and was properly expelled); Esteban v. Cent. Mo. State Coll., 415 F.2d 1077, 1082 (8th Cir. 1969) (rejecting vagueness challenge to regulation requiring students to abide by "all local, state and federal laws"). It is a wise practice to cite other campus rules if relevant to the alleged misconduct, rather than to rely upon this rule, in order to avoid the criminal defense

Commentary. It is an appropriate practice to cite another rule that a student's conduct may also have violated whenever this rule is cited so that the institution is enforcing its rules rather than the standards set by persons outside the academic community for law enforcement purposes. This practice will help to avoid the mistaken notion that the institution is enforcing the criminal laws.

10. Use, possession, manufacturing, or distribution of marijuana, heroin, narcotics, or other controlled substances except as expressly permitted by law.

11. Use, possession, manufacturing, or distribution of alcoholic beverages (except as expressly permitted by [College] [University] regulations), or public intoxication. Alcoholic beverages may not, in any circumstance, be used by, possessed by or distributed to any person under twenty-one (21) years of age.

Commentary. This rule should be consistent with the institution's alcohol policy, for example, by making reference to the policy or to special features of it (such as a "three strikes and you're out" policy, or a parental notification policy, if applicable). Rules such as 10 and 11 comply with the Drug-Free Schools and Communities Act[92], and 34 C.F.R. Part 86, requiring higher education institutions receiving any federal financial aid to have "standards of conduct that clearly prohibit, at a minimum, the unlawful possession, use, or distribution of illicit drugs and alcohol by students"[93] for which the institution will impose sanctions.[94]

12. Illegal or unauthorized possession of firearms, explosives, other weapons, or dangerous chemicals on [College] [University] premises or use of any such item, even if legally possessed, in a manner that harms, threatens or causes fear to others.[95]

13. Participating in an on-campus or off-campus demonstration, riot or activity that disrupts the normal operations of the [College] [University] and/or infringes on the rights of other members of the [College] [University] community; leading or inciting others to disrupt scheduled and/or normal activities within any campus building or area.

14. Obstruction of the free flow of pedestrian or vehicular traffic on [College] [University] premises or at [College] [University] sponsored or supervised functions.

---

lawyer's argument that a violation of this rule should be predicated upon a prior final determination of criminal responsibility.

92.   Pub. L. No. 99-570, 100 Stat. 3207 (1986) (codified as amended in scattered sections of 20 U.S.C.).

93.   34 C.F.R § 86.100(a)(1) (2004).

94.   *Id.* § 86.100(a)(5).

95.   This would be the spot to make it a rules violation to possess even a legal firearm on campus if that is the institution's choice but an administrator at a public institution would be well advised to consult campus counsel on this choice. Under such a rule, one court upheld the suspension of a student who refused to promise that he would not bring a gun onto a private institution's campus. Ali v. Stetson Univ., Inc. ___ F. Supp. 2d ___, No. 6:03-CV-975-ORl28, 2004 WL 2309552 (M.D. Fla. Oct. 8, 2004) (lawsuit brought under 42 U.S.C. § 1981).

15. Conduct that is disorderly, lewd, or indecent; breach of peace; or aiding, abetting, or procuring another person to breach the peace on [College] [University] premises or at functions sponsored by, or participated in by, the [College] [University] or members of the academic community. Disorderly Conduct includes but is not limited to: Any unauthorized use of electronic or other devices to make an audio or video record of any person while on [College][University] premises without his/her prior knowledge, or without his/her effective consent when such a recording is likely to cause injury or distress. This includes, but is not limited to, surreptitiously taking pictures of another person in a gym, locker room, or restroom.

Commentary. The provisions set forth in rule fifteen (adapted in part from a rule at the University of Denver) are intended to give student affairs professionals some tools to deal with inappropriate conduct in the ever-changing electronic age.

16. Theft or other abuse of computer facilities and resources, including but not limited to:
    a. Unauthorized entry into a file, to use, read, or change the contents, or for any other purpose.
    b. Unauthorized transfer of a file.
    c. Use of another individual's identification and/or password.
    d. Use of computing facilities and resources to interfere with the work of another student, faculty member or [College] [University] Official.
    e. Use of computing facilities and resources to send obscene or abusive messages.
    f. Use of computing facilities and resources to interfere with normal operation of the [College] [University] computing system.
    g. Use of computing facilities and resources in violation of copyright laws.
    h. Any violation of the [College][University] Computer Use Policy.[96]

17. Abuse of the Student Conduct System, including but not limited to:
    a. Failure to obey the notice from a Student Conduct Board or [College] [University] official to appear for a meeting or hearing as part of the Student Conduct System.
    b. Falsification, distortion, or misrepresentation of information before a Student Conduct Board.
    c. Disruption or interference with the orderly conduct of a Student Conduct Board proceeding.
    d. Institution of a student conduct code proceeding in bad faith.

---

96. Each public institution will want to have its counsel review the institution's computer use policy to consider speech issues. It is recommended that each institution have a separate computer use policy and that reference be made to it in the student conduct code. Many excellent policies are maintained by EDUCAUSE/Cornell Institute for Computer Policy and Law, *at* http://www.educause.edu/icpl (last visited Oct. 12, 2004). *See* AM. COUNCIL ON EDUC., UNIV. POLICIES AND PRACTICES ADDRESSING IMPROPER PEER-TO-PEER FILE SHARING, *available at* http://www.acenet.edu/hena/pdf/P2P2.pdf (Apr. 2004).

e. Attempting to discourage an individual's proper participating in, or use of, the student conduct system.

f. Attempting to influence the impartiality of a member of a Student Conduct Board prior to, and/or during the course of, the Student Conduct Board proceeding.

g. Harassment (verbal or physical) and/or intimidation of a member of a Student Conduct Board prior to, during, and/or after a student conduct code proceeding.

h. Failure to comply with the sanction(s) imposed under the Student Code.

i. Influencing or attempting to influence another person to commit an abuse of the student conduct code system.

Commentary. Colleges or universities are, of course, free to include in their lists of misconduct as many types of acts as they choose. The list of acts of misconduct that constitute violations of the Student Code should give students notice of the types of conduct that may result in sanctions but not every specific type of misconduct is listed because it would not be possible to do so.

Courts give college and university officials much greater freedom concerning purely academic decisions than they do concerning purely disciplinary decisions.[97] Academic misconduct cases involving cheating or plagiarism, for example, present a unique hybrid of academic and disciplinary decisions.[98] Because courts have a real challenge in deciding whether misconduct is academic or disciplinary,[99] the authors suggest that public institutions review with campus counsel each case of

---

97. *See* Regents of Univ. of Mich. v. Ewing, 474 U.S. 214 (1985); Bd. of Curators v. Horowitz, 435 U.S. 78, 87–91 (1978). The dichotomy has developed because "disciplinary determinations are based on objective findings of fact so that hearings are useful and appropriate in this context. However, academic determinations are quite different because they are more subjective and evaluative." Ronald M. Levin, *Constitutional Law - Due Process of Law*, 47 U. CIN. L. REV. 514, 517 (1978). *See generally* Emogene C. Wilhelm, *Academic or Disciplinary Decisions: When is Due Process Required?*, 6 U. BRIDGEPORT L. REV. 391 (1985); M. Michele Fournet, *Due Process and the University Student: The Academic/Disciplinary Dichotomy*, 37 LA. L. REV. 939 (1977); KAPLIN & LEE, *supra* note 8, at 491–97; Pugel v. Univ. of Ill., 378 F.3d 689 (7th Cir. 2004).

98. Dutile, *supra* note 8; Bernard, *supra* note 8; Steve Milam & John Marshall, *Impact of Regents of the University of Michigan v. Ewing on Academic Dismissals from Graduate and Professional Schools*, 13 J.C. & U.L. 335 (1987). The safest approach is clear: "When dismissal or other serious sanctions depend more on disputed factual issues concerning conduct than on expert evaluation of academic work, the student should be accorded procedural rights akin to those for disciplinary cases." KAPLIN & LEE, *supra* note 8, at 491.

99. *See, e.g.*, Jaksa v. Univ. of Mich., 597 F. Supp. 1245, 1248 n.2 (E.D. Mich. 1984), *aff'd per curiam*, 787 F.2d 590 (6th Cir. 1986); Hall v. Medical Coll. of Ohio, 742 F.2d 299, 308–09 (6th Cir. 1984). *But see* Corso v. Creighton Univ., 731 F.2d 529, 532 (8th Cir. 1984) (holding that "[c]heating on exams is clearly an academic matter. . . ."); Garshman v. Pa. State Univ., 395 F. Supp. 912, 921 (M.D. Pa. 1975) (holding that "a determination as to the academic honesty of a student is . . . peculiarly within the discretion of a college administration."); McDonald v. Bd. of Trs. of Univ. of Ill., 375 F. Supp. 95, 104 (N.D. Ill 1974). *See also* Robert N. Roberts, *Public University Responses to Academic Dishonesty: Disciplinary or Academic*, 15 J.L. & EDUC. 369, 384 n.16–32 (1986) (noting that "even if a public university classifies the punishment of cheating as an academic matter, the courts may not hold the same view").

"academic misconduct" which might result in suspension or expulsion to assure that the minimal procedural due process required in the particular circumstance is provided. No such dilemma is presented at private institutions. Academic misconduct also may be grounds for academic sanctions, such as the imposition of a lower grade. This system must be dovetailed with the institutional process for disciplinary review of misconduct in the academic setting if additional sanctions are possible.

Concerning items number three, thirteen, fifteen, sixteen, and seventeen, a public institution must ensure that regulations that may infringe upon the right of free speech do not violate the First Amendment because of overbreadth or vagueness.[100]

Generally, it is not considered to be a separate student code violation for a student to remain mute in his/her hearing, as if the Fifth Amendment (applicable in criminal cases) applied. Some schools expressly give Accused Students that option. Of course, mute students give up the chance to explain their side of the story. Moreover, a violation of the Student Code may nevertheless be found based upon the other evidence presented.[101]

18. Students are required to engage in responsible social conduct that reflects

---

100. Courts have traditionally taken a dim view on the efforts of public colleges and universities to regulate the content of student speech. *See, e.g.,* Bair v. Shippensburg State Univ., 280 F. Supp. 2d 357 (M.D. Pa. 2003).

Many commentators also have called into question the efficacy of such policies in responding to underlying prejudices and bigotry. For example, Robert O'Neil, the former president of the University of Virginia who is currently professor of law at the University of Virginia and director of the Thomas Jefferson Center for the Protection of Free Expression, states:

Speech that wounds or insults or demeans by reason of gender, religion or sexual preference has no place on a university campus. In fact, such expression seems least tolerable in an academic setting, where the values of rational discourse and the quest for truth are paramount. Universities also have a special need to establish an environment hospitable to persons who have felt unwelcome there for far too long and whose very ability to learn may depend on civility and respect. Yet it is also in this setting – and for the most central educational reasons, that, in the words of the recent AAUP statement, 'no viewpoint or message may be deemed so hateful or disturbing that it may not be expressed.' And, as the statement adds, 'by proscribing ideas, a university sets an example that profoundly disserves its academic mission.' Thus, penalties or policies that might be found acceptable in the industrial workplace simply do not belong in the classroom or the laboratory, or even the dormitory or the locker room.

Robert O'Neil, *A Time To Re-Evaluate Campus Speech Codes*, CHRON. HIGHER EDUC., July 8, 1992, at A40 (internal citations omitted). *Compare.* Harvey Silverglate & Greg Lukianoff, *Speech Codes: Alive and Well at Colleges . . .*, CHRON. HIGHER EDUC., August 1, 2003, at B7 (arguing that speech codes are the rule rather than the exception in higher education) *with* Robert O'Neil, . . . *but Litigation is the Wrong Response*, CHRON. HIGHER EDUC., August 1, 2003, at B9 (arguing that the number of genuine "speech codes" is much smaller).

101. A student who exercised his choice to remain silent was, nevertheless, expelled. Mallory v. Ohio Univ., 76 Fed. Appx. 634, 634 (6th Cir. 2003). *Compare* Morale v. Grigel, 422 F. Supp. 988, 1003 (D.N.H. 1976) (finding that it was proper to draw an inference from a student's silence that he had violated the state institution's rule against drug possession), *with* SILVERGLATE & GEWOLB, *supra* note 8, at 109 (stating that no right to remain silent exists in student disciplinary process).

credit upon the [College][University] community[102] and to model good citizenship in any community.[103]

Commentary. Although it is most common to enforce negatively worded community standards, ones stated in the affirmative are permissible, too. They are used most commonly at private institutions. Endorsing the view of one commentator who urged that detailed codes of prohibition not be used in higher education, the Missouri judges noted:

The notice of the scholastic and behavioral standards to the students may be written or oral, or partly written and partly oral, but preferably written. The standards may be positive or negative in form . . . . For this reason, general affirmative statements of what is expected of a student may in some areas be preferable in higher education. Such affirmative standards may be employed, and

---

102. A rule using this language was sustained against an attack of being too vague when it was enforced, resulting in suspensions and expulsions at a public institution, Southern University in New Orleans. French v. Bashful, 303 F. Supp. 1333, 1339 (E.D. La. 1969). Some other older cases involving private institutions, which may be followed cautiously, endorse the practice of basing student discipline on religious standards. Carr v. St. John's Univ., New York, 231 N.Y.S.2d 403, 407 (N.Y. App. Div. 1962), (holding permissible rule under which students were expelled provided that "in conformity with the ideals of Christian education and conduct, the university reserves the right to dismiss a student at any time on whatever grounds the university judges advisable"), *aff'd*, 187 N.E.2d 19 (N.Y. 1962). *–See also* Denham v. Brandeis Univ., 150 F. Supp. 626, 627 (D. Mass. 1957) (holding that the university may reserve "the right to sever the connection with any student with the university for appropriate reason."). A later New York case required "procedures which are fair and reasonable and which lend themselves to a reliable determination." Kwiatkowski v. Ithaca Coll., 368 N.Y.S.2d 973 (N.Y. Sup. Ct. 1975).

103. A rule using this language was sustained against an attack by students suspended from the University of Southern Mississippi for possessing false and inflammatory literature. Speake v. Grantham, 317 F. Supp. 1253, 1270–71 (S.D. Miss. 1970). The court explained:

> An institution may establish appropriate standards of conduct, both scholastic and behavioral, in any form and manner reasonably calculated to give adequate notice to the scholastic attainments and behavior expected of the student. The notice of these standards may be written or oral, or partly written and partly oral, but preferably written and may be positive or negative in form. . . . [T]here was no confusion or unawareness on [the part of the Accused Students]. The exercise of common sense is all that was required. Each plaintiff as a reasonably intelligent college student certainly was given adequate, sufficient and reasonable notice of what he was charged with and certainly he knew what he was doing and knew the consequences thereof. Secondly, it is not sound to draw an analogy between student discipline and a criminal procedure . . . . the attempted analogy of student discipline to criminal proceedings against adults and juveniles is not sound.

Id. at 1257.

The *Speake* court took a different tack than the Seventh Circuit had a year earlier. In *Soglin v. Kauffman*, 418 F.2d 163 (7th Cir. 1969), the court ruled that the University of Wisconsin had acted unconstitutionally in sanctioning students for "misconduct" when no rules specifically defined what the university viewed as "misconduct." *Id.* at 166–67. The court ruled that while a university had the power to punish misconduct, it had to promulgate rules describing such misconduct to avoid punishing students on the basis of unconstitutionally vague, overbroad criteria. *Id.* at 167–68.

Given this difference of judicial perspectives, it would be wise to combine violation of such an affirmative expectation with a allegation that a negatively worded expectation was violated, as well.

discipline of students based thereon.[104]

C. Violation of Law and [College] [University] Discipline

1. [Alternative A]

[College] [University] disciplinary proceedings may be instituted against a student charged with conduct that potentially violates both the criminal law and this Student Code (that is, if both possible violations result from the same factual situation) without regard to the pendency of civil or criminal litigation in court or criminal arrest and prosecution. Proceedings under this Student Code may be carried out prior to,[105] simultaneously with, or following civil or criminal proceedings off campus at the discretion of [the person identified in Article I (13)]. Determinations made or sanctions imposed under this Student Code shall not be subject to change because criminal charges arising out of the same facts giving rise to violation of University rules were dismissed, reduced, or resolved in favor of or against the criminal law defendant.

[Alternative B]

If a violation of law which also would be a violation of this Student Code is alleged, proceedings under this Student Code may go forward against an Accused Student who has been subjected to criminal prosecution only if the [College] [University] determines that its interest is clearly distinct from that of the community outside the [College] [University]. Ordinarily, the [College]

---

104. *General Order*, *supra* note 2, at 146.

105. The imposition of college or university discipline need not await the outcome of other proceedings. Hart v. Ferris State Coll., 557 F. Supp. 1379, 1384–85 (W.D. Mich. 1983); Gossner v. Columbia Univ., 287 F. Supp. 535 (S.D.N.Y. 1968); Goldberg v. Univ. of Cal., 57 Cal. Rptr. 463 (Cal. Ct. App. 1967). *See generally* DeVita v. Sills, 422 F.2d 1172, 1178–1180 (3d Cir. 1970) (holding that the Fifth Amendment does not require postponement of civil proceedings whenever related criminal charges are pending). Even commentators writing to support accused students conclude, "Courts have held, however, that due process does not require campus disciplinary proceedings to be postponed until related criminal matters are settled." SILVERGLATE & GEWOLB, *supra* note 8, at 59.

When a student testifies in a campus proceeding before a criminal process takes place, the student may argue that his oral testimony to the student conduct board (and the "fruits" of it) should be excluded from a later criminal proceeding as "compelled" testimony. *Compare* Furutani v. Ewigleben, 297 F. Supp. 1163, 1164-65 (N.D. Cal. 1969) (holding that testimony from student discipline proceeding could not be used in criminal trial) *and* Garrity v. N.J., 385 U.S. 493 (1967) (holding that testimony from job investigation could not be used in criminal proceeding), *with* Nzuve v. Castleton State Coll., 335 A.2d 321, 326 (Vt. 1975) (holding that student conduct code testimony was voluntary and could be used in criminal trial) *and* Gabrilowitz v. Newman, 582 F.2d 100 (1st Cir. 1978) (allowing attorney to advise student quietly in student conduct matter to ameliorate the problem). Elizabeth L. Grossi & Terry D. Edwards, *Student Misconduct: Historical Trends in Legislative and Judicial Decision-Making in American Universities,* 23 J.C. & U.L. 829, 848 (1997) ("[W]hile the student's decision [to remain silent in the college proceeding or to participate, knowing that statements made on campus may be used in a later judicial trial] is a difficult one, it must be made. The courts refuse to require the university to delay disciplinary proceedings until completion of a criminal trial."). For a discussion of practical considerations involved when a student is charged with violations of both campus rules and the criminal law, see Capone III, *surpa* note 8, at 7–9.

[University] should not impose sanctions if public prosecution of a student is anticipated or until law enforcement officials have disposed of the case.[106]

Commentary. A college or university may take student disciplinary action before possible criminal charges arising out of the same facts are resolved. There are two basic approaches to the recurring dilemma of how a college or university should proceed when a student is accused not only of violating school regulations, but also of breaking the criminal law. Alternative A is the proactive approach, in which the institution has reserved the authority to take action under the Student Code in all such situations. A college or university may choose this approach because it does not wish to trivialize its code. To postpone the use of its disciplinary code and system of factual determinations and appeals in those cases involving criminal conduct would lead, in the words of one court, to an "absurd situation:" A student who violated a rule or regulation short of committing a crime receives immediate discipline, while a student who committed a more serious

---

106. THE UNIVERSITY OF KANSAS, YOU AND THE UNIVERSITY OF KANSAS, STUDENT HANDBOOK, 1988–89, as quoted in Douglas. R. Richmond, *Students' Right to Counsel in University Disciplinary Proceedings,* 15 J.C. & U.L. 289, 312 n.166 (1989). In the view of the authors of this Model Code a college could, of course, voluntarily adopt the policy of not imposing student discipline if the conduct might also violate a criminal law or ordinance and might be the subject of a criminal prosecution. While this would be legal, there are a number of policy issues to consider before proceeding down that path. Here are a few:

Aside from minor residence hall infractions such as violating quiet hours for studying, virtually all student discipline is based upon misconduct that does overlap with some criminal law proscription. For example, the criminal code prohibits underage alcohol use, throwing things out windows, turning in false fire alarms, stealing property, fighting, hazing, dating violence, and other types of student-on-student violence. Adopting a policy of delay whenever conduct might violate a criminal standard will prevent the school from responding promptly to virtually all misconduct that undermines a positive living/learning environment.

The criminal law process is a slow one. Deference to it would mean that campus discipline standards would go unresolved for a long period of time. Worse, the criminal law often reaches no resolution at all because witnesses move away (or graduate) or become discouraged by the repeated delays or by the discomfort of being "put on trial" by criminal defense counsel. Thus, delay pending the completion of criminal processes is unlikely to result in prompt reinforcement of living/learning standards on campus. To the contrary, delay in enforcing the college's rules may mean that no one deals with the behavior, ever.

. . . .

Prompt response to campus misconduct reinforces our values and delay does not. Deferral to criminal law process does not create campus conduct standards that support a quality living/learning environment. Instead, delay creates standards that mimic the environment in the society at large, and the quality of life on campus will suffer by being reduced to "the law of the street." By contrast, prompt response to campus misconduct helps to convince students that the institution is, indeed, committed to creating a quality environment for them. On every campus in this country, student leaders and student affairs professionals urge student victims of dating violence to come forward.

Edward N. Stoner, *Reviewing Your Student Discipline Policy: A Project Worth The Investment,* 9–10 (2000), *available at* http://www.nacua.org/publications/pubs/pamphlets/StudentDiscipline-Policy.pdf.

offense is entitled to attend school without immediate disciplinary action.[107] *Alternative B illustrates the other approach. Although such an approach is not often admitted explicitly, it is not uncommon in practice. It does, however, lead to a Student Code which deals only with minor offenses. The authors recommend Alternative A.*

2.   When a student is charged by federal, state, or local authorities with a violation of law, the [College] [University] will not request or agree to special consideration for that individual because of his or her status as a student. If the alleged offense is also being processed under the Student Code, the [College] [University] may advise off-campus authorities of the existence of the Student Code and of how such matters are typically handled within the [College] [University] community. The [College] [University] will attempt to cooperate with law enforcement and other agencies in the enforcement of criminal law on campus and in the conditions imposed by criminal courts for the rehabilitation of student violators (provided that the conditions do not conflict with campus rules or sanctions). Individual students and other members of the [College] [University] community, acting in their personal capacities, remain free to interact with governmental representatives as they deem appropriate.

Commentary. It is important to establish a solid relationship with the local prosecuting attorney in anticipation of such situations. The prosecuting attorney should be educated about the institution's student code and the general philosophy regarding discipline. By doing this, the institution may better coordinate its efforts with that of the prosecuting attorney when a disciplinary problem overlapping criminal charges arises. In addition, the prosecuting attorney who understands that the college or university will handle matters appropriately may choose instead to allow the institution to handle the situation. Finally, familiarizing the prosecuting attorney with the student code before an incident arises helps to avoid misunderstandings and media errors when an incident arises.

This area requires a delicate balance, good judgment, and an appreciation of the separate rules of student discipline and law enforcement. College and university officials must take care not to attempt, or appear to attempt, to influence prosecutorial decision making. This is the same balance followed by law enforcement when they avoid suggesting to college and university officials when or how to proceed in enforcing campus rules or what campus sanctions to impose. Although the campus and criminal systems must remain distinct, with neither dictating to the other, it is nevertheless important to have a clear line of communications. In addition, college officials must take care not to discourage or to appear to discourage the student "victim" from pursuing criminal charges.[108]

---

107.   *See* Johnson v. Bd. of Educ., 310 N.Y.S.2d 429 (N.Y. Sup. Ct. 1970).

108.   Claims that victims of sexual assault were discouraged from reporting to authorities are common. *E.g.,* Catherine Lucey, *Group Asks State to Investigate Handling of Rape Allegation at LaSalle,* MONTEREY HERALD, June 29, 2004, *available at* http://www.montereyherald.com/mld/ montereyherald/sports/9035385.htm. The Jeanne Clery Disclosure of Campus Security Policy

In addition to working with the prosecuting attorney, the college or university attorney should establish a relationship with the attorney(s) for the Accused Student or for a student who feels s/he has been a victim of another student's conduct. This is important because the college or university attorney can help the outside attorney make an informed decision as to how his/her client will interact with the student code system. For example, if the Accused Student is found to have violated college or university rules, sanctions will be imposed and law enforcement may decide, at their discretion, to take these sanctions into account in making prosecutorial decisions. Campus sanctions most likely will be different than criminal sanctions. Complainants who feel vindicated and satisfied with the result of the institutional disciplinary hearing may be inclined to drop the criminal charges. In any case, the institution's representative must be mindful of trying to provide a process that reinforces campus values and that is fair for both the student who has alleged a violation of the Student Code and the alleged violator.

ARTICLE IV: STUDENT CONDUCT CODE PROCEDURES

A. Charges and Student Conduct Board Hearings

1. Any member of the [College] [University] community may file charges against a student for violations of the Student Code. A charge shall be prepared in writing and directed to the Student Conduct Administrator. Any charge should be submitted as soon as possible after the event takes place, preferably within [specify time period].

Commentary. This section not only describes who may file charges, but also requires that such charges be in writing and that they all be submitted to the same person. Such measures are desirable because: (1) they ensure that college or university officials can immediately assess the gravity of each complaint; and (2) they help to provide notice in an orderly fashion.[109] The use of a standard form for charges will ensure the receipt of all the necessary information.

Practice varies widely concerning the time in which charges may be presented. For example, at Westminster College, Complainants are asked to file charges within forty-eight (48) hours.[110] At Pratt Institute, charges of discriminatory treatment must be submitted within twenty-eight (28) days of the date the Complainant first attempted to resolve the matter, which must be done within

---

and Campus Crime Statistics Act requires that the Annual Security Report include "[i]nforming students of their options to notify proper law enforcement authorities, including on-campus and local police, and the option to be assisted by campus authorities in notifying such authorities, if the student so chooses." 20 U.S.C. §1092(f)(8)(v) (2000). *See also* 34 C.F.R. § 668.46 (2004) (providing further guidance on obligations of an institution).

109. *See* Dutile, *supra* note 8; Grier & Stoner, *supra* note 8. James M. Picozzi, *University Disciplinary Process: What's Fair, What's Due, and What You Don't Get*, 96 YALE L.J. 2132, 2157 n.107 (1987).

110. *See, e.g.,* OFFICE OF STUDENT AFFAIRS, WESTMINSTER COLLEGE, STUDENT HANDBOOK BULLETIN 14 (1989–90) (on file with author).

ninety (90) days of the incident.[111] *At Northwestern University, Complainants have one year during which to file charges.*[112] *Finally, Indiana University's Code of Student Rights, Responsibilities, and Conduct contains no "statute of limitations" period at all.*[113] *The key, however, is to provide a flexible guideline, so that student victims will come forward even if they are "late" in doing so.*

2. The Student Conduct Administrator may conduct an investigation to determine if the charges have merit and/or if they can be disposed of administratively by mutual consent of the parties involved on a basis acceptable to the Student Conduct Administrator. Such disposition shall be final and there shall be no subsequent proceedings. If the charges are not admitted and/or cannot be disposed of by mutual consent, the Student Conduct Administrator may later serve in the same matter as the Student Conduct Board or a member thereof. If the student admits violating institutional rules, but sanctions are not agreed to, subsequent process, including a hearing if necessary, shall be limited to determining the appropriate sanction(s).

Commentary. As noted previously,[114] *courts have recognized that it is not easy in the college and university setting to ensure that the participants in the disciplinary process have not had prior contact with the student(s) involved or prior knowledge of the events which are the subject of the proceeding. Where staffing permits, it is preferable to separate the administrative and mediation*[115] *functions from the fact finding and sanctioning functions.*

3. All charges shall be presented to the Accused Student in written form. A time shall be set for a Student Conduct Board Hearing, not less than five nor more than fifteen calendar days after the student has been notified. Maximum time limits for scheduling of Student Conduct Board Hearings may be extended at the discretion of the Student Conduct Administrator.

Commentary. Notice and an opportunity to be heard are essential to all student disciplinary proceedings, at least in the public college and university settings.[116]

---

111. PRATT INSTITUTE NON-DISCRIMINATION GRIEVANCE PROCEDURES 1-2 (on file with author).

112. NORTHWESTERN UNIV., OFFENSES AND HEARING PROCEDURES 24 (on file with author).

113. IND. UNIV., CODE OF STUDENT RIGHTS, RESPONSIBILITIES, AND CONDUCT, *available at* http://www.dsa.indiana.edu/Code (last visited Oct. 12, 2004).

114. *See supra* notes 68–69 and accompanying text.

115. *See, e.g.,* Eugene L. Zdziarski, *Alternative Dispute Resolution: A New Look at Resolving Campus Conflict, in* THE ADMINISTRATION OF CAMPUS DISCIPLINE: STUDENT, ORGANIZATIONAL AND COMMUNITY ISSUES 237–252 (Brent G. Paterson & William L. Kibler eds., 1998). The Association for Student Judicial Affairs sponsors tracks of introductory and advanced mediator training at its annual Donald D. Gehring Institute. *See* ASS'N FOR STUDENT JUDICIAL AFFAIRS, *at* http://asja.tamu.edu (last visited Oct 12, 2004).

116. Goss v. Lopez, 419 U.S. 565 (1975); Dixon v. Ala. Bd. of Educ., 294 F.2d 150 (5th Cir. 1961).

Requiring that the Accused Student receive written notice of the charge ensures that the Accused Student receives adequate notice of the alleged violations. Such notice should be "reasonably calculated, under all the circumstances, to apprise interested parties of the pendency of the action and afford them an opportunity to present their objections."[117]

Further, there is no bright-line rule governing how far in advance of a Student Conduct Board Hearing notice should be given.[118] Indeed, some courts have indicated that notice of charges may be given at the same time the student has an opportunity to defend against those charges at least in less serious cases.[119] Nevertheless, it seems fairer to give some reasonable amount of time to allow an Accused Student to prepare. The institution must, however, be sure to follow its own rules once it establishes an amount of time which is to pass between notice and the Student Conduct Board Hearing.[120]

Granting the Student Conduct Administrator discretion to extend the maximum time limits permits the institution flexibility in cases in which examination periods, breaks, holidays, and other occurrences disrupt the time at which Student Conduct Board Hearings would otherwise be scheduled. Some institutions may wish to deal with break and/or holiday issues more explicitly by providing in their codes for dates certain to be used in such situations. For example, a college or university may wish to provide that, in cases in which an examination period or break intervenes between the time of notice and the Student Conduct Board Hearing date, such hearings always will be held during the first week in which classes are again in session.

4. Student Conduct Board Hearings[121] shall be conducted by a Student Conduct Board according to the following guidelines except as provided by article IV(A)(7) below:

    a. Student Conduct Board Hearings normally shall be conducted in private.[122]

---

117.   Memphis Light, Gas & Water Div. v. Craft, 436 U.S. 1, 13 (1978) (quoting Mullane v. Cent. Hanover Trust Co., 339 U.S. 306, 314 (1950)). The court in *Goss v. Ala. Bd. of Educ.,* stated that the student must be told "what he is accused of doing and what the basis of the accusation is." 419 U.S. at 582. The court in *Dixon* required "a statement of the specific charges and grounds." 294 F.2d at 158.

118.   *See* Nash v. Auburn Univ., 812 F.2d 655, 661 (11th Cir. 1987).

119.   *Goss,* 419 U.S. at 582.

120.   *See supra* notes 33–34.

121.   The guidance of the Supreme Court in *Goss* was that "there be at least an informal give-and-take between student and disciplinarian." 419 U.S. at 584.

122.   Fact finding in student discipline matters is rarely done in public. Disciplinary records are education records covered by the Family Educational Rights and Privacy Act of 1974, 20 U.S.C.A. § 1232g (2000 & West Supp. 2004) [hereinafter FERPA]. United States v. Miami Univ., 294 F.3d 797 (6th Cir. 2002). Dr. William Bracewell, former director of Judicial Programs at the University of Georgia, described some of problems with open hearings at that institution:

The *Red & Black* decision [Red & Black Publishing Co. v. Board of Regents, 427 S.E.2d 257 (Ga. 1993)] has produced two significant results. First, complaining parties do not wish to participate in a hearing. The individuals report incidents to the

    b.   The Complainant, Accused Student and their advisors,[123] if any, shall be allowed to attend the entire portion of the Student Conduct Board Hearing at which information is received (excluding deliberations).[124] Admission of any other person to the Student Conduct Board Hearing shall be at the discretion of the Student Conduct Board and/or its Student Conduct Administrator.[125]

    c.   In Student Conduct Board Hearings involving more than one Accused Student, the Student Conduct Administrator, in his or her discretion, may permit the Student Conduct Board Hearings concerning each student to be conducted either separately or jointly.

    d.   The Complainant and the Accused Student have the right to be assisted by an advisor they choose, at their own expense. The advisor[126] must be a

---

university, but when told that the matter needs to be referred to a hearing they decline to pursue it. Without their participation, the university can not meet its obligation of showing with clear and convincing proof whether a university rule was violated.

    Second, those hearings which are held are shallow. Members of the hearing panel or the administrative hearing officer are reluctant to ask questions which might expose a personal matter, for fear it will be printed in the paper. Many of the details which give context to the incident and lead to sound decisions in terms of student development are not discussed.

    The university continues to work to find ways to respond to student misconduct in a way that is educational and fair. The presence of undergraduate student reporters makes this task very difficult.

John Wesley Lowery, *The Family Educational Rights and Privacy Act and Student Disciplinary Records*, 6 SYNTHESIS 464, 465 (1995).

    Under 1998 FERPA amendments, institutions may release the final results of the disciplinary process including the name, violations of institutional rules, and sanctions imposed, for students found responsible for violating campus rules that correspond to the criminal offenses of arson, assault and battery, burglary, destruction/damage/vandalism of property, criminal homicide-manslaughter by negligence, criminal homicide-murder and non-negligent manslaughter, forcible and nonforcible sex offenses, kidnapping/abduction, and robbery. *See* 34 C.F.R. § 99.39 (2004). *See also* 34 C.F.R. pt. 99, app. A (providing definitions of the stated offenses).

    123.   The Jeanne Clery Disclosure of Campus Security Policy and Campus Crime Statistics Act provides that an alleged sexual assault victim and an Accused Student have the same rights to have others present at the Student Conduct Board Hearing. 20 U.S.C. § 1092(f)(8)(B)(iv)(I) (2000).

    124.   If a Student Conduct Board visits the location of an alleged violation, the Accused Student, Complainant and their advisors should be allowed to participate. Univ. of Tex. Med. Sch. at Houston v. Than, 901 S.W.2d 926, 932 (Tex. 1995). In *Than*, an ex parte visit to the classroom site of a cheating allegation which was attended by a hearing officer and the person advocating violation of rules but excluding the Accused Student violated a Texas constitutional guarantee of due course of law and new hearing was ordered. *Id.*

Similarly, an Accused Student should be allowed to make his/her presentation to the person or entire group of persons who are to decide the matter if credibility is an issue. *E.g.*, Esteban v. Cent. Mo. State Coll., 277 F. Supp. 649, 651 (W.D. Mo. 1967) (ordering that a new hearing before the entire board be held when students were allowed to present to only one person of a group that recommended suspension).

    125.   Normally, other witnesses are permitted to attend the Student Conduct Board Hearing only when they are providing information.

    126.   One court quoted with approval former Princeton President Dr. William G. Bowen's explanation about the roles of an advisor:

member of the [College][University] community[127] and may not be an attorney.[128] The Complainant and/or the Accused Student is responsible for presenting his or her own information, and therefore, advisors are not permitted to speak or to participate directly in any Student Conduct Board

---

The University is an institution which proceeds very much on the basis of freely given cooperation, and . . . with a very limited set of punishments . . . for being sure that conduct stays within certain specified bounds. There are, of course, rules and regulations of a general kind that we do our best to uphold. But we do not have a whole set of arrangements concerning perjury or whatever that guide and protect the proceedings of a court of law . . . . And since we do not have that whole panoply of protections . . . or means of enforcing those guidelines, we do expect advisers who are meant to be peers and not meant to be attorneys, to be direct and clear, helpful [and] not deliberately misleading in their relationship to the Committee and to the University.

Clayton v. Princeton Univ., 608 F. Supp. 413, 439 (D.N.J. 1985).

127. The rule that a student facing dismissal could be assisted "by an advisor of his choice who is a member of the University community" but not by legal counsel complies with minimal procedural due process at a public institution. Garshman v. Pa. State Univ., 395 F. Supp. 912, 914 (M.D. Pa. 1975). The court stated: "Judicial reluctance to force the inclusion of a non-University individual into this delicate decision-making process should be that much greater where, as here, the procedures involve elaborate efforts to insure that a fair result is reached." *Id.* at 921.

128. An institution concerned about the interaction with a subsequent pending parallel criminal matter could add a sentence at the end to provide: "If an Accused Student is also the subject of a pending subsequent criminal matter arising out of the same circumstances, s/he may be allowed to have an attorney serve as his/her advisor, at his/her own expense, to behave in the same manner as any other advisor."

Some institutions reach a different conclusion and allow the participation of attorneys on the same basis as other advisors. If that choice is made, the language may read:

The Complainant and the Accused Student have the right to be assisted by any advisor they choose, at their own expense. The advisor may be an attorney. The Complainant and/or the Accused Student is responsible for presenting his or her own information and, therefore, advisors are not permitted to speak or to participate directly in any Hearings before a student conduct board.

A university process was approved as complying with procedural due process at a public institution in which an attorney was allowed "to advise his clients during the hearing, but he was not permitted to participate in the proceedings." Nash v. Auburn Univ., 812 F.2d 655, 658 (11th Cir. 1987).

As noted in the commentary immediately below, there is no requirement to allow either the presence or participation of attorneys, except in a few circumstances in some jurisdictions at public institutions. In a male/male sexual conduct case resulting in expulsion at a public institution, the court denied a student's claim that he was denied procedural due process when he was allowed to have the assistance of a second year law student but not his own private attorney:

We first address plaintiff's contention that he was denied procedural due process because he was not permitted to have a private attorney represent him at the disciplinary hearing. . . . Plaintiff does not appear to contend, however, that he had a constitutional right to be represented by a private attorney at the hearing. In any event, such an argument is without merit. The consensus of the courts of appeal that have directly addressed the issue is that a university student has no constitutional right to counsel at a university disciplinary hearing. Although the Court of Appeals for the Third Circuit has not addressed the issue, there is no reason to believe that it would reach a different result on similar facts.

Woodard v. Univ. of Pittsburgh, No. 95-1299, at 4–5 (W.D. Pa. 1995) (internal citations omitted).

Hearing before a Student Conduct Board. A student should select as an advisor a person whose schedule allows attendance at the scheduled date and time for the Student Conduct Board Hearing because delays will not normally be allowed due to the scheduling conflicts of an advisor.[129]

e. The Complainant, the Accused Student and the Student Conduct Board may arrange for witnesses to present pertinent information to the Student Conduct Board. The [College][University] will try to arrange the attendance of possible witnesses who are members of the [College][University] community, if reasonably possible, and who are identified by the Complainant and/or Accused Student at least two weekdays prior to the Student Conduct Board Hearing.[130] Witnesses will provide information to and answer questions from the Student Conduct Board. Questions may be suggested by the Accused Student and/or Complainant to be answered by each other or by other witnesses.[131] This will be conducted by the Student Conduct Board with such questions directed to the chairperson, rather than to the witness directly. This method is used to preserve the educational tone of the hearing and to avoid creation of an adversarial environment. Questions of whether potential information will be received shall be resolved in the discretion of the chairperson of the Student Conduct Board.

f. Pertinent records, exhibits, and written statements (including Student Impact Statements) may be accepted as information for consideration by a Student Conduct Board at the discretion of the chairperson.

g. All procedural questions are subject to the final decision of the chairperson of the Student Conduct Board.[132]

---

129. Unfortunately, some advisors (particularly attorneys) try to delay the student discipline process by contending that their "other commitments," personal and professional, conflict with the dates scheduled, even though they are not participants in the process. It is a bad practice to allow such manipulation. For another view, see Pavela, *supra* note 8, at 825. If you do accommodate conflicts of advisors' schedules, be careful, in cases involving a student who feels s/he has been victimized by another, to consider the scheduling conflicts of the advisors of both students.

130. While there is no constitutional requirement for this offer to arrange the attendance of witnesses, it is common practice. One court noted that a college could not do more. Hart v. Ferris State Coll., 557 F. Supp. 1379, 1389 (W.D. Mich. 1983) ("It is not clear how the College could be required to compel the attendance of witnesses over whom it has no power by subpoena or otherwise.").

131. This method of "cross-examination" was specifically approved by the Court of Appeals for the Eleventh Circuit. In a case of two students who had been suspended from a public institution, the court ruled that "there was no denial of appellants' constitutional rights to due process by their inability to question the adverse witnesses in the usual, adversarial manner." Nash v. Auburn Univ., 812 F.2d 655, 664 (11th Cir. 1987). Similarly, a court approved a process in which a student submitted a written statement, followed by a roundtable discussion. "The Constitution does not confer on plaintiff the right to cross-examine his accuser in a school disciplinary proceeding." Jaksa v. Univ. of Mich., 597 F. Supp. 1245, 1252 (E.D. Mich. 1984), *aff'd per curiam*, 787 F.2d 590 (6th Cir. 1986). "[A] student charged in a disciplinary process has no right to call or cross-examine witness[es] as long as the student has a full opportunity to defend herself or explain her position." Grier & Stoner, *supra* note 8, at 7.

132. The chair can set a good tone for the fact finding process and it is a normal expectation that s/he will do so. In *Henderson State Univ. v. Spadoni*, S.W.2d 951, 954 (Ark. Ct. App. 1993),

h. After the portion of the Student Conduct Board Hearing concludes in which all pertinent information has been received, the Student Conduct Board shall determine (by majority vote if the Student Conduct Board consists of more than one person) whether the Accused Student has violated each section of the Student Code which the student is charged with violating.

i. The Student Conduct Board's determination shall be made on the basis of whether it is more likely than not that the Accused Student violated the Student Code.

j. Formal rules of process, procedure, and/or technical rules of evidence, such as are applied in criminal or civil court, are not used in Student Code proceedings.[133]

Commentary. The law requires no particular form of hearing.[134] For two reasons, however, the institution should establish guidelines pursuant to which hearings are to be conducted. First, doing so will ensure that the institution treats students accused of misconduct evenhandedly. That is, a college or university can feel safe in knowing that, as long as the student disciplinary board follows the procedures set forth in its code, each Accused Student will receive the same treatment. Thus, there is less opportunity for any student to complain of unequal treatment. Second, establishing such guidelines in advance will avoid ad hoc decisions on many difficult issues.

This compendium of hearing guidelines incorporates the following legal principles: the hearing need not be open to the public,[135] and neither the Federal Rules of Evidence nor any state's rules of evidence apply in student disciplinary proceedings.[136]

---

the court upheld the chair's actions to run an orderly hearing, noting "that [the Accused Student's] witnesses were required to testify in response to questions instead of being permitted to tell whatever they wanted to say, but this is normal procedure even in a judicial proceeding."

133. It is wise to include an express statement such as this within the body of the Student Code so that no one has an expectation that such formalistic legal rules are pertinent. This rule is not a new one. Esteban v. Cent. Mo. State Coll., 415 F.2d 1077 (8th Cir. 1969). Recent cases approve of such express statements. Schaer v. Brandeis Univ., 735 N.E.2d 373, 380 n. 15 (Mass. 2000):

> Although these statements would be excluded from a courtroom under the rules of evidence, a university is not required to abide by the same rules. Brandeis may choose to admit all statements by every witness or it may choose to exclude some evidence. It is not the business of lawyers and judges to tell universities what statements they may consider and what statements they must reject.

134. Goss v. Lopez, 419 U.S. 565, 583–84 (1975); Dixon v. Ala. State Bd. of Educ., 294 F.2d 150, 158–59 (5th Cir. 1961).

135. Hart v. Ferris State Coll., 557 F. Supp. 1379, 1389 (W.D. Mich. 1983).

136. *Nash*, 812 F.2d at 665 (11th Cir. 1987) (holding that "student disciplinary hearings follow flexible rules and need not conform to formal rules of evidence"); Boykins v. Fairchild Bd. of Educ., 492 F.2d 697, 701 (5th Cir. 1974). Indeed, one court noted that the absence of "complex rules of evidence or procedure" in the student discipline hearing helped to explain why the Accused Student was not entitled to any representative to be with him, whether an attorney or lay advisor. Jaksa v. Univ. of Mich., 597 F. Supp. 1245, 1252 (E.D. Mich. 1984), *aff'd per curiam*, 787 F.2d 590 (6th Cir. 1986); Wasson v. Trowbridge, 382 F.2d 807, 812 (2d Cir. 1967)

Third, a student has no right to be represented by an attorney in the adversarial manner in which attorneys represent clients in judicial proceedings, at student disciplinary hearings at private institutions,[137] *and in most proceedings at public institutions, even including public K-12 schools at which, unlike public colleges, attendance is mandatory.*[138]

(describing a process that resulted in a student's expulsion from the Merchant Marine Academy, the Court stated that "[t]he hearing may be procedurally informal and need not be adversarial."), *rev'd on other grounds*, 269 F. Supp. 900 (E.D.N.Y. 1967).

137.   Ahlum v. Adm'rs of Tulane Educ. Fund, 617 So.2d 96 (La. Ct. App. 1993) (holding that there was no right to counsel in a sexual assault rules violation hearing resulting in suspension).

> Again it must be noted that the standards of due process imposed upon a public institution do not apply to a private actor. Thus, Tulane, as a private actor is not required to abide by the United States Supreme Court pronouncements of what process is due to students of public educational facilities.

Id. at 99 n.1.

138.   *Compare* Goss v. Lopez, 419 U.S. 565 (1975) (holding that in K–12 setting, short suspensions include no right to counsel) *and General Order*, *supra* note 2, at 147 *and* Madera v. Bd. of Educ., 386 F.2d 778, 788–89 (2d Cir. 1967) (holding that even in public seventh grade, no right to counsel in superintendent's process that resulted in suspension: "Law and order in the classroom should be the responsibility of our respective educational systems. The courts should not usurp this function and turn disciplinary problems, involving suspension, into criminal adversary proceedings--which they definitely are not."), *and* Brown v. W. Conn. State Univ., 204 F. Supp. 2d 355 (D. Conn. 2002) (holding that there is no constitutional right to counsel), *and* Fedorov v. Univ. of Ga., 194 F. Supp. 2d 1378, 1393 (S.D. Ga. 2002) (holding that although student was prohibited from having an attorney, university "exceeded" due process requirements), *and* Everett v. Marcase, 426 F. Supp. 397 (E.D. Pa. 1977) (holding that there is no right to counsel in K–12 disciplinary setting), *and* Wasson v. Trowbridge, 382 F.2d 807, 812 (2d Cir. 1967) (stating that there was no right to counsel at Merchant Marine Academy disciplinary hearing resulting in expulsion) ("[T]he proceeding is non-criminal in nature, . . . the hearing is investigative and not adversarial and the government does not proceed through counsel"), *rev'd on other grounds*, 269 F. Supp. 900 (E.D.N.Y. 1967), *and* Haley v. Va. Comm. Univ., 948 F. Supp. 573, 582 (E.D. Va. 1996); *and* Woodard v. Univ. of Pittsburgh, No. 95-1299, at 4–5 (W.D. Pa. 1995) (declaring that attorney need not be permitted at public university at hearing resulting in expulsion), *and* Jaksa v. Univ. of Mich., 597 F. Supp. 1245, 1251–52 (E.D. Mich. 1984) (declaring that student was not entitled to have *any* representative with him at disciplinary hearing resulting in one semester suspension, whether representative was an attorney or a lay person, the court noted that "there was nothing mysterious about the Academic Judiciary procedures" and that "[t]he Manual of Procedures for the Academic Judiciary is written in plain English, and is comprehensible to the average college student."), *aff'd per curiam*, 787 F.2d 590 (6th Cir. 1986), *and* Bleicker v. Ohio State Univ., Coll. of Veterinary Med., 485 F. Supp. 1381, 1387–88 (S.D. Ohio.1980), *and* Haynes v. Dallas County Jr. Coll. Dist., 386 F. Supp. 208, 211–12 (N.D. Tex. 1974), *and* Barker v. Hardway, 283 F. Supp. 228, 236–38 (S.D. W.Va. 1968) (holding that students disciplinarily suspended from Bluefield State College had no right counsel in discipline hearing), *and* Due v. Fla. A&M Univ., 233 F. Supp. 396, 402 (N.D. Fla. 1961) (holding that students convicted of criminal contempt had no right to counsel in student disciplinary hearing in which they were suspended for "misconduct"), *with* Marin v. Univ. of P.R., 377 F. Supp. 613, 623–24 (D.P.R. 1974) (holding that when institution imposed suspension without notice or hearing, court's remedy included allowing students to have the "assistance" of their retained attorney "if his or her attendance does not unduly delay the hearing."), *and* French v. Bashful, 303 F. Supp. 1333, 1337 (E.D. La. 1969) (stating that a new hearing was required where Southern University at New Orleans, a public university, had process in which "prosecution" was done by third year law student "chosen to prosecute because of his familiarity with legal proceedings" and student was refused participation of his attorney but the court refused to require University to pay for student's attorney).

There are two exceptions to this rule that are applicable to public institutions. First, a public institution's disciplinary board may be considered a state agency in some situations. Being deemed a state agency may bring into play certain state administrative agency laws, which may allow full courtroom-like representation by an attorney.[139] *Thus, as always, one must consider the requirements of state law. Second, if parallel criminal charges are pending,*[140] *some courts have required a*

---

139. *Compare* Kusnir v. Leach, 439 A.2d 223, 226–27 (Pa. 1982) (holding that Clarion State College was a commonwealth agency under state law), *and* Mull v. Or. Inst. of Tech., 538 P.2d 87 (Or. 1975) (applying state administrative procedures act to suspension for misconduct and remanding for statement of findings of fact and conclusions of law), *with* Mary M. v. Clark, 473 N.Y.S.2d 843 (N.Y. App. Div. 1984) (refusing to apply New York administrative procedure act to disciplinary suspension).

140. *See, e.g.,* Gabrilowitz v. Newman, 582 F.2d 100, 106 (1st Cir. 1978) (involving student who was also facing criminal charge of assault with intent to commit rape of another student). The Court of Appeals noted, that the student had not requested that the University of Rhode Island delay its process until after the criminal trial and emphasized that there was no constitutional right to counsel in the discipline proceeding per se, but only to advise about the pending criminal case. *Id.* at 105, 106 n.6. It added:

> Counsel would be present only to safeguard appellee's rights at the criminal proceeding, not to affect the outcome of the disciplinary hearing. Counsel's principal function would be to advise appellee whether he should answer questions and what he should not say so as to safeguard appellee from self-incrimination, and to observe the proceeding first-hand so as to be better prepared to deal with attempts to introduce evidence from the hearing at a later criminal proceeding. To fulfill these functions, counsel need speak to no one but appellee.

Id. at 106.

The Seventh Circuit disagreed with the First Circuit's decision in *Gabrilowitz*, siding instead with the dissenter in *Gabrilowitz* who had noted that the Supreme Court had rejected the argument that prisoners were entitled to the advice of counsel in prisoner disciplinary proceedings in *Baxter v. Palmingiano,*. Osteen v. Henley, 13 F.3d 221, 225–26 (7th Cir. 1993) (internal citations omitted). The court explained:

> Even if a student has a constitutional right to *consult* with counsel—an issue not foreclosed by *Baxter,* as we shall see—we do not think he is entitled to be represented in the sense of having a lawyer who is permitted to examine or cross-examine witnesses, to submit and object to documents, to address the tribunal, and otherwise to perform the traditional functions of a trial lawyer. To recognize such a right would force student disciplinary proceedings into the mold of adversary litigation. The university would have to hire its own lawyer to prosecute these cases and no doubt lawyers would also be dragged in—from the law faculty or elsewhere—to serve as judges. The cost and complexity of such proceedings would be increased, to the detriment of discipline as well as of the university's fisc. Concern is frequently voiced about the bureaucratization of education, reflected for example in the high ratio of administrative personnel to faculty at all levels of American education today. We are reluctant to encourage bureaucratization by judicializing university disciplinary proceedings, mindful also that one dimension of academic freedom is the right of academic institutions to operate free of heavy-handed governmental, including judicial, interference.

Id. at 225 (emphasis in original).

Compare Wimmer v. Lehman, 705 F.2d 1402, 1404 (4th Cir. 1983) (deciding that when parallel criminal prosecution was pending, due process requirements of *Gabrilowitz* were met when the student "could have counsel present to advise him with respect to safeguarding his interests regarding his pending state criminal trial, but that in all other respects he must conduct his own defense."), *and* Hart v. Ferris State Coll., 557 F. Supp. 1379, 1386–88 (W.D. Mich. 1983)

public college or university to permit the student to have his/her own attorney present. [141] *Even in these cases, however, the attorney may be restricted to the same quiet advisory role served by non-attorney advisors.* [142]

It is not required that either students or their advisor be given the opportunity to cross-examine witnesses directly. Cross-examination by or through the Student Conduct Board, as suggested in the appended model Student Conduct Board Hearing script, is sufficient at the college and university level. [143]

It is rare that college or university counsel take part in student conduct hearings, [144] *although they often attend to make sure that other attorneys attending as advisors behave properly.*

A college or university may wish to institute either an arbitration or a mediation requirement prior to reaching the more formal Student Conduct Board Hearing

---

(holding that with parallel criminal matter pending, attorney's role was as a consultant, but not as participant, complies with due process), *with* Gorman v. Univ. of R.I., 837 F.2d 7, 16 (1st Cir. 1988) (finding that there is no right to counsel in case where no criminal charges were pending).

141.   Esteban v. Cent. Mo. State Coll., 277 F. Supp. 649, 651–52 (W.D. Mo. 1967) (holding that counsel for suspended students could be present at hearing "to advise them" and students "not their attorney" could ask questions of witnesses). Interestingly, the *General Order, supra* note 2, at 147 states: "There is no general requirement that procedural due process in student disciplinary cases provide for legal representation . . . ."

142.   In *Donohue v. Baker*, 976 F. Supp. 136, 146 (N.D.N.Y. 1997), a student at the State University of New York at Cobleskill College had been accused both of the felony of rape and violating university rules. He challenged not being allowed to be represented by an attorney in the university proceeding, citing *Gabrilowitz*. *Id.* He had not, however, limited his request to having his attorney sit quietly and advise him only about the interplay with his criminal matter. This, the court held, meant he had no right to an attorney at all, even under *Gabrilowtiz*. *Id.* "Plaintiff thus claims that he was denied due process because the defendants prevented him from using his attorney as a sword to challenge [his accuser's] credibility, rather than as a shield to protect his Fifth Amendment rights. . . . [This] did not infringe upon his due process rights." *Id.*

143.   Roach v. Univ. of Utah, 968 F. Supp. 1446, 1452 (D. Utah 1997) (finding no due process violation applying *Dixon* when student was not allowed to cross-examine or hear witnesses but was allowed to present his side); Reilly v. Daly, 666 N.E.2d 439, 444 (Ind. Ct. App. 1996) (holding that student dismissed from Indiana University Medical School for cheating was not denied due process when conduct board read a transcript of her meeting with accusing professors but the professors were not present for her to cross-examine at the hearing itself, with Court noting, "[W]here basic fairness is preserved a student subject to dismissal for disciplinary reasons is not entitled to formal cross-examination of her accusers."); Nash v. Auburn Univ., 812 F.2d 655, 664 (11th Cir. 1987) (holding that Accused Students' ability to submit questions to the disciplinary board, to be asked of the witnesses, rather than direct cross-examination, was sufficient); Univ. of Houston v. Sabeti, 676 S.W.2d 685, 689 (Tex. Ct. App. 1984) (holding that a student expelled from public institution was afforded procedural due process when he was allowed to submit questions for other witnesses to the hearing officer, who then asked some, but not all, of the questions, because "a form of cross-examination was allowed"); Wimmer v. Lehman, 705 F.2d 1402, 1404 (4th Cir. 1983) (denying any requirement that attorney be allowed to do cross-examination rather than the student); Hart v. Ferris State Coll., 557 F. Supp. 1379, 1386–87 (W.D. Mich. 1983) (holding that the probable value of cross-examination by student's counsel is minimal compared to significant burden it would impose); Gorman v. Univ. of R.I., 837 F.2d 7, 16 (1st Cir. 1988) (holding that the right to unlimited cross-examination is not an essential requirement of due process).

144.   *See* George M. Shur, *The Role of University/College Counsel at Student Disciplinary Proceedings,* 3rd Annual Conf. of the Ass'n for Student Judicial Affairs (1991) (on file with author).

stage. Such an option is acceptable because the concept of due process is flexible, requiring no more than is necessary to provide fair notice and an opportunity to be heard. In other words, in some cases a formal fact finding process is not required; an informal meeting between the students involved and college or university administrators suffices, as long as Accused Students are informed of the charges and given an opportunity to tell their side of the story.

Other schools may not want to require such an initial meeting because such meetings could consume all of the administrator's time with little benefit. Local experience will dictate whether it is effective to attempt to resolve alleged Student Code violations through such a meeting, although the most common practice is to emphasize efforts at mediation or other informal resolution.

This Model Student Code advocates using a "more likely than not" or "preponderance of the evidence" standard for disciplinary decision making. This is because the "beyond a reasonable doubt" standard applied in criminal cases is too demanding for college and university disciplinary proceedings.[145] After all, criminal law standards were never intended to be standards for student behavior within an academic community. Some codes use a "clear and convincing" standard, but such a standard is not as common, nor is it required by law.[146] The use of the "more likely than not" standard is normal for important civil judicial proceedings.[147] More importantly, it reflects the difference between college and

---

145.   Sill v. Pa. State Univ., 462 F.2d 463, 467 (3d Cir. 1972); *Speake v. Grantham*, 317 F. Supp. 1253, 1281–82 (S.D. Miss. 1970); Jones v. State Bd. of Educ., 407 F.2d 834, 836 (6th Cir. 1969); *Keene v. Rodgers*, 316 F. Supp. 217, 221(D. Me. 1970); *Esteban*, 415 F.2d 1077, 1088–90 (8th Cir. 1969). *See also* Nicholas Trott Long, *The Standard of Proof in Student Disciplinary Cases,* 12 J.C. & U.L. 71, 81 (1985) ("No court will require school discipline to rest on 'proof beyond a reasonable doubt'. . . .").

146.   Smyth v. Lubbers, 398 F. Supp. 777, 797–99 (W.D. Mich. 1975) (stating, in dicta, in a matter arising at Grand Valley State University, that the court "believed" that a clear and convincing standard "may be required" and, thus, the court "recommended" that the university "give serious consideration to adopting" clear and convincing as the standard for future cases, citing no education law to support this mild recommendation); Long, *supra* note 145, at 80–82; Schaer v. Brandeis Univ., 735 N.E.2d at 379 n.9 (Mass. 2000) (stating that clear and convincing standard voluntarily used by Brandeis was not judicially required). *But see* Charles F. Carletta, *The Campus Judicial Process* at 10, 7th Annual Donald D. Gehring Training Inst. of the Ass'n for Student Judicial Affairs (1999) (on file with author) (recommending use of "more likely than not" standard); Swem, *supra* note 47, at 359–360 (1987) ("[T]he substantial evidence standard remains the norm" [as opposed to "clear and convincing"] . . . . Unless an institution's code of conduct provides otherwise, basing a decision on substantial evidence is acceptable."). One survey found that the "more likely than not" standard was the most common standard of proof used in campus sexual assault cases. Sophie W. Penney, Lawrence Tucker & John Wesley Lowery, *National Baseline Study on Campus Sexual Assault: Adjudication of Sexual Assault Cases* 11 (Ass'n for Student Judicial Affairs 2000), *available at* http://asja.tamu.edu/news/ASJA%20-%20Baseline%20Study%20Report%20Published.pdf. Another commentator noted that the "vast majority" of colleges and universities use the "more likely than not" standard. SILVERGLATE & GEWOLB, *supra* note 8, at 101.

147.   In *Concrete Pipe & Prods. v. Construction Laborers Pension Trust,* 508 U.S. 602, 622 (1993) Justice Souter, speaking for the Court, wrote:

The burden of showing something by a 'preponderance of the evidence,' the most common standard in the civil law, 'simply requires the trier of fact 'to believe that the existence of a fact is more probable than its nonexistence before [he] may find in favor of the party who has the burden to persuade the [judge] of the fact's existence."

university student discipline and judicial processes. The "clear and convincing" and "beyond a reasonable doubt" standard inaccurately treat the Accused Student as more important than the student who believes s/he was a victim of misconduct and/or as having more important interests than all other members of the academic community have in the maintenance of a calm, peaceful and productive living/learning environment. The "preponderance" standard correctly treats each one of these constituencies as equally important when a fact finder tries to decide what happened when the facts are disputed.

Courts review disciplinary decisions of colleges or universities under a "substantial evidence" standard. Courts examine whether there was enough information in the fact finding process to support the determination that it was "more likely than not" that the Accused Student violated the Student Code. In doing so, courts do not make new credibility determinations but assume that the information supporting the determination was deemed credible by the fact finder. In this sense, the "substantial evidence" review is a relatively easy standard to meet. The same standard applies as one of the standards for internal appellate review under most student conduct codes.[148]

5. There shall be a single verbatim record, such as a tape recording, of all Student Conduct Board Hearings before a Student Conduct Board (not including deliberations). Deliberations shall not be recorded. The record shall be the property of the [College] [University].[149]

Commentary. This provision has several purposes. First, it assures that a record will be made of the hearing,[150] *and deters students from asking to make*

(internal citations omitted).

148. *See* Model Code, art. IV(D)(2)(b).

149. The tape recording or other verbatim record of the hearing will be an education record under FERPA that a student with FERPA access rights would be allowed to review but not to copy. 34 C.F.R. § 99.10 (2003).

150. Most authorities agree that no transcript is required, even for public institutions, as a matter of minimal procedural due process. A recent ruling to this effect involved Brandeis University, where no verbatim transcripts of hearings are kept—not even tape recordings. In one hearing concerning sexual conduct, at which there were thirteen witnesses and over five hours of testimony, the Supreme Judicial Court of Massachusetts approved a "summary" only twelve lines long. Schaer v. Brandeis Univ., 735 N.E. 2d at 382 (Mass. 2000) The Court noted that the report correctly reflected the credibility judgments upon which the decision turned: "The report, although short, reflects a judgment by the board that the Complainant and the corroborating witnesses were credited; Schaer and his witnesses were not credited." Id. at 379 n.9. *See* Trahms v. Columbia Univ., 245 N.E.2d 124 (N.Y. Sup. Ct. App. Div. 1997) (holding that no transcript of an Honor Board Hearing is required in expulsion case); *Gorman v. Univ. of R.I.*, 837 F.2d 7, 16 (1st Cir. 1988) (holding that summary handwritten notes was sufficient); Jaksa v. Univ. of Mich., 597 F. Supp. 1245, 1252 (E.D. Mich. 1984) ("I am not persuaded that the due process clause requires the University to provide a verbatim transcript of the hearing. While this case illustrates the wisdom of recording such hearings, it is clear that the Constitution does not impose such a requirement."), *aff'd per curiam*, 787 F.2d 590 (6th Cir. 1986); Due v. Fla. A&M Univ., 233 F. Supp. 396, 403 (N.D. Fla. 1961) ("There need be no stenographic or mechanical recording of the proceedings.").

At least one court, however, has required that a transcript be made of student disciplinary hearings. Marin v. Univ. of P.R., 377 F. Supp. 613, 623 (D.P.R. 1973). When this need arises, an institution should explore having a careful typist transcribe statements from an

their own copies. Second, it establishes that the record is the property of the institution. Third, it can be used to assist the fact-finder when deliberating over whether a student violated the institution's rules or in setting sanctions. Fourth, it can be used by a person appealing in preparation for his/her appeal. Finally, it enables an appellate reviewer (internal or external) to know what "really" happened before the Student Conduct Board and keeps others from misrepresenting what occurred. [151]

In some cases, a student may request permission to make a record of the proceedings. An institution may not wish to permit a student to do so because, for example, it may not want its students to replay tapes of the disciplinary proceedings as a form of entertainment, in addition to other privacy concerns.

6. If an Accused Student, with notice, does not appear before a Student Conduct Board Hearing, the information in support of the charges shall be presented and considered even if the Accused Student is not present.

Commentary. "Judgment by default" without considering the information available about the student's conduct is a rather harsh penalty to impose upon a student.

7. The Student Conduct Board may accommodate concerns for the personal safety, well-being, and/or fears of confrontation of the Complainant, Accused Student, and/or other witness during the hearing by providing separate facilities, by using a visual screen, and/or by permitting participation by telephone, videophone, closed circuit television, video conferencing, videotape, audio tape, written statement, or other means, where and as determined in the sole judgment of [title of administrator identified in Article I, number 13] to be appropriate.[152]

---

audio tape rather than going to the expense of using a court reporter.

151. A discussion of considerations to observe in audiotaping appears in Stoner, *supra* note 106, at 14.

152. This provision is modeled after one appearing in the *Alfred University Judicial System Policies and Regulations*. ALFRED UNIV., JUDICIAL SYS. POLICIES AND REGULATIONS, *at* http://www.alfred.edu/policies/index.cfm?fuseaction=viewPolicy&id=10 (last revised July 2004). The need for this type of accommodation occurs most often in sexual conduct cases, in which the alleged victim fears visual or verbal confrontation during courtroom-type "cross-examination," and/or retaliation. *See* William Fischer & Lori Fox, *The Sexual Assault Case and the Student Judiciary*, 42nd Annual Conf., Nat'l Ass'n of Coll. & Univ. Attys 10 (2002) (on file with author) (stating that "one of the most traumatic aspects of [sexual assault] cases for Complainants is cross-examination by the Accused Student"); Maryalice (Qui Qui) Ledee, *Due Process Rights and Special Considerations in Sexual Assault Cases,* 1 STUDENT AFF. L. & POL'Y Q. 18, 19 (2004), *at* http://www.clhe.org/lawpolicyquarterly/salpq1_1.pdf. Witnesses in violent cases not involving sexual conduct and other cases, such as those involving academic dishonesty, also may be reticent to testify for various reasons. While it is important to respect these concerns, most college and university students are adults of eighteen years of age or older—not children of tender years. *See supra* note 10 and accompanying text. Thus, student affairs professionals will be careful not to create such concerns accidentally. In academic dishonesty cases, the reluctant student witnesses may not even be necessary to a fair review process, as those witnesses may not have anything valuable to add. This is especially true if they provide only the anonymous "tip"

Commentary. This section concerns what to do about a witness who is reluctant to tell his/her story to a conduct board, because, for example, s/he does not desire a confrontation.[153] *The accommodations discussed below should be used rarely, only after efforts to educate and to reassure the reluctant witness about how the student discipline process functions normally have failed. Student affairs professionals dealing with these fearful students must be careful to be sensitive to genuine concerns while also realizing that the students involved are adults, not children of tender years.*

As in all student discipline cases, the students involved must first be educated about the student discipline process because they may not understand how the process works. Worse, they may assume that campus procedures resemble criminal law processes. Furthermore, victim support groups unfamiliar with the student discipline process may discourage student accusers from sharing information in the normal manner in the student conduct board hearing because victim advocates, too, confuse campus processes with witness-unfriendly systems, such as the ones used in criminal court. Once they realize that the student discipline process has an educational tone rather than an adversarial one, student

---

that leads the accusing faculty member to investigate the incident. *See, e.g., Jaksa*, 597 F. Supp at 1252 (asserting that the real accuser in an academic dishonesty case is the professor, whom the student does have an opportunity to confront). Thus, while an alleged victim's testimony in student conduct proceedings is usually critical to a fair outcome, "victim-less" infractions such as academic dishonesty can often be fairly resolved without the testimony of a reluctant student witness. Therefore, this section will be most important where the reluctant witness is an alleged victim.

153. Only a few colleges and universities have provisions in their discipline codes dealing with this issue expressly. *See, e.g.,* ALFRED UNIV. JUDICIAL SYS. POLICIES AND REGULATIONS, *supra* note 152; PA. STATE UNIV., JUDICIAL AFFAIRS VICTIMS' RIGHTS, *available at* http://www.sa.psu.edu/ja/rights.shtml (last visited Oct. 12, 2004) (providing for the opportunity to testify with special accommodations); GA. INST. OF TECH., STUDENT CODE OF CONDUCT: PROCEDURAL RIGHTS, ADJUDICATION, AND SANCTIONS, *available at* http://www.deanofstudents.gatech.edu/integrity/policies/code_of_conduct.html (last visited Oct. 12, 2004) ("Testimony may be taken in person, in writing, or by other reliable means of communication including, but not limited to electronic, email, telephone or video conferencing."); FLA. INT'L UNIV., JUDICIAL AND MEDIATION SERVICES, VICTIM RIGHTS *available at* http://www.fiu.edu/~jms/ (last modified Dec. 2002) (stating that "victims" have the right "to testify in limited privacy, as long as the process does not compromise the charged students' right to confront and question witnesses") (The authors note that this language may not give the student affairs professional the discretion that was intended because it may be viewed as giving complete priority to confrontation and questioning of witnesses.); WRIGHT STATE UNIV. OFFICE OF JUDICIAL AFFAIRS, STUDENT RIGHTS: RIGHTS OF COMPLAINANT, *at* http://www.wright.edu/students/judicial/rights.html (last updated August 2004) (making provisions "in cases of sexual assault only" whereby "victims" are given the "right to answer questions posed by the accused out of the presence of the accused"). The authors suggest that, once a determination is made that such fears are genuine, they be accommodated when *any* type of offense is alleged rather than limiting a response to such fears only in situations in which the misconduct at issue is sexual. In addition, it is suggested that the label of "victim" not be formally attached to a student in a student conduct code hearing. Attaching such a label gives the erroneous impression that the institution has determined that a rules violation occurred prior to hearing the case; moreover, an Accused Student may feel that s/he has been wrongly accused and is, therefore, also entitled to be called the "victim" of someone else's wrongful accusation. The authors suggest that the better practice is to call students "students" or "witnesses" rather than to give them judgment-laden labels. *See supra* note 50.

witnesses who were initially fearful often feel differently. Thus, they may agree to testify without special accommodations. In addition, once wary support groups realize that the campus discipline process is purposefully not run like an adversarial criminal proceeding, student accusers may be encouraged to participate in the normal manner.

When a witness remains fearful even after reassurance attempts by student affairs professionals, however, there are competing concerns. The student discipline process aims to treat alleged victims and Accused Students with equal care and dignity and also to reach fair and correct results. A witness may need to feel safe and ought not be re-victimized by reliving any traumatic experiences. The Accused Student desires not to be wrongly sanctioned. The community desires a safe living and learning environment and wishes to be confident in its discipline process; that is, if a rule violation is found, the community seeks to be confident that one actually occurred. In addition, student affairs professionals need to have conduct code language that enables them to accommodate genuine fears appropriately without creating a lawsuit alleging failure to follow the college or university's own rules once the difficult job of determining responsibility and/or sanctions is completed. The language proposed in article IV(A)(7), coupled with the other provisions of this Model Code, attempts to address the two process issues that contribute to making witnesses reluctant: fear of visual confrontation and fear of direct cross-examination confrontation in the abrasive style used by attorneys in criminal and civil cases in court.

At first blush, it may appear that private institutions have more flexibility in dealing with this challenge than their public counterparts.[154] Upon closer scrutiny, however, the same solutions appear to be available at all institutions. As we have discussed elsewhere in this Model Code,[155] part of the solution is that direct adversarial cross-examination in the criminal law sense is not required in student discipline hearings unless it is provided by the institution as a matter of

---

154. Public colleges and universities, as state actors, are required to provide minimal constitutional procedural due process to students when disciplining them for violating campus rules. *See supra* notes 29–31 and accompanying text. Private institutions are not subject to this standard. *See supra* note 30. It is, however, easy to comply with the requirement of providing a student minimal constitutional procedural due process. *See supra* notes 43–45 and accompanying text. Even commentators writing to support accused students concluded, while citing a sexual conduct case, "Due process, as indicated by [Donohue v. Baker, 976 F. Supp. 136, 146 (N.D.N.Y. 1997)], does not generally require face-to-face confrontation in campus disciplinary proceedings." SILVERGLATE & GEWOLB, *supra* note 8, at 105 (speculating, however, that such face-to-face confrontation might be required in a case of alleged mistaken identity).

155. *See* Model Code, *supra* article IV(A)(4)(e); *supra* note 142 and accompanying text; Model Student Conduct Board Hearing Script, *infra* notes 196, 203, and 222. Scholars agree that some form of cross-examination is appropriate when credibility is at issue. *See, e.g.,* Wright, *supra* note 20, at 1076 (arguing that "if the case resolves itself into a problem of credibility, and the tribunal must choose to believe either the accused or his accuser, cross-examination is . . . required in the interest of fairness"); Thomas R. Baker, *Judicial Complaint Resolution Models and Schemes: An Administrator's Reference Guide for Self-Assessment* 10–12, 12th Annual Conf., Ass'n for Student Judicial Affairs (2000) (on file with author) (noting that where a long suspension is imposed upon the accused student and he or she denies the allegations, the U.S. Constitution may require . . ." that accused students have the opportunity to pose questions to accusers in some manner).

educational preference. Cross-examination through the Student Conduct Board, through questions suggested to the chair, as urged in this model, suffices.

As the language in article IV(A)(7) suggests, there are several options available if a witness remains reluctant even if s/he understands that the abrasive criminal law model of cross-examination is not to be used. One option, if technologically feasible, is to proceed with the hearing through closed-circuit television, with the reluctant witness in another room from the Student Conduct Board and the Accused Student but remaining visually and aurally available to all. Another approach is to allow the reluctant witness to participate by telephone, again from a location remote from the Student Conduct Board and the Accused Student. This is a less desirable approach because visual contact is lost. A third option that addresses the issue of visual confrontation might be to use a hearing room with a one-way mirror (sometimes available in counseling centers) so that the Student Conduct Board, Accused Student, and reluctant witness can all see and hear each other, except that the reluctant witness cannot see the Accused Student. Others have set up a physical screen to shield the reluctant witness and Accused Student from seeing each other.[156] These approaches have the advantage of allowing both students to be "present" in some sense while information is received by the Student Conduct Board.[157]

Another option, but one that does not have the advantage of having all parties present simultaneously in any sense, is for the Student Conduct Board to hold separate interviews with the reluctant witness and the Accused Student and to allow the Accused Student to read a verbatim transcript of the reluctant witness's interview (or to allow the Accused Student to hear that portion of the tape recording) and to allow the Accused Student an opportunity to respond.[158] This

---

156. *See* Ledee, *supra* note 152, at 19 (suggesting use of speakerphones, screens or dividers); Fernand N. Dutile, *Students and Due Process in Higher Education: Of Interests and Procedures,* 2 FL. COAST. L. REV. 243, 271 n.198 (2000) (suggesting possibility of closed-circuit television use); Baker, *supra* note 158, at 10 ("If live video technology is available, institutions may prefer to seat the complainant and accused student in separate rooms and permit the accused student to view the proceedings via a television camera."). Also, *Dillon v. Pulaski County Special School District* recognized that "the need for anonymity of student accusers . . . could prevail over the right to confrontation," suggesting the possibility of less direct confrontation such as with the use of a screen separating the parties. 468 F. Supp. 54, 58 (E.D. Ark. 1978). The use of a screen was approved in *Cloud v. Boston University,* in which a law student accused of peeping was separated from his accusers as they testified behind a screen, although his attorney and the panel could see the witness. 720 F.2d 721, 725 (1st Cir. 1983). The court dismissed the plaintiff's argument that the use of a screen and anonymous testimony was prejudicial because it gave the impression he was threatening, observing that "the balance of the equities favored protecting the witness's identity." Note that Boston University is a private university, but other courts have cited *Cloud* favorably in the public institution context. *See, e.g.,* Gomes v. Univ. of Me. Sys., 304 F. Supp. 117 (D. Me. 2004).

157. *See* Dutile, *supra* note 156 (noting "one could hear all evidence (for example, through close[d]-circuit television) and still not be physically present.").

158. A verbatim transcript (video or tape recording) is required to use this option so that the Accused Student may hear the information against him, and also to insure compliance with minimal procedural due process at public institutions. *See Nash v. Auburn Univ.*, 812 F.2d 655, 664 (11th Cir. 1987) at 664 (emphasizing that the accused students heard all testimony against them and holding that the process afforded was sufficient); *Dixon* v. *Ala. State Bd. of Educ.*, 294 F.2d 150, 159 (5th Cir. 1961) (holding that "the student should be given . . . an oral or written

may be a practical solution because of cost (if a regular tape recorder is used) and time concerns, but it is the least desirable because it does not provide the Student Conduct Board an opportunity to clarify or to probe further with either student after receiving information from the other.

If this last procedure is modified a bit, however, it can provide the Student Conduct Board such an opportunity, even if the description sounds a bit silly. The Student Conduct Board can sit in a room and invite the Complainant to give information that is either audio or videotape recorded. The Complainant would exit the room, and the Accused Student would be invited in. The recording would be played back for the Accused Student, who then would suggest questions for the Complainant to the Student Conduct Board. The Accused Student would leave again, and the Complainant would come back in and answer questions asked by the board. Then the Accused Student would come back in and listen to the Complainant's responses. The board could follow the same procedure for the Accused Student. This would continue until all questioning was completed. Other than the revolving door and the necessity to play back portions of the testimony, this rudimentary solution preserves all aspects of the ideal Student Conduct Board Meeting set out in Article IV(A)(4), while avoiding a visual confrontation.

B. Sanctions

1. The following sanctions may be imposed upon any student found to have violated the Student Code:
   a. Warning—A notice in writing to the student that the student is violating or has violated institutional regulations.
   b. Probation—A written reprimand for violation of specified regulations. Probation is for a designated period of time and includes the probability of more severe disciplinary sanctions if the student is found to violate any institutional regulation(s) during the probationary period.
   c. Loss of Privileges—Denial of specified privileges for a designated period of time.
   d. Fines—Previously established and published fines may be imposed.
   e. Restitution—Compensation for loss, damage, or injury. This may take the form of appropriate service and/or monetary or material replacement.
   f. Discretionary Sanctions—Work assignments, essays, service to the [College] [University], or other related discretionary assignments.
   g. Residence Hall Suspension—Separation of the student from the residence halls for a definite period of time, after which the student is eligible to return. Conditions for readmission may be specified.
   h. Residence Hall Expulsion—Permanent separation of the student from the residence halls.

---

report on the facts to which each witness testifies"). It is not clear whether a summary of the evidence by the Student Conduct Board would suffice based on the language in *Dixon* but, at least in cases where the sanctions imposed are great, it is safer and relatively easy for the college or university to provide some form of transcript. In addition, this Code recommends that a verbatim record such as a tape recording be taken of the entire meeting. *See supra* Model Code, art. IV(A)(5).

    i.   [College] [University] Suspension—Separation of the student from the [College] [University] for a definite period of time, after which the student is eligible to return. Conditions for readmission may be specified.

    j.   [College] [University] Expulsion—Permanent separation of the student from the [College] [University].[159]

    k.   Revocation of Admission and/or Degree—Admission to[160] or a degree awarded from the [College][University] may be revoked for fraud, misrepresentation, or other violation of [College][University] standards in obtaining the degree, or for other serious violations committed by a student prior to graduation.[161]

    l.   Withholding Degree—The [College][University] may withhold awarding a degree otherwise earned until the completion of the process set forth in this Student Conduct Code, including the completion of all sanctions imposed, if any.[162]

Commentary. Colleges and universities may, within certain limitations,[163] authorize as many types of sanctions as they wish. This section gives the institution maximum flexibility by permitting the Student Conduct Administrator to

---

159.   A student who is expelled or suspended may ask a court to enjoin the discipline. Courts have held that suspension does not constitute irreparable harm so as to support a motion for injunctive relief. Boehm v. Univ. of Pa. Sch. of Veterinary Med., 573 A.2d 575 (Pa. 1990); *Schulman v. Franklin and Marshall Coll.*, 538 A.2d 49, 51–52 (Pa. Super. Ct.); Barker v. Bryn Mawr Coll., 122 A. 220 (Pa. 1923) (refusing to enjoin college's decision to expel student after conclusion of internal process). This reluctance to disturb internal decisions extends beyond student affairs to employment. *See, e.g.,* Murphy v. Duquesne Univ. of the Holy Ghost, 777 A.2d 418 (Pa. 2001) (refusing to allow de novo review of university's reasons for terminating employment of tenured professor after conclusion of internal process); Baker v. Lafayette Coll., 532 A.2d 399 (Pa. 1987) (refusing to allow de novo review of college's reasons for not continuing employment of non-tenured teacher after conclusion of internal process); Stoner & Showalter, *supra* note 16, at 583. This deference, however, does not extend to situations in which a college does not follow its own express rules. *See supra* note 33.

160.   Martin v. Helstad, 699 F.2d 387 (7th Cir. 1987) (involving revocation of acceptance to law school for omitting securities fraud conviction).

161.   Courts support the revocation of degrees in these circumstances in order to protect the integrity of the institution's degrees and to protect the public from being victimized by a person displaying false credentials. Crook v. Baker, 813 F.2d 88, 93 (6th Cir. 1987); Waliga v. Kent State Univ., 488 N.E.2d 850, 852 (Ohio 1986). *See* Jayme L. Butcher, MIT v. Yoo: *Revocation of Academic Degrees for Non-Academic Reasons,* 51 CASE WEST. L. REV. 749 (2001); Gary Pavela, *For the Same Reasons That Students Can Be Expelled, Degrees Ought to be Revocable,* CHRON. HIGHER EDUC., Oct. 22, 1999 at B6; Bernard Reams Jr., *Revocation of Academic Degrees by Colleges and Universities,* 14 J.C. & U.L. 283, 300 (1987). *See also* Pavela, *supra* note 8, at 829 (discussing another formulation of this sanction).

162.   Vandereerden v. Yale Sch. of Mgmt., No. 0438876, 2000 WL 727515, at *2 (Conn. Super. Ct. May 18, 2000) (upholding right to withhold degree pending six month suspension imposed after completion of course work, even in the absence of a specific clause).

163.   The district court in *Gorman v. University of Rhode Island,* for example, found that the University of Rhode Island's sanction of compulsory psychiatric treatment was a "shocking extreme" and would violate the student's right to privacy. 646 F. Supp. 799, 814 (D.R.I. 1986). A commentator, no doubt intending to be thought provoking, proposed that colleges and universities impose sanctions to change both the wrongdoer and the entire community. She proposed shaming. Katharine R. Baker, *Sex, Rape and Shame,* 79 B.U. L. REV. 663 (1999).

impose any sanction(s) for any infraction of the Student Code. An experienced student affairs administrator will consider all of the facts and circumstances to apply a sanction appropriate for the offender, the community, and the victim (if there is one).[164] *An alternative approach is to enumerate those offenses carrying the more serious sanctions (i.e., expulsion and suspension), and to allow the Student Conduct Administrator to choose among the remaining sanctions as to other offenses.*[165] *As to discretionary sanctions, the language is purposefully broad to allow an educator to impose sanctions from a wide range of possibilities in order to help the student to understand more fully the consequences of his/her conduct.*

2. More than one of the sanctions listed above may be imposed for any single violation.
3. (a) Other than [College] [University] expulsion or revocation or withholding of a degree, disciplinary sanctions shall not be made part of the student's permanent academic record,[166] but shall become part of the student's disciplinary record. Upon graduation, the student's disciplinary record may be expunged of disciplinary actions other than residence hall expulsion, [College] [University] suspension, [College] [University] expulsion, or revocation or withholding of a degree, upon application to the Student Conduct Administrator. Cases involving the imposition of sanctions other than residence hall expulsion, [College] [University] suspension, [College] [University] expulsion or revocation or withholding of a degree shall be expunged from the student's confidential record [insert preferred number] years[167] after final disposition of the case.

    (b) In situations involving both an Accused Student(s) (or group or organization) and a student(s) claiming to be the victim of another student's conduct, the records of the process and of the sanctions imposed, if any, shall be considered to be the education records of both the Accused Student(s) and the student(s) claiming to be the victim because the educational career and chances of success in the academic community of each may be impacted.

Commentary. Institutions may define that such records are education records of the complaining students, as well as of the Accused Student. Educationally speaking, this is surely valid, as the incident may directly impact the educational environment and performance of each student. Treating such records as education

---

164. In *Haley v. Virginia Commonwealth University* a student-on-student harassment case, the accused student was suspended for two years to permit the victim to complete school without him present. 948 F. Supp. 573, 576 (E.D. Va. 1996).

165. *See, e.g.,* Gary Pavela, *Limiting the "Pursuit of Perfect Justice" on Campus: A Proposed Code of Student Conduct,* 6 J.C. & U.L. 137, 143 (1979).

166. Some institutions include information regarding suspensions from the institution on the student's permanent academic transcript, at least for the period of the suspension.

167. Records substantiating the statistics must be maintained for three years after publication (approximately seven years after the conduct). *See* Jeanne Clery Disclosure of Campus Security Policy and Campus Crime Statistics Act, 20 U.S.C. § 1092(f)(1)(F) (2000); 34 C.F.R. § 668.46 (c)(1) (2004).

records of the complaining student, as well as of the Accused Student, also avoids strange results under the Family Education Right to Privacy Act ("FERPA")[168] *because the complaining student would then have access to his/her own records— rather than being told that the result of the process concerning them could not be disclosed because they were records only of another student. Thus, the results of the student discipline process are communicated to the complaining student.*[169]

4.   The following sanctions may be imposed upon groups or organizations[170]:
   a.   Those sanctions listed above in article IV(B)(1)(a)–(e).
   b.   Loss of selected rights and privileges for a specified period of time.
   c.   Deactivation. Loss of all privileges, including [College] [University] recognition, for a specified period of time.

Commentary. When a recognized student organization engages in some act of misconduct, the college or university may take action not only against the student(s) involved, but also against the organization itself. This procedure does not violate the double jeopardy clause of the Constitution[171] *for two reasons. First, the double jeopardy clause applies only to criminal, not civil, proceedings.*[172] *Proceedings under a school's student code are not criminal proceedings.*[173] *Furthermore, the actors (student(s) and organization) are separate offenders. Punishing each of them for the same act is not punishing the same offender twice for one act of misconduct.*[174] *Similarly, it does not violate the*

---

168.   20 U.S.C.A. § 1232g (2000 & West Supp. 2004). One court discussed the conclusion that discipline records are education records under FERPA in student-on-student violence situations:

> First, the disciplinary records at issue in this case clearly 'contain information directly related to a student.' The offenders being disciplined, and often the victims of the offense, are students of the respective universities, and the matters addressed in the disciplinary records pertain to actions committed or allegedly committed by or against those students.

United States v. Miami Univ., 91 F. Supp. 1132, 1150 (S.D. Ohio 2000), *aff'd*, 294 F.3d 797 (6th Cir. 2002).

169.   *See infra* Model Code, art. IV(B)(5).

170.   *See* Grier, *supra* note 88.

171.   The Fifth Amendment to the United States Constitution provides in part: "[N]or shall any person be subject for the same offence to be twice put in jeopardy of life or limb." U.S. CONST. amend. V. This provision applies to the states through the Fourteenth Amendment. Benton v. Maryland, 395 U.S. 784, 794 (1969). *See supra* note 46 and accompanying text.

172.   Paine v. Bd. of Regents, 355 F. Supp. 199, 203 (W.D. Tex. 1972), *aff'd*, 474 F.2d 1397 (5th Cir. 1973). *Cf.* Oliver v. U.S. Dept. of Justice, 517 F.2d 426, 428 (2d Cir. 1975) (holding that deportation proceedings following a criminal conviction do not violate double jeopardy clause); United States v. Forty-Two Jars "Bee Royale Capsules," 160 F. Supp. 818, 821 (D.N.J. 1958) (holding that double jeopardy does not apply to drug misbranding proceedings); Attorney Grievance Comm. v. Andresen, 379 A.2d 159, 160 (Md. 1977) (holding that double jeopardy clause does not apply to attorney disciplinary proceedings). *See also* George C. Thomas III, *An Elegant Theory of Double Jeopardy*, 4 U. ILL. L. REV. 827, 837 (1988). *See supra* note 46 and accompanying text.

173.   *See, e.g.,* Nzuve v. Castleton State Coll., 335 A.2d 321, 323 (Vt. 1975).

174.   *See* United States v. Richmond, 700 F.2d 1183, 1195 n.7 (8th Cir. 1983) (holding that

double jeopardy clause for the same student to be subjected to both criminal and student-code (civil) sanctions for the same misconduct.[175]

The private/public institution distinction remains important. As elsewhere in student discipline, a private institution has more discretion in disciplining student organizations, mainly needing just to follow institutional rules.[176] *Public institutions must follow the requirements of minimal procedural due process and may be limited by other constitutional provisions as well.*[177]

5.   In each case in which a Student Conduct Board determines that a student and/or group or organization has violated the Student Code, the sanction(s) shall be determined and imposed by the Student Conduct Administrator. In cases in which persons other than, or in addition to, the Student Conduct Administrator have been authorized to serve as the Student Conduct Board, the recommendation of the Student Conduct Board shall be considered by the Student Conduct Administrator in determining and imposing sanctions. The Student Conduct Administrator is not limited to sanctions recommended by members of the Student Conduct Board. Following the Student Conduct Board Hearing, the Student Conduct Board and the Student Conduct Administrator shall advise the Accused Student, group and/or organization (and a complaining student who believes s/he was the victim of another student's conduct) in writing of its determination and of the sanction(s) imposed, if any.[178]

Commentary. Imposition of sanctions by the Student Conduct Administrator ensures some consistency among the sanctions meted out over time. A college or university may choose to allow the Student Conduct Board, rather than a college or university official, to impose sanctions in each case.[179] *Such a choice is not unusual. It may be more equitable, however, to have the Student Conduct Administrator choose the sanction in all situations, so as to avoid putting students who sit on the Student Conduct Board in the position of imposing a sanction on a*

---

punishment of both a corporation and its officers does not constitute double punishment).

175.   *See Paine*, 355 F. Supp. at 203.

176.   Mu Chapter of Delta Kappa Epsilon v. Colgate Univ., 176 A.2d 11 (N.Y. App. Div. 1992); Psi Upsilon of Phila. v. Univ. of Pa., 591 A.2d 755 (Pa. 1991) (holding that withdrawal of recognition for hazing permitted under fundamental fairness standard).

177.   *See, e.g.,* Iota Xi Chapter of Sigma Chi Fraternity v. George Mason Univ., 993 F.2d 386 (4th Cir. 1993) (holding that First Amendment prohibited sanction for racially and sexually offensive skit).

178.   At the Pennsylvania State University, the "victim" has the right to "hear" the results of the disciplinary process even if the "victim" is not a student. PA. STATE UNIV. DIV. OF STUDENT AFFAIRS, JUDICIAL AFFAIRS, VICTIM'S RIGHTS, *available at* http://www.sa.psu.edu/ja/rights. shtml (last visited Oct. 12, 2004).

179.   *See, e.g.,* UNIV. OF S.C., CODE OF STUDENT CONDUCT 11.3. DELIBERATIONS AND DECISIONS OF THE COUNCIL, *available at* http://www.sa.sc.edu/carolinacommunity/judicial.html (last visited Oct. 12, 2004); NORTHEASTERN UNIV., STUDENT HANDBOOK, CODE OF STUDENT CONDUCT, *available at* http://www.neu.edu/handbook/studenthandbook.pdf (last visited Oct. 12, 2004).

peer. In this manner, the administrator could take into account sanctions given in prior similar cases in order to provide consistency—without disclosing all prior details to the current conduct board. Moreover, the administrator would be an appropriate witness for a court challenge, if one arises. Finally, the administrator may be better trained than the board to bring educational judgment to bear in setting the sanction(s). In this Model, the authors recommend that, when the board consists of more persons than just the administrator, the board recommend sanctions to the administrator, who makes the final decision.[180]

C. Interim Suspension

In certain circumstances, the [title of administrator identified in Article I, number 13], or a designee, may impose a [College] [University] or residence hall suspension prior to the Student Conduct Board Hearing before a Student Conduct Board.

1. Interim suspension may be imposed only: 1) to ensure the safety and well-being of members of the [College] [University] community or preservation of [College] [University] property; b) to ensure the student's own physical or emotional safety and well-being; or c) if the student poses an ongoing threat of disruption of, or interference with, the normal operations of the [College] [University].

2. During the interim suspension, a student shall be denied access to the residence halls and/or to the campus (including classes) and/or all other [College] [University] activities or privileges for which the student might otherwise be eligible, as the [title of administrator identified in Article I, number 13] or the Student Conduct Administrator may determine to be appropriate.

3. The interim suspension does not replace the regular process, which shall proceed on the normal schedule, up to and through a Student Conduct Board Hearing, if required.[181]

Commentary. It is permissible to impose an interim suspension in certain limited instances.[182] *It has been noted:*

---

180.   As to the practice of informing student "victims" of the results of the process, see *supra* Model Code, art. IV(B)(3)(b) and *infra* Model Hearing Script, n. 219.

181.   Suspending a student on an interim basis without following the Ohio State University hearing process converted the interim suspension to a permanent expulsion in violation of due process principles. Ashiegbu v. Williams, No. 97-3173, 1997 WL 720477 (6th Cir. Nov. 12, 1997), *discussed in* KAPLIN & LEE, *supra* note 8, at 319.

182.   Rollins v. Cardinal Stritch Univ., 626 N.W.2d 464 (Minn. Ct. App. 2001) (approving interim suspension in sexual harassment matter). Ali v. Stetson Univ., Inc. ___ F. Supp. 2d ___, No. 6:03-CV-975-ORI28, 2004 WL 2309552 (M.D. Fla. Oct. 8, 2004) (granting summary judgment to university on lawsuit challenging interim suspension following off campus arrest on felony aggravated assault with a firearm charge). This concept stems from a passage in *Goss v. Lopez*, 419 U.S. 565, 582–83 (1975), stating that "[s]tudents whose presence poses a continuing danger to persons or property or an ongoing threat of disrupting the academic process may be immediately removed from school. In such cases, the necessary notice and . . . hearing should follow as soon as practicable." In *Cleveland Board of Education. v. Loudermill*, 470 U.S. 532,

However, the student should be notified in writing of this action and the reasons for the suspension. The notice should include the time, date, and place of a subsequent hearing at which the student may show cause why his or her continued presence on the campus does not constitute a threat [and at which they may contest whether a campus rule was violated].[183]

An unusual case allowed the immediate dismissal of a student at a Kentucky private college without using the process for resolving what happened.[184]

D. Appeals

1. A decision reached by the Student Conduct Board or a sanction imposed by the Student Conduct Administrator may be appealed by the Accused Student(s) or Complainant(s) to an Appellate Board within five (5) school days of the decision. Such appeals shall be in writing and shall be delivered to the Student Conduct Administrator or his or her designee.

Commentary. This is another point at which it may be wise to grant students more rights than they might otherwise have. Although there is some authority for the proposition that students need not be given the right to appeal from a decision rendered as a result of a hearing,[185] *providing an appellate process promotes an image of fairness. Further enhancing the image of fairness, this model affords not*

---

538 (1985), however, the Supreme Court indicated that in most cases an interim suspension without some sort of hearing beforehand is something to be avoided if possible. *Loudermill* was not a school case, but it indicated that, at least in the public employment context, a predetermination hearing serves as "an initial check against mistaken decisions." *Id.* at 545. *See* Picozzi, *supra* note 51, at 2158 n.111, in which the author indicates that judgments of whether the imminent danger necessary to justify an interim suspension is present should be left to the discretion of the administrator responsible for implementing the student code but that the administrator's decision should be reviewed as soon thereafter as is practicable.

183. Gehring & Bracewell, *supra* note 9, at 97–98. As Professor Wright noted, "[T]here must be power in a University, when circumstances compel it, to suspend students summarily pending a later hearing at which they will be given all of the ordinary procedural protections." Wright, *supra* note 20, at 1074.

184. Centre Coll. v. Trzop, 127 S.W.3d 562 (Ky. 2003) (upholding dismissal of student who admitted possessing a five inch knife on campus, a violation of campus rules, although he explained that it was part of his National Guard equipment). The Kentucky Supreme Court upheld his dismissal, done with minimal notice and hearing and without following the college's usual procedure, explaining:

> In its "contract" with Trzop, Centre never guaranteed the right to due process. In fact, the Centre Student Handbook clearly states that such process may be withheld in certain circumstances:
>
>> Although students are ordinarily disciplined through the judicial process involving the Student Judiciary or the executive committees of the Intrafraternity Council or the Panhellenic Association, the college administration may invoke sanctions including dismissal from the College in unusual circumstances. The need for confidentiality, for immediate action, or for protection of others might prompt such action.

Id. at 568.

185. *Goss,* 419 U.S. at 582–83.

only the Accused Student but also the Complainant a right to appeal.[186] *This is*
consistent with the basic student affairs precept that all students are entitled to be
treated with equal care, concern, honor, and dignity. Particulars, such as the
amount of time within which to permit appeals, may vary from school to school.
Regardless of the result initially, the appeals process further assists the institution
to get the "right" result.

2.   Except as required to explain the basis of new information, an appeal shall be
limited to a review of the verbatim record of the Student Conduct Board
Hearing and supporting documents for one or more of the following purposes:

    a.   To determine whether the Student Conduct Board Hearing was conducted
fairly in light of the charges and information presented, and in conformity
with prescribed procedures giving the complaining party a reasonable
opportunity to prepare and to present information that the Student Code
was violated, and giving the Accused Student a reasonable opportunity to
prepare and to present a response to those allegations. Deviations from
designated procedures will not be a basis for sustaining an appeal unless
significant prejudice results.

    b.   To determine whether the decision reached regarding the Accused Student
was based on substantial information, that is, whether there were facts in
the case that, if believed by the fact finder, were sufficient[187] to establish

---

186.   At the Pennsylvania State University, the "victim" has the right to appeal the results of
the disciplinary process, perhaps even if the "victim" is not a student. *See supra* note 178 and
accompanying text.

187.   Papachristou v. Univ. of Tenn., 29 S.W.3d 487 (Tenn. Ct. App. 2000) (deferring to fact
finder's decision and sanction of indefinite suspension once the court concluded there was
substantial evidence to support the conclusion). The court held:

> The testimony in this record is in conflict. Therefore, what really happened in that
> classroom and what motivated Mr. Papachristou to do what he did requires the fact
> finder to assess the credibility of many witnesses. . . . When reviewing administrative
> decisions, the courts do not make de novo decisions about the credibility of
> witnesses. . . . Neither the trial court nor this court may review issues of fact de novo
> or substitute the court's judgment for that of the agency as to the weight of the
> evidence. . . . With substantial and material proof in the record on which the university,
> Chancellor's findings could be based, the action taken must be affirmed.

Id. at 490–91.

    The information from a single witness found to be credible by the finder of fact is
sufficient to sustain a finding that a student violated institutional rules. This happens often on
campus when the incident involves two persons and it must be determined who is credible. In a
male/male sexual conduct case resulting in expulsion, United States District Judge Lancaster
explained that the testimony of one credible witness was sufficient to sustain the expulsion from a
public institution:

> Plaintiff's argument appears to be that because the tribunal based its decision on the
> student's uncorroborated version of the events, the evidence was insufficient to warrant
> expulsion. We disagree.
>
>   Tribunals of every level, whether trial courts, administrative agencies or school
> disciplinary boards, by their very nature, must resolve disputes of fact. In doing so,
> they weigh the evidence, assess the credibility of witnesses, and make factual findings
> based on the testimony they find most credible. *Merely because a tribunal decides to*
> *rely on one witness's word rather than another's does not mean that the procedure was*

that a violation of the Student Code occurred.

    c.   To determine whether the sanction(s) imposed were appropriate for the violation of the Student Code which the student was found to have committed.

    d.   To consider new information, sufficient to alter a decision, or other relevant facts not brought out in the original hearing, because such information and/or facts were not known to the person appealing at the time of the original Student Conduct Board Hearing.

Commentary. The appellate body should review the Student Conduct Board's decision in order to determine whether it was supported by substantial information or, synonymously legally speaking, substantial evidence.[188] *Substantial evidence is "more than a mere scintilla. It means such relevant evidence as a reasonable mind might accept as adequate to support a conclusion."*[189] *In making such a determination, the Appellate Board should not substitute its judgment for the judgment of the Student Conduct Board. Instead, it should respect the credibility judgments made by the Student Conduct Board and review the Student Conduct Board's determination only to see whether there was information before the Student Conduct Board that supported the result it reached.*[190]

3.   If an appeal is upheld by the Appellate Board, the matter shall be returned to the original Student Conduct Board and Student Conduct Administrator for re-opening of Student Conduct Board Hearing to allow reconsideration of the original determination and/or sanction(s).[191] If an appeal is not upheld, the matter shall be considered final and binding upon all involved.

---

    unfair. It simply means that the tribunal made credibility determinations, its primary purpose.
Woodard v. Univ. of Pittsburgh, No. 95-1299, at 6 (W.D. Pa. 1995) (emphasis added).

    188.   Speake v. Grantham, 317 F. Supp. 1253, 1282 (S.D. Miss. 1971); Jones v. State Bd. of Educ., 407 F.2d 834, 836 (6th Cir. 1969); Givens v. Poe, 346 F. Supp. 202, 209 (W.D.N.C. 1972); Herman v. Univ. of S.C., 341 F. Supp. 226, 231 (D.S.C. 1971), *aff'd per curiam*, 457 F.2d 902 (4th Cir. 1972); Center for Participant Educ. v. Marshall, 337 F. Supp. 126, 136 (N.D. Fla. 1972). *See also* Swem, *supra* note 47, at 379–80 ("University officials bear the burden of proof in producing evidence to sustain the charges against the student and must base their disciplinary decisions on substantial evidence.").

    189.   Sill v. Pa. State Univ., 318 F. Supp. 608, 621 (M.D. Pa. 1970), (quoting Universal Camera Corp. v. NLRB, 340 U.S. 474 (1951)), *aff'd*, 462 F.2d 463 (3d Cir. 1972). A student may be held responsible if the information supports a "reasonable inference" that he violated institutional rules, even in the absence of direct, eye-witness testimony of the precise conduct alleged. *E.g.*, Esteban v. Cent. Mo. State Coll., 290 F. Supp. 622, 631 (W.D. Mo. 1968).

    190.   *Cf.* Mullins v. Sec'y of Health & Human Services, 680 F.2d 472 (6th Cir. 1982).

    191.   In a process that allowed the president, upon appeal, to reset the sanction, his decision to increase the sanction's severity was upheld even though he only reviewed the record and did not "hear" the testimony anew himself. The court approved this process because the Accused Student had had a "meaningful" hearing before the hearing board. Smith v. Univ. of Va., 78 F. Supp. 2d 533, 538–541 (W.D. Va. 1999)

Commentary. A smaller institution may choose to permit yet another step in the appeal process by providing that a person disagreeing with the decision of the Appellate Board may appeal to the president or other top-ranking official. In such cases, the institution may want to provide that the decision of the president shall be "final."[192] *Doing so would open the door to arguing that, as in labor disputes in which the parties have agreed that disputes be submitted to binding arbitration, the decision of the president as "arbitrator" should not be disturbed by a court as long as it is reasonable and derives its essence from the student code.*[193]

ARTICLE V: INTERPRETATION AND REVISION

A.   Any question of interpretation or application of the Student Code shall be referred to the [title of administrator identified in Article I, number 13] or his or her designee for final determination.

Commentary. Typically, the person making these decisions would be the institution's chief student affairs officer. This is a very important provision and should be included in every institution's code of student conduct. It allows ambiguous situations to be resolved by a person with training in educational development of students and in the context of the institution's mission, instead of leaving such judgment calls to persons outside of the academic community.

B.   The Student Code shall be reviewed every [__] years under the direction of the Student Conduct Administrator.

Commentary. Every Student Code should be reviewed periodically, at least every three years. Specifying some "normal" period for review may help to ensure that such a review is done.

---

192.   *See, e.g.,* COMPASS, 2003-2004 STUDENT HANDBOOK OF ALLEGHENY COLLEGE, JUDICIAL SYSTEM Art. IV, 3.D (on file with author).

193.   *See, e.g.,* Baker v. Lafayette Coll., 516 Pa. 291, 299–300, 532 A.2d 399, 403 (Pa. 1987); United Paperworkers Int'l Union v. Misco, Inc., 484 U.S. 29, (1987); United Steelworkers of Am. v. Enterprise Wheel & Car Corp., 363 U.S. 593 (1960).

A Twenty-First Century Model Student
Conduct Board Hearing Script

An important component of the Model Student Code is the Student Conduct Board. It is composed of one or more members of the college or university community and is designated to hear cases under the student code system, especially the more serious cases. One resource that members of Student Conduct Boards often find useful both in training[194] and in conducting hearings to determine what happened and to recommend sanctions, if necessary, is a script for the Student Conduct Board Hearing.

The following Model Student Conduct Board Hearing Script was developed to reflect the procedures outlined in the Model Student Code. The script provides an outline to be followed during the Student Conduct Board Hearing so that the necessary procedural steps may be followed without intervention by the Student Conduct Administrator. The Model Student Conduct Board Hearing Script should be revised to fit the institution's specific procedures.

This Model Script is intended to suggest "some kind of hearing" that follows the lead of *Goss v. Lopez*.[195] Courts have consistently recognized that a college or university may (if not *should*) consciously design its process for determining facts about student conduct *not* so that it models a criminal prosecution[196] because that is contrary to creating an educational atmosphere.[197] Rather, it should be tailored to fit the circumstances of what is to be heard[198] and the educational mission that is to

---

194.   Diane M. Waryold, *Increasing Campus Judicial Board Effectiveness: Are Two Heads Truly Better Than One?* in The Administration of Campus Discipline: Student, Organizational, and Community Issues 227–36 (Brent G. Paterson & William L. Kibler, eds. 1998).

195.   419 U.S. 565, 583 (1975) (noting that "further formalizing the suspension process and escalating its formality and adversary nature may not only make it too costly as a regular disciplinary tool but also destroy its effectiveness as part of the teaching process"). See *supra* note 40 and accompanying text.

196.   *See* Esteban v. Cent. Mo. State Coll., 277 F. Supp. 649, 651 (W.D. Mo. 1967) (asserting that "the Court does not hold that the procedural due process which must be afforded these plaintiffs before they can be validly suspended implies a formal court type judicial hearing such as is required in criminal cases").

197.   "This is not to imply that a full-dress judicial hearing, with right to cross-examine witnesses, is required. Such a hearing, with the attending publicity and disturbance of college activities, might be detrimental to the college's educational atmosphere and impractical to carry out." Dixon v. Ala. State Bd. of Educ., 294 F.2d 150, 159 (5th Cir. 1961) (contemplating that a disciplinary hearing could be "not before the Board directly" and that student could give his version of events "to the Board, or at least to an administrative official of the college" instead).

198.   The court notes that the observations of the Supreme Court in *Mathews* are appropriate here:

> The judicial model of an evidentiary hearing is neither a required, nor even the most effective, method of decision-making in all circumstances. . . . All that is necessary is that the procedures be tailored, in light of the decision to be made, to 'the capacities and circumstances of those who are to be heard to insure that they are given a meaningful opportunity to present their case.

Hart v. Ferris State Coll., 557 F. Supp. 1379, 1390 (W.D. Mich. 1983) (quoting Mathews v.

be accomplished.[199]

Thus, this model of a script for the Student Conduct Board Hearing envisions a process that is calm rather than confrontational. It challenges us to achieve an atmosphere more consistent with the educational and academic setting in which it is occurring,[200] as contrasted to the "trial by combat" behaviors often exhibited in courtroom proceedings.[201] "The hearing may be procedurally informal and need not be adversarial."[202]

It is believed that this script provides dignity for all students involved and that the finders of fact are enabled to do their job: resolving questions of credibility, determining whether institutional rules were violated, and, if so, recommending sanctions to fit the misconduct and the institution's mission.

This Model empowers the chair and the Student Conduct Board to set the tone for the hearing.[203] All questions are directed to all witnesses by or through the Student Conduct Board, including questions that are in the nature of cross-examination.[204]

This method was specifically approved by the Court of Appeals for the Eleventh Circuit.[205] In a case of two students who had been suspended from a public institution, the court ruled that "there was no denial of appellants' constitutional rights to due process by their inability to question the adverse witnesses in the usual, adversarial manner."[206] The court explained that:

> Although appellants were not allowed to ask questions directly of the adverse witnesses, it is clear that they heard all of the testimony against them. Appellants were told they could pose questions to the presiding

---

Eldridge, 424 U.S. 319, 348–349 (1976)) (internal citations omitted).

199. Wright v. Tex. So. Univ., 392 F.2d 728 (5th Cir. 1968)

This does not mean that the student is entitled to the formality of a trial, in the usual sense of that term, but simply requires that he must be given a fair and reasonable opportunity to make his defense to the charges and to receive such a hearing as meets the requirements of justice both to the school and to himself.

Id. at 729.

200. In a student discipline hearing that resulted in a one semester suspension, the court approved an informal process: "At the hearing itself, plaintiff read a prepared statement to the panel, and participated in an informal discussion of his case." Jaksa v. Univ. of Mich., 597 F. Supp. 1245 (E.D. Mich. 1984), *aff'd per curiam*, 787 F.2d 590 (6th Cir. 1986). See *supra* note 191 and accompanying text.

201. One commentator contrasts his campus process with the "adversarial" model by calling it the "investigatory" model, such as is used in Europe and in American "drug courts." Pavela, *supra* note 8 at 827.

202. Wasson v. Trowbridge, 382 F.2d 807, 812 (2d Cir. 1967), (affirming expulsion of student from Merchant Marine Academy), *rev'd on other grounds*, 269 F. Supp. 900 (E.D.N.Y. 1967).

203. "The hearing was non-criminal, and was conducted in a non-adversarial manner, there was no opposing counsel, and the hearing was conducted entirely by the Investigating Officer." Wimmer v. Lehman, 705 F.2d 1402 (4th Cir. 1983) (upholding dismissal of student from United States Naval Academy).

204. *See Jaksa*, 597 F. Supp. at 1252 ("The Constitution does not confer on plaintiff the right to cross-examine his accuser in a school disciplinary proceeding.").

205. Nash v. Auburn Univ., 812 F.2d 655, 664 (11th Cir. 1987).

206. *Id.*

board chancellor, who would then direct appellants' questions to the witnesses. Appellants were clearly informed when the time came for them to ask questions in the prescribed manner.[207]

The Court of Appeals of Texas also approved this approach. At the University of Houston, a public institution, this same process was followed in reaching the decision to expel a student:

> The [Accused Student] was assisted by his counsel of choice, a law student. This counsel attended the hearing and advised the [Accused Student] during the hearing; however, he was not allowed to speak, argue, or question witnesses during the hearing. The [Accused Student], speaking for himself, was allowed to testify and to make opening and closing statements, but was not permitted to question witnesses directly. All questions were referred to the hearing officer, who would ask the question directly of the witness. The hearing officer asked some, but not all the questions requested by the [Accused Student].[208]

In a civil action for money damages in connection with an arrest for rape (that was allegedly a wrongful arrest) when the student was expelled from a public institution for the same alleged conduct, the court approved the method of allowing the Accused Student to direct questions to his accuser through the Student Conduct Board:

> It is understandable that the panel would wish to alter the proceedings in an effort to protect the alleged victim from additional trauma. . . . At the very least, in light of the disputed nature of the facts and the importance of witness credibility in this case, due process required that the panel permit the plaintiff to hear all evidence against him and to direct questions to his accuser through the panel.[209]

Thus, legal authorities clearly permit, if not urge, colleges and universities to create an atmosphere for student conduct boards, like the script proposed here, that is adopted because it fits the goals of the educational community it serves. Student affairs professionals also see educational value in conducting hearings in this manner.[210]

Student development theorists support the notion that peer influences can be extremely persuasive for traditional aged students. Therefore, students dialoguing with students in a disciplinary hearing regarding the behavioral expectations of the college or university community can be the best method for redirecting behavior.[211]

---

207. *Id.*

208. Univ. of Houston v. Sabeti, 676 S.W.2d 685, 686 (Tex. Ct. App. 1984).

209. Donohue v. Baker, 976 F. Supp. 136, 147 (N.D.N.Y. 1997).

210. *See, e.g.,* Thomas R. Baker, *Judicial Complaint Resolution Models and Schemes: An Administrator's Reference Guide for Self-Assessment* at 11–12, Annual Conf. of the Ass'n for Student Judicial Affairs (2000) (discussing many of the details involved in what he calls "non-confrontational" and "quasi-confrontational" "adjudications"—including use of video equipment to avoid confrontations of students—in an excellent practitioner's guide).

211. Diane M. Waryold, *Increasing Campus Judicial Board Effectiveness: Are Two Heads Truly Better Than One? in* THE ADMINISTRATION OF CAMPUS DISCIPLINE: STUDENT,

The approach recommended here has an added advantage. There is no "prosecutor" or specially trained expert to "present" the case "against" the Accused Student. Instead, the institution is not "against" any student at all. It makes a forum available—not as an advocate but as a stake holder—to determine what happened and to recommend sanctions, if necessary. The organizing and questioning is done primarily by the Student Conduct Board (the Complainant and Accused Students may identify and invite witnesses and pertinent documents as well). This allows all witnesses who come before the board to be treated with equal dignity. Whether they are students, faculty members, security officers, or others, they are likely to be adults, and each has the same role: to share the pertinent information they have with the Student Conduct Board.

This arrangement dispenses with feelings that it is "unfair" to pit an expert "prosecutor," professor, or person trained in the law "against" a "mere" student. Thus, this approach creates a fair hearing and avoids either the imposition of attorneys to "equalize" the skills of "presenters"[212] or the requirement to start over because the skills of the presenters were not equal.[213]

The Model Student Conduct Board Script follows.

Pre-Student Conduct Board Hearing of the Student Conduct Board Without the Parties Present

It can be useful for the Student Conduct Administrator to conduct a meeting with the members of the Student Conduct Board prior to the beginning of the Student Conduct Board's Student Conduct Board Hearing without the parties present. Issues to be considered during this meeting include:

A review of any written materials.

A review of procedures to be followed during the Student Conduct Board Hearing.

A discussion of any potential for bias on the part of any Student Conduct Board member.

Organizational, and Community Issues 228 (Brent G. Paterson & William L. Kibler, eds. 1998).

212. *Jaksa*, 597 F. Supp. 1245, 1252 (E.D. Mich. 1984), *aff'd per curiam*, 787 F.2d 590 (6th Cir. 1986).

> Significantly, the University did not proceed against plaintiff through an attorney or other representative. Had an attorney presented the University's case, or had the hearing been subject to complex rules of evidence or procedure, plaintiff may have had a constitutional right to representation. But here, Professor Rothman presented the case against plaintiff and there was nothing mysterious about the Academic Judiciary proceedings.

Id. at 1252.

In *Wasson v. Trowbridge*, 382 F.2d 807, 812 (2d Cir. 1967), *rev'd on other grounds*, 269 F. Supp. 900 (E.D.N.Y. 1967), the Accused Student had no right for an attorney to present his case "where the hearing is investigative and not adversarial and the government does not proceed through counsel."

213. French v. Bashful, 303 F. Supp. 1333 (E.D. La. 1969) (requiring new hearing where Southern University at New Orleans, a public university, had process in which "prosecution" was done by third year law student "chosen to prosecute because of his familiarity with legal proceedings" and Accused Student was refused participation of his attorney).

Student Conduct Board Hearing Script

Begin tape recorder.[214]

Good afternoon, my name is [_____], and I will be serving as the chair of the Student Conduct Board. My role is to oversee the Student Conduct Board Hearing that will be conducted today.

Please note that today's Student Conduct Board Hearing is being tape recorded. This recording represents the sole official verbatim record of the Student Conduct Board Hearing and is the property of this institution.

At this time, I will ask the members of the Student Conduct Board to introduce themselves.

Would the Accused Student(s) introduce himself/herself (themselves).[215]

Would the Accused Student's advisor introduce himself/herself *(if present)*?[216]

Would the Complainant introduce himself/herself?

Would the Complainant's advisor introduce himself/herself *(if present)*?

Would the individuals who are here today as possible witnesses introduce themselves?

If the Complainant or the Accused Student has an advisor read the following statement. The role of the advisor during this Student Conduct Board Hearing is limited. It reflects that this process is not a courtroom proceeding but is part of the institution's programs that are designed to provide a good living/learning environment for all members of our academic community. An advisor may not question witnesses or make statements before the Student Conduct Board. The only appropriate role for the advisor is to provide advice to the student who has requested his/her presence in a manner which does not disturb the proceedings of

---

214. It is important to maintain a verbatim record, such as a tape recording, of the Student Conduct Board Hearing for use in deliberations by the Student Conduct Board and in any subsequent internal appeal. Such a record is anticipated by the Model Student Code. It is necessary to test the recorder prior to the beginning of the Student Conduct Board Hearing to ensure that the recorder will capture the voices of all present. The tape should be retained until after all appeals under the Code have been completed, at least. *See also* Edward N. Stoner, *Reviewing Your Student Discipline Policy: A Project Worth the Investment* 14 (2000), *at* http://www.nacua.org/publications/pubs/pamphlets/StudentDisciplinePolicy/pdf   (discussing important considerations to follow in making an audiotape record).

215. Throughout the Student Conduct Board Hearing, the chair should be careful to assure that each speaker is identified, even if s/he spoke earlier, so that the audio recording may be understood by a subsequent listener, such as on appeal.

216. In cases in which an advisor is present, it is important for the board chair to communicate clearly the appropriate role of the advisor in the Student Conduct Board Hearing and to respond immediately if the advisor oversteps these bounds. The courts have not created a legal right for students to have an advisor present in student discipline proceedings except in certain limited circumstances at public institutions and, even then, their role is to quietly advise their client, not to participate directly in the Student Conduct Board Hearing. *See supra* Model Code, art. IV(A)(4)(d). The Campus Security Provisions of the Student-Right-to-Know and Campus Security Act as amended do, however, require, in sexual assault cases, that the accused and the accuser be allowed the same rights to have others present during the Student Conduct Board Hearing. Rather than creating separate procedures for sexual assault cases, it is advisable to apply the same standard to all cases. This is the normal practice under the student affairs maxim that all students (including alleged victims and alleged rule violators alike) be treated with equal care, concern, fairness, and dignity.

the Student Conduct Board. If an advisor fails to act in accordance with the procedures of the Student Conduct Board, he/she will be barred from these proceedings.

I would like to remind everyone participating in this Student Conduct Board Hearing that falsification, distortion, or misrepresentation before the Student Conduct Board is a violation of the Student Code. Any person who abuses the Student Code System in this way may face disciplinary charges for that violation.

Witnesses, other than the Accused Student and the Complainant, are present in the Student Conduct Board Hearing only while offering their information.[217] Would all witnesses, other than the Accused Student and the Complainant, please leave the Student Conduct Board Hearing room and wait outside. You will be asked to reenter the Student Conduct Board Hearing to offer your testimony.

Before we proceed, are there any questions?

The Accused Student and the Complainant may challenge any member of the Student Conduct Board for bias if you believe that he or she cannot be fair in this Student Conduct Board Hearing.

Does the Accused Student wish to challenge any member of the Student Conduct Board for bias?

Does the Complainant wish to challenge any member of the Student Conduct Board for bias? [If so, the student should be asked to explain what might prevent the member from participating fairly in the Student Conduct Board Hearing and the chair may then recess the Student Conduct Board Hearing briefly to consider and to decide the challenge.]

The Student Conduct Board is considering charges which have been brought against [_____], the Accused Student, by [_____], the Complainant in today's Student Conduct Board Hearing.

Under the Student Code, [_____], the Accused Student, has been charged with the following violations of the Student Code:

The Student Conduct Board Chair reads each of the violations of the Student Disciplinary Code which the Accused Student is alleged to have violated.

Would the Accused Student please respond to each of the charges which I have just read indicating whether you accept responsibility for violating this provision of the Student Code?

If the Accused Student does not accept responsibility for violating each of the provisions of the Student Code listed above, then the Student Conduct Board Hearing shall proceed.

If the Accused Student does accept responsibility for violating each of the provisions of the Student Code listed above, then the Student Conduct Board

---

217. Witnesses other than the Accused Student and the Complainant are present in the Student Conduct Board Hearing only while providing information. This is to prevent them from being influenced by what they hear others say and is designed to preserve the confidentiality of the process. It is important to provide a location where the witnesses may wait until they are called into the Student Conduct Board Hearing. If there are two contentious "sides," two rooms may be provided. If, under an institution's process, a "victim" student is not considered to be the "Complainant," this language must be modified to allow him/her to attend the entire process because that result is contemplated by the Model Student Conduct Code.

Hearing shall proceed with the presentation of information limited to that which should be considered in the imposition of sanctions.

At this time, we will begin the portion of the Student Conduct Board Hearing during which information is presented for consideration in determining if the Accused Student has or has not violated the Student Code. *Witnesses may be asked to swear or affirm to tell the truth at this point if the institution wishes to follow this practice.*

The Complainant and Accused Student will be provided the opportunity to share introductory remarks which should not exceed five (5) minutes. You are not required to do so.[218] If you have prepared an Impact Statement[219] in writing or wish to make one orally, you may do so at this time.[220]

Are there any questions before we proceed with any introductory remarks?

Would the Complainant in this case like to make introductory remarks? If so, please proceed.

Would the Accused Student in this case like to make introductory remarks? If so, please proceed.

At this time, the Student Conduct Board will hear witnesses offer testimony for consideration in determining if the Accused Student has or has not violated the Student Code. The Student Conduct Board will begin by calling witnesses to present testimony. After the Student Conduct Board has called all the witnesses it considers appropriate, the Complainant, followed by the Accused Student, will be afforded the opportunity to call additional witnesses.[221]

The members of the Student Conduct Board will have the opportunity to question each witness.[222] Witnesses called by the Student Conduct Board may be questioned by the Complainant, followed by the Accused Student, after the Student

---

218. There is no requirement that students be allowed to make "introductory remarks" and some have found them unnecessary and, possibly, redundant or confusing when compared to the students' subsequent "testimony."

219. Some courtroom proceedings contemplate a similar presentation, commonly called a "Victim Impact Statement." In an educational setting, the term "Victim" is not used. This reflects that some Accused Students consider themselves to be "Victims" because they feel they have been unjustly accused. It also reflects the educational perspective that the academic community is concerned about the impact of the events and the process upon all students equally. Thus, a more appropriate terminology is "Impact Statement" or "Student Impact Statement."

220. One practice is to reserve the presentation of Student Impact Statements unless and until a rules violation is found, in the sanctioning phase. There is no requirement to break up the process in this manner, and this Model reflects the choice to allow each student to share with the board the impact that events and the process have had upon him/her as part of the board's work to determine what happened.

221. The Complainant and the Accused Student will have advised the Student Conduct Administrator prior to the Student Conduct Board Hearing of the names of the witnesses s/he wishes to have offer information at the Student Conduct Board Hearing. This allows the Student Conduct Administrator to require these persons to attend the Student Conduct Board Hearing and for the Hearing to proceed smoothly. There is no requirement that a witness be identified as "for" one student or "for" a version of "what happened." Indeed, all community members are presumed to be doing their best to assist the community, not to act as advocates for a particular student.

222. By having the Student Conduct Board question each witness first, it is hoped that the educational nature of the Hearing will be emphasized and the potential adversarial nature will be downplayed.

Conduct Board has concluded its questioning. Witnesses called by the Complainant and Accused Student will be questioned initially by the Student Conduct Board. Following the conclusion of the Student Conduct Board's questioning, the individual calling the witness will have the opportunity to have questions asked of the witness. Following the conclusion of this questioning, the other individual will have the opportunity to have questions asked of the witness. Before a witness is excused, the chair will ask members of the Student Conduct Board and the Complainant and Accused Student if they have any final questions.

All questions by the Complainant and Accused Student of witnesses should be directed to the chair of the Student Conduct Board.[223]

Are there any questions before witnesses testify? [Typically, the Complainant will be asked to testify first, followed by the Accused Student, and then other witnesses.]

At this time, the Board will hear from the Complainant.

Do the members of the Student Conduct Board have any questions for this witness?

After completion of questioning by the Student Conduct Board: Does the Complainant wish to provide any additional information to the Board?

Does the Accused Student have any questions to be directed to the Complainant? Please remember to direct your questions to the chair of the Student Conduct Board.

At this time, the board will hear from the Accused Student.

Do the members of the Student Conduct Board have any questions for this witness?

After completion of questioning by the Student Conduct Board, does the Accused Student wish to provide any additional information to the board?

Does the Complainant have any questions to be directed to the Accused Student? Please remember to direct your questions to the chair of the Student Conduct Board.

After the Complainant and the Accused Student have testified, the following procedures will be followed for additional witnesses called by the Student Conduct Board.

The next witness to be called by the Student Conduct Board is [_____].

Do the members of the Student Conduct Board have any questions for this witness?

After the completion of the questioning by the Student Conduct Board. Does the Complainant have any questions for this witness? Please remember to direct your questions to the chair of the Student Conduct Board.

After the completion of questions suggested by the Complainant. Does the Accused Student have any questions for this witness? Please remember to direct your questions to the chair of the Student Conduct Board.

After the completion of questions suggested by the Accused Student. Are there

---

223. The purpose of directing cross-examination questions to the chair is twofold: to set an educational instead of adversarial tone for of the Hearing and to provide the opportunity for the chair to regulate inappropriate questions.

any final questions before this witness is excused?[224] Thank you very much for taking the time to participate in this Student Conduct Board Hearing of the Student Conduct Board. Your participation is appreciated. Please do not discuss with other potential witnesses the information you have shared with us today.

This process is repeated until the Student Conduct Board has called each witness.

Does the Complainant wish for the Board to call any additional witnesses?

The next witness is called into the Student Conduct Board Hearing.

Do the members of the Student Conduct Board have any questions for this witness?

After the completion of the questioning by the Student Conduct Board. Does the Complainant have any questions for this witness? Please remember to direct your questions to the chair of the Student Conduct Board.

After the completion of questions suggested by the Complainant. Does the Accused Student have any questions for this witness? Please remember to direct your questions to the chair of the Student Conduct Board.

After the completion of questions suggested by the Accused Student. Are there any final questions before this witness is excused?[225] Thank you very much for taking the time to participate in this Student Conduct Board Hearing of the members of the Student Conduct Board. Your participation is appreciated. Please do not discuss with other potential witnesses the information you have shared with us today.

This process is repeated until each of these witnesses have been called.

Does the Accused Student wish for the Board to call any additional witnesses?

The next witness is called into the Student Conduct Board Hearing.

Do the members of the Student Conduct Board have any questions for this witness?

After the completion of questions by the Student Conduct Board. Does the Accused Student have any questions for this witness? Please remember to direct your questions to the chair of the Student Conduct Board.

After the completion of questions suggested by the Accused Student. Does the Complainant have any questions for this witness? Please remember to direct your questions to the chair of the Student Conduct Board.

After the completion of questions suggested by the Complainant. Are there any final questions before this witness is excused?[226] Thank you very much for taking the time to participate in this Student Conduct Board Hearing of the members of the Student Conduct Board. Your participation is appreciated.

This process is repeated until each of these witnesses have been called. At this point, the chair should ask the members of the Student Conduct Board if they have

---

224. Final questions may be proposed by board members, the Complainant, or the Accused Student.

225. Final questions may be proposed by board members, the Complainant, or the Accused Student.

226. Final questions may be proposed by board members, the Complainant or the Accused Student.

any final questions for the Complainant or the Accused Student. Please do not discuss with other potential witnesses the information you have shared with us today.

At this time, the Complainant and the Accused Student will be provided the opportunity to make concluding remarks. You are not required to do so.[227]

Are there any questions before we proceed?

Would the Complainant in this case like to make concluding remarks? If so, please proceed.

Would the Accused Student in this case like to make concluding remarks? If so, please proceed.

At this time, we would ask that the Complainant, Accused Student, and their advisors (*if any*) leave the Student Conduct Board Hearing room so that the members of the Student Conduct Board may determine if the Accused Student is responsible for any of the violations of the Student Code with which he/she has been charged.[228]

After the determination regarding responsibility is made, you will be asked to return to this room. The Student Conduct Board will announce its decision regarding responsibility. If the Accused Student is found not responsible concerning all charges, the Student Conduct Board Hearing will be adjourned. If the Accused Student is found responsible concerning any charges, the Student Conduct Board will consider the following additional information related to sanctioning.

A.   Character witnesses on behalf of the Accused Student;[229]

B.   Any prior violations of the Student Code by the Accused Student; and

C.   Recommendations for sanctioning from the Complainant and the Accused Student.

Turn the tape recorder off.[230]

Once the Student Conduct Board has concluded its deliberations concerning responsibility on each alleged violation, the Complainant, and Accused Student are called back into the Student Conduct Board Hearing.

Turn the tape recorder on.

This Student Conduct Board Hearing of the Student Conduct Board is now back in session. The Student Conduct Board has considered the charges against [_____], the Accused Student. The Student Conduct Board has evaluated all of the information shared with it and has determined which information was more credible, when the information was in conflict.

---

227.   This is another occasion at which a student may be given the opportunity to share an Impact Statement.

228.   Under these Student Conduct Board Hearing procedures, the determination of responsibility and sanctions have been separated so that the introduction of character witnesses, prior violations, and recommendations for sanctioning may be heard after the determination of responsibility is made. It is permissible to combine the determination of responsibility and sanctions into one deliberation.

229.   This Model allows for the possibility of character witnesses; they are not required.

230.   In the Model Student Conduct Board Hearing Script, the presentation of information during the hearing is recorded, but the deliberations of the Student Conduct Board are not.

Regarding the charge of [_____], the Student Conduct Board finds you [responsible] [not responsible]. *Repeat this sentence for each violation of the Student Code with which the Accused Student has been charged.*

If the Accused Student is found not responsible of all charges, read the following statement. This Student Conduct Board Hearing of the Student Conduct Board is now concluded.

Any further questions regarding the student code system or this decision of the Student Conduct Board should be directed to [_____]. Questions regarding this case should not be directed to any member of Student Conduct Board. The members of Student Conduct Board are cautioned not to discuss this matter with anyone to respect the privacy of all persons involved. Thank you very much for your participation.

If the Accused Student is found responsible of any charge, read the following statement. At this time, the Accused Student may ask the Board to call a reasonable number of character witnesses.

Does the Accused Student wish to do so?

Would the character witness please state your name and tell us the nature of your acquaintance with the Accused Student and comment on the student's character?

Do the members of the Student Conduct Board have any additional questions for this character witness?

Does the Accused Student wish to have any questions asked of this character witness? Please remember to direct any questions to the chair of the Student Conduct Board.

Does the Complainant wish to have any questions asked of this character witness? Please remember to direct any questions to the chair of the Student Conduct Board.

Repeat as necessary for each witness.

Would the Complainant like to offer any comments for consideration in the imposition of sanctions?[231]

Would the Accused Student like to offer any comments for consideration in the imposition of sanctions?

At this time, we would ask that the Complainant, Accused Student, and their advisors leave the Student Conduct Board Hearing room so that the members of the Student Conduct Board may determine the sanctions to be recommended in this case.

The Student Conduct Board will now request information regarding the Accused Student's prior violations of the Student Code, if any. Has the Accused Student been found responsible for violating the Student Code in any prior incidents?[232]

---

231. If the Complainant wishes to make an Impact Statement, this would be the time to do so if the choice is made to present these statements during the sanctioning phase.

232. The Student Conduct Administrator should bring this information to each Student Conduct Board Hearing, but it is recommended that information regarding the Accused Student should be shared with the Student Conduct Board only if it is determined that the Accused Student has violated the Code in the current case.

After the Student Conduct Administrator considers the Student Conduct Board's sanctioning recommendations, and determines what sanctions to impose, the Accused Student and Complainant have the opportunity to return to this room. The decision regarding sanctions will be announced. You may choose not to attend the announcement of the sanctions. Regardless, the Accused Student and Complainant (if a student) will receive written notification of the outcome of the Student Conduct Board Hearing.[233]

Turn the tape recorder off.

Once the Student Conduct Board has concluded its deliberations the Accused

---

233. For institutions at which all matters involving student versus student conduct are considered part of the educational records of each student, the same written notification should be given to each student. *See supra* Model Code, art. IV(B)(3)(b) and art. IV(B)(5). Complainants who are not students but need to know the result to do their jobs as institutional employees (e.g., security or a professor in a plagiarism case) may also be given the results, consistent with FERPA.

It seems an appropriate choice to consider records of the process initiated by a student to address an experience that occurred during his/her educational experience (e.g., a rules violation as to which he/she was the "victim") as equally that student's educational records as they are of the accused rules violator's. If one takes this approach, the "victim" student is entitled to see his/her own records under FERPA. Some schools, probably without considering the point that such records are surely records pertaining to the impacted student, define such records as "only" those of the Accused Students. This has led to absurd results of victims not being told the results of their own processes—and of congressional responses to "correct" this misidentification of whose record it is, by the institution. Thus, for institutions who choose to define a record of the process used by an impacted student as being *not* part of his/her educational records, Congress has nevertheless provided FERPA exceptions in extreme cases. It remains inexplicable, however, why an institution would define the process of records of a non-violent rules violation (e.g., theft of a TV from a residence hall room) to be *not* the record of the impacted student (and, thus, to refuse to tell the student whether he would get his TV back). Here are the Congressional responses.

The Jeanne Clery Disclosure of Campus Security Policy and Campus Crime Statistics Act requires that the victim of a sexual assault be informed of the final outcome of any campus disciplinary proceeding against the alleged attacker in the matter of the sexual assault. 20 U.S.C. § 1092(f)(8)(B)(iv)(II) (2000). FERPA allows institutions to share the outcome of a disciplinary proceeding with the alleged victim of a "crime of violence." 20 U.S.C. § 1232g(b)(6)(A) (2000). In 1998, FERPA was further amended to allow institutions to release to the public the final results of a campus disciplinary proceeding alleging a "crime of violence" when the Accused Student is found responsible, and to release information to parents of a student under the age of 21 when the institution determines that the student violated a campus rule or law governing the use of alcohol or drugs. *Id.* § 1232g(b)(6)(B) (2000). Institutions should carefully examine their policies to insure compliance with these provisions, to consider that records of a hearing's results are education records of a "victim" student, and to consider whether to release information to the public or to parents.

In a decision dated July 16, 2004, the U.S. Department of Education ruled that Georgetown University had violated the Campus Security Act by requiring that victims sign an agreement promising not to re-release the final results of the disciplinary proceeding before the university would make the required notification. *See* Letter from M. Geneva Coombs, Director, Case Management Teams—Northeast, U.S. Dept. of Educ. to Dr. John J. DeGioia, President, Georgetown University (July 16, 2004) *available at* http://www.securityoncampus.org/reporters/releases/degioia071604.pdf.

At the Pennsylvania State University, the "victim" has the right to "hear" the outcome of the disciplinary process even if the "victim" is not a student. PA. STATE UNIV. DIV. OF STUDENT AFFAIRS, *supra* note 178.

Student and Complainant are called back into the Student Conduct Board Hearing.
   Turn the tape recorder on.
   This Student Conduct Board Hearing of the Student Conduct Board is now back in session. The following sanction(s) will be imposed in this case:[234]
   Read each of the sanctions.
   This decision may be appealed within five (5) working days of receipt of written notification of the decision in this case. Appeals should be made in writing and delivered to [_____]. Decisions of the Student Conduct Board and/or the Student Conduct Administrator may be appealed on the following grounds only:

A. The original Student Conduct Board Hearing was not conducted fairly in light of the charges and information presented, and not in conformity with prescribed procedures giving the Complainant a reasonable opportunity to prepare and to present information that the Student Code was violated, and giving the Accused Student a reasonable opportunity to prepare and to present a rebuttal of those allegations.

B. The decision reached in this case was not based on substantial information.

C. The sanctions were not appropriate for the violation of the Student Code which the Accused Student was found to have committed.

D. New information, sufficient to alter a decision, is now available which was not available to the person appealing at the time of the original Student Conduct Board Hearing.

For more information, please refer to the Student Code which is published in the [_____].
   Are there any final questions at this time?
   Any further questions regarding the student code system or this decision of the Student Conduct Board should be directed to [_____], the Student Conduct Administrator. Questions regarding this case should not be directed to any member of Student Conduct Board. The members of Student Conduct Board are cautioned not to discuss this matter with anyone, to respect the privacy of all persons involved.
   This Student Conduct Board Hearing of the Student Conduct Board is now concluded. Thank you very much for your participation.
   Turn tape recorder off.

END OF STUDENT CONDUCT BOARD HEARING SCRIPT

   The written record of the process need not include a lengthy "opinion" like judges sometimes issue in certain courtroom proceedings.[235] On the other hand, it

---

234. If the Student Conduct Administrator needs additional time to consider which sanction(s) to impose, the Accused Student and Complainant should be advised as to when and how they will be told about the sanctions.

235. Jaksa v. Univ. of Mich., 597 F. Supp. 1245, 1253 (E.D. Mich. 1984) (upholding one semester suspension despite being told only that he was found in violation "as a result of the case presented by Professor Rothman," and finding no requirement for a more detailed explanation), *aff'd per curiam*, 787 F.2d 590 (6th Cir. 1986); Herman v. Univ. of S.C., 341 F. Supp. 226, 232 (D.S.C. 1971), *aff'd*, 457 F.2d 902 (4th Cir. 1972) (finding that the university's procedures adequately protected student's interests). "There is no requirement in law or reason that suggests

is advisable to provide at least a little more information than the "responsible/not responsible" conclusion given by courtroom juries. The board could state, "We carefully considered the testimony of all persons who provided information to the board and we considered all documents we received. We evaluated the credibility of each witness and the relevance and importance of all information we received. We resolved conflicts in the information we received in this manner." Use of an explanation, like this, will enable a subsequent reviewer—whether an internal appeal or a court—to respect the factual determinations made by the board.[236]

---

or demands the Board to issue written findings of fact or conclusions of law similar to those required by Rule 52 of the Federal Rules of Civil Procedure." *Id.*

236. *See, e.g.,* Schaer v. Brandeis Univ., 735 N.E. 2d 373, 379 n.9 (Mass. 2000) ("The report, although short, reflects a judgment by the board that the complainant and the corroborating witnesses were credited; Schaer and his witnesses were not credited."); Stoner & Martineau, *supra* note 39, at 313 (recommending, if possible, this type of additional statement: "On disputed issues of credibility, we believed student X rather than student Y.").

Appendix I

List of Acronyms and Abbreviations

ACEP	American College of Emergency Physicians
ACHA	American College Health Association
AODs	alcohol and other drugs
APRI/BC	American Prosecutors Research Institute and Boston College
BASICS	Brief Alcohol Screening and Intervention for College Students
CDC	Centers for Disease Control
Clery Act	The Jeanne Clery Disclosure of Campus Security Policy and Campus Crime Statistics Act
DFSA	Drug-facilitated sexual assault
DOE	U.S. Department of Education
FERPA	Family Educational Right to Privacy Act of 1974
FN-CSA	Forensic Nurse Certified in Sexual Assault
FNE	Forensic Nurse Examiner
GHB	gamma hydroxybutyrate
GLBT	gay, lesbian, bisexual, transgender
HEA	Higher Education Act of 1992
HIV	human immunodeficiency virus
HSV	herpes simplex virus
IAFN	International Association of Forensic Nurses
IHEs	institutions of higher education (IHEs)
DOJ	U.S. Department of Justice
LSD	lysergic acid diethylamide
NCWSV	National College Women Sexual Victimization Survey
NIAAA	National Institute on Alcohol Abuse and Alcoholism
OVC	Office of Victims of Crimes
OVW	Office on Violence Against Women
RA	resident advisor
RBS	responsible beverage service
SAE	Sexual Assault Examiner
SAFE	Sexual Assault Forensic Examiner
SANC	Sexual Assault Nurse Clinician
SANE	Sexual Assault Nurse Examiner

SART   Sexual Assault Response Team
SJA   Student Judicial Affairs
STI   sexually transmitted infection
U.S. DOJ   United States Department of Justice

Index

[References are to pages.]